1997

Directory of American Poetry Books

Third Edition

Volume II

1997

Directory of American Poetry Books

Third Edition, Volume II

Compiled by Poets House through the Poetry Publication Showcase
With "Publishing Options for Poetry in the 1990's," by Marie Brown

POETS HOUSE

New York

Published by Poets House

Third Edition, Volume II

**LIBRARY OF CONGRESS
CATALOGING-IN-PUBLICATION DATA**

Directory of American Poetry books/
[edited by] Poets House.—3rd ed., vol II

p.   cm.
Includes Index
1.   American   poetry—Bibliobraphy.   2.   Literature
publishing—United States—Directories. I. Poets House (Firm)
Z1231.P7D57 1997
[PS303]   93-17778
016.811008—dc20   CIP
ISBN 1-890695-01-7 (pb.)

Printed in the United States of America
Distributed by Poets House
72 Spring St., New York, NY 10012
(212-431-7920)

Contents

Acknowledgments

We wish to thank Deborah Pease and the Middlecott Foundation, Mary Kaplan and the J.M. Kaplan Fund, without whose help this volume of the Directory would not have been published. We thank all of those whose work on the Poetry Publication Showcase helped to gather the information reflected here, as well as those who assisted in the preparation of this volume, including: Neil Azevedo, Gabrielle Bendiner-Viani, Sarah Borden, Anne Hasley, Dan Islam, Ellen Ivey, David Johnson, Jennifer Knox, Marne Ludwig, Molly Ralkstein, Andre Spears, Michael Thomas, Esther Trepal, Sylvia Williams, and Maggie Vaisman. Special thanks to Chermayeff & Geismar Inc., especially Ivan Chermayeff and Chuck Rudy, for the design of the cover, part of a new look they have created for Poets House.

We thank the poets and publishers who continue to advise us on these projects, and all of those who contribute their books to the Showcase exhibit, whose enthusiasm encourages and supports us.

About Poets House

Poets House is a comfortable, accessible place for poetry—a 35,000 volume poetry library and meeting place that invites poets and the public to step into the living tradition of poetry. Its resources and literary events document the wealth and diversity of modern poetry and stimulate dialogue on issues of poetry in culture.

Founded in 1985 by Stanley Kunitz and the late Elizabeth Kray, Poets House is one of the only independent literary centers in the nation devoted to poetry. Through programs such as the annual Poetry Publication Showcase and Poetry in The Branches, Poets House is building a national archive of poetry while seeking to encourage broader readership and better representation of poetry in bookstores and libraries around the country.

Poets House is located at 72 Spring Street, New York, NY 10012 and welcomes visitors between the hours of 11:00 and 7:00, Tuesday through Friday, and 11:00 and 4:00 on Saturday. A non-profit organization, Poets House depends on donations for its support. For information about making a donation or becoming a member of Poets House, or for information about our programs and services, please write or call 212–431–7920.

About This Directory

The *Directory of American Poetry Books* is a buyer's guide for poetry readers, a publishing guide for poets, and a chart of the current status of the poetic voice in America. The only bibliographic resource that attempts to reflect the incredible diversity of poetry publishing during the 1990's, the *Directory* provides information about all books published since the fall of 1991 by publishers of every kind from all parts of the country.

This volume includes information on books published since the fall of 1994. It includes comprehensive listings for books published through the spring of 1996 and many that were published during the fall. The prior volume (Third Edition, Volume I) covers the period between June of 1991 and November of 1994.

The *Directory* grows out of the Poetry Publication Showcase, inaugurated by Poets House in June, 1992. An annual exhibition and series of events celebrating the year's new books, the Showcase was established by Executive Director Lee Briccetti to reflect the Poets House mission to make the range of modern poetry available to the public and to stimulate public dialogue on issues of poetry in culture.

Each year approximately 1,000 books are exhibited, first at Poets House and later at the American Library Association's annual conference, a gathering of over 18,000 librarians from around the country. In tandem with the exhibit, readings, panel discussions, and other kinds of events bring together poets, publishers, reviewers, booksellers, and librarians. By exploring the mechanisms by which poetry books reach readers, the Showcase attempts to articulate the complex relationship between the perception of poetry and the availability of poetry to the public.

Together, the two volumes of the *Directory* extend the reach of the Showcase, providing bibliographic detail for all of the books displayed since the start of the project. As an inclusive rather than a selective listing, the *Directory* lists all books of poetry sent to us except those intended for children and those published outside the United States. Works of poetry-related prose—biographical, auto-biographical, and critical works listed in previous editions—are not included here. Though we use the broadest possible sense of the word "poetry," we define "book" in the more traditional sense of a paper product with at least eight pages and, minimally, a traditional binding. We provide information about poetry cassettes and videos only when they were published coincidentally with a paper edition. While we salute the producers of poetry on-line and on disk, their publications are not yet included here.

While we make every effort to insure that these listings are complete, Poets House depends on the active participation of publishers for the information included in the *Directory*. We include information about books from commercial, university, and independent presses. In addition, due to the long literary tradition of self-publishing, self-published books are included if they find their way into our hands. Further, we believe that no source book could adequately reflect the range of the poetic voice of America in the 1990's if it excluded author subsidized works. Our goal in editing this volume has been to draw a distinction between subsidized and vanity presses, excluding the latter.

These are difficult distinctions to draw and complete information is often difficult to obtain. Therefore, inclusion in these pages should not be interpreted as an endorsement by Poets House of any publishing enterprise. For further discussion of these issues please see "Publishing Options in the 1990's" by Marie Brown, beginning on page xiii.

Organized by author, each main entry also provides the editor (anthologies and posthumous publications only), translator, title, number of pages, ISBN, city and state of publication, publisher, and publication date, as well as a brief description of each book. If both paper and hardcover editions are available, both are described. For a paper edition, the abbreviation "pap." precedes the price. When publication dates differ for cloth and paper editions, we list only the earlier date. The descriptions provided for each book are excerpts from published reviews, recommendations provided by other poets, or descriptive prose written by the publisher. In each case, the source of the quotation is identified.

A complete index of publishers begins on page 327. For each publisher we provide an office address and, when it differs, an ordering address, as well as phone and fax numbers. Wherever addresses provided in Volume I differ from those provided here, these are the more recent. Where the abbreviation "Cont:" appears, it precedes a listing of publishing staff members, ideally members of both the editorial and the publicity departments. Distributors and wholesalers are indicated next. For a list of frequently used abbreviations and for phone numbers of those distributors and wholesalers who appear most often, see the Key to the Index by Publisher on page 398.

If used properly this *Directory* is an excellent source of information for poets seeking a publisher. When submitting your work, look first to see who publishes work similar to your own in aesthetic and in thematic content, and consider the track record of those poets already on their list. If, for instance, yours will be a first book, look for publishers of other first books. Examine the main entry for each of the books listed in the index for that publisher. Ideally, read some of the books themselves. Confirm that the publisher accepts unsolicited manuscripts by consulting *Poets Market*, or one of the other resources available. Remember the "tao" of poetry publishing: poets must support the all too often fragile literary journals and presses if they want their own work to be supported by them.

As a reader and/or buyer of poetry, you can use the Directory in much the same way, profiting from the editorial choices of the publishers as well as from the recommendations by reviewers or other poets provided in the main entries. Readers seeking to buy books of poetry are urged to visit their local bookstores. Many bookstores participate in STOP (Single Title Order Plan) and will be able to place a special order for you. You can also contact the publisher directly. However, we suggest that you call or write to the publisher before ordering by mail, as shipping and handling charges are not included in the prices listed here and most publishers can only fill pre-paid orders.

Remember that placing orders through your local bookstore supports the art of poetry both by supporting the bookseller and by demonstrating publicly your demand for poetry. Remember too that urging the acquisitions librarian at your local library to order poetry books for the collection ensures better access to poetry for everyone in your community.

Jane Preston
Project Director

Options for Publishing
Poetry in the 1990's

People come to the publishing process with an intention to reach an audience with their work, to speak within and to a community. The sculpting of an identity as a poet and the development of a career are nested within each other and are intrinsically connected to this notion of reaching an audience.

The 1990's have witnessed a proliferation of means by which a poet can reach an audience—and a reciprocal burgeoning of interest in poetry. Readings, performances, literally hundreds of literary journals and small presses, CD-Rom, and the internet all are vehicles for poetry. And all are means for reaching and developing an audience.

The multiplicity of American voices reflected here in the *Directory* also reflects a multiplicity of poetry audiences. It is important to recognize that publishers no longer have the means of tapping a monolithic entity, "the poetry reading public." The publication of a book of poems must be supported by the development of an audience if the book is to be read.

A poet becomes known either through performance or publication, or both. While the publication of a book of poems will increase a poet's visibility, the audience a poet has already developed is one of the factors a publisher considers when looking at a body of work. The path to publication is, more often than not, determined by the poet's visibility, whether in performance, on the literary circuit—from workshops and seminars to cocktail parties—or in prior publication.

Most writers do not know what it costs to publish a book. Printing is not publishing. Publishing is a process which includes editorial services, promotion, advertising (which is always minimal), marketing, sales, warehousing and distribution. No matter how small a publisher is, if they have a distributor, they can get a book to the marketplace. However, effective marketing for a book of poems often relies on the active participation of the poet.

Just as there are many poetries and many poetry audiences, there are many kinds of poetry publishers, generally categorized by size and structure as 1) trade publishers, Norton or Knopf, for example; 2) university presses; and 3) independents, including literary presses such as Copper Canyon and Milkweed. These publishers acquire a manuscript, negotiate a contract and take a book through the various processes that bring it to its readers.

Trade publishers produce a broad range of materials including literary titles. Since they publish in fairly large print runs, only writers who have published broadly in reputable literary journals, who have received significant critical attention, or who have developed sizeable audiences through other means, should consider sending their manuscripts to a trade publisher.

It is essential for every writer to understand that any publishing enterprise requires capital to produce and distribute the work. Though large trade publishers often consider the publication of poetry to be subsidized by the better sales of other books on their list, and the maintenance of poetry on their lists as an investment in their literary reputation, they will still be cautious about the potential for actually losing money on a book.

University presses, supported as they are by the larger financial structure of the university, are somewhat freer from the domination of sales projections (traditionally very low for poetry) and the bottom line. Some university presses have developed extremely reputable poetry series, including Yale and Pitt. In general, university presses have an excellent reputation for keeping books in print over the long haul.

Much of the diversity of poetry books represented in these pages is due to the vitality of the independent press. The National Endowment for the Arts reports a 500% increase in the number of small presses over the last 30 years. In effect, desktop publishing has put the production of books of poetry into the hands of a wider range of Americans.

Most independent presses publish specifically what interests them. It may be a style of writing (Story Line Press, for example, is known for publishing narrative poetry) or a kind of voice or subject matter they feel is otherwise inadequately represented in print. By focussing on one kind of work independent presses are often extremely successful in reaching specific audiences.

Independent presses vary greatly in their goals, their resources, and their reach. While the largest are nationally distributed, others seek to reach a regional, or even local, audience. Some excellent presses struggle with severe under-capitalization and lack of distribution. Those which are not-for-profit sometimes struggle with these problems as well as an unreliable funding climate.

Because of these difficulties some publishers are unable to publish all of the work in which they are interested without an investment from the poet to help meet the costs of publication. This is usually done under a separate imprint and is called subsidy publishing. Due to chronically low sales figures for poetry, many publishers who will pay advances to authors for works in other categories may require subsidies from poets for the publication of poetry.

Another option is self publishing which, with Walt Whitman as an early example, has a long literary tradition. The independence self-publishing allows, as well as the personal control over both the process and the product, makes self-publishing very attractive to some poets. There are some small presses which can trace their origins to the successful self-publishing of their founders.

Self-publishing is particularly viable when a poet is just beginning to read or perform publicly and is unlikely to attract a publisher, yet wants to have a chapbook available for sale. In this way, self-publishing can serve as one of the earliest tools a poet uses to interact with a developing audience.

However, self-publishing also means that the poet must be prepared to take on all the activities of a publisher if the book is to reach readers. Self-published writers who believe that the act of publishing *is* printing often face a deep sense of frustration when they find that their book reaches only people with whom they personally interact. Poets planning to distribute their own work in the way that a publisher would should be aware that it is a very difficult, time consuming and expensive task.

All of these publishing options have the basic intention of getting the work to an audience. This is not the case with vanity presses. The vanity press solicits business from writers seeking publication. They often present themselves as legitimate publishers, however their intent is to profit not from the sales of the book but from the its "publication," for which they will charge from $5,000 to $15,000, often providing minimal promotion and no distribution.

When seeking to publish, poets should evaluate their options carefully in the light of the kind of visibility their work has already achieved. They should seek a publisher who has published work which has something in common with their own. The *Directory* can be very useful in that regard. They should ask what aspects of the publisher's role are most important at this particular point in their development as a writer. A good match between poet and publisher is essential.

It is useful for poets to read widely about the book publishing industry. Reference materials are available in a variety of publications both in bookstores and libraries. Literary organizations such as Poets

House, Poets and Writers and the Council for Literary Presses can also help. As in any field, writers benefit from gaining as much knowledge as possible as they seek to bring their work into print.

Book publication is part of a process of getting poems to their potential audience. The process is complemented by readings and the development of reciprocal relationships with new audiences. This is more than marketing. It is community building. Its rewards are often slow.

Marie Brown
Marie Brown Associates, Literary Services

Abbott, Steve. *A Short History of the Word.* 32p. pap. $6.95 (0-944754-077). Johnstown, OH: Pudding House Publications, Spring 1996. Poems of a mystic's interaction with the cityscape and popular culture. —Pudding House Publications

Abramson, Lillian. *Not So Idle Notions.* 120p. $15.95 (0-944957-52-8). New York, NY: Rivercross Publishing, Fall 1995.

Ackerman, Pat. *Nine Poems.* 16p. San Francisco, CA: Thin Ice Press, Fall 1996. Handprinted and handsewn, numbered and signed edition. —Thin Ice Press

Adair, Virginia Hamilton. *Ants on the Melon.* 160p. $21.00 (0-679-44881-0). New York, NY: Random House, Spring 1996. Gravity of thought, lightness of touch, complex feelings balanced by a supple formal prowess—all these make V. H. Adair's ripe harvest of poems a heady mixture of humor, rapture, and metaphysics. —Eamon Grennan. Tart, knowledgeable poems by a woman who has lived long and felt deeply. They surprise and delight us with their passion. —Maxine Kumin

Adams. *The Two Headed God.* 90p. pap. $9.95 (1-879-384-262-4). Fort Bragg, CA: Cypress House, Fall 1995. In the poems of *The Two Headed God*, few words suffice to conjure up the world. The poet becomes the sage who can connect nature and culture, the future with the past. —Francisco X. Alarcón

Adams, Joseph D. ed. *Criterion for Tune.* 128p. pap. $8.00 (1-880016-19-2). Painter, VA: Road Publishers, Spring 1995.

Adams, Joseph D., ed. *Those Move Easiest Who Have Learned To Dance.* 160p. pap. $7.50 (1-880016-15-X). Painter, VA: Road Publishers, Fall 1994.

Adams, Joseph D., ed. *What One Beholds of a Woman Is the Least Part of Her.* 128p. pap. $8.00 (1-880016-21-4). Painter, VA: Road Publishers, Fall 1995. This is a theme-based anthology, commemorating *The Year of the Woman*. —Road Publishers

Adcock, Betty. *The Difficult Wheel*. 71p. $17.95 (0-8071-2022-7); pap. $9.95 (0-8071-2023-5). Baton Rouge, LA: Louisiana State University Press, Fall 1995. Winner of the Natalie Ornish Poetry Award, sponsored by the Texan Institute of Letters. Betty Adcock takes her truth neat, with humor, melody, and intelligence. She writes poems that are as upright as houses, and as flighty as clouds. —Mary Oliver. Word-driven, at times gloriously intoxicated on their own vowels and consonants, the poems in Betty Adcock's *The Difficult Wheel* are exhilarating. —Andrew Hudgins. This is substantial, first-rate poetry. It can carry you long distances three feet off the ground. —*The Texas Observer*.

Adcock, Fleur, and Jacqueline Simms, eds. *The Oxford Book of Creatures*. 387p. (0-19-214226-7). New York, NY: Oxford University Press, Fall 1995. *The Oxford Book of Creatures* selects from the work of naturalists, philosophers, novelists, diarists, and, outstandingly, poets to celebrate the creatures with whom we share this planet. It includes the work of writers ranging from Aristotle to Orwell, Montaigne to Miriam Rothschild, John Clare to E. Nesbit. —Oxford University Press

Addeo, Samuel J. *Caribbean Journal: Notes in the Sun*. 47p. (0-964277-0-9). Asbury Park, NJ: Broken Star Press, Fall 1994.

Addeo, Samuel J. *Caribbean Journal: This Land Bonaire*. 96p. (0-9642774-1-7). Asbury Park, NJ: Broken Star Press, Spring 1995.

Adler, Frances Payne. *Raising the Tents*. 64p. $19.95 (0-934971-33-1); pap. $9.95 (0-934971-33-1). Corvallis, OR: Calyx Books, Spring 1995. A Jewish pulse with feminist vision and wise humor. [Adler is a] woman who is probing the crevices of memory, with a wide lens, cherishing all peoples. —Bettina Aptheker

Adnan, Etel. *The Indian Never Had a Horse and Other Poems*. 103p. pap. $12.00 (0-942996-04-6). Sausalito, CA: Post-Apollo Press, reissued Fall

1994. Adnan has an exceptional gift for the mystical delineation of an experience and achieves an otherworldly density of image, line after line. It is obvious that Etel Adnan is a major poet. —Eric Sellin

Adoff, Arnold. *Slow Dance Heart Break Blues.* 80p. $14.00 (0-688-10569-6). New York, NY: Lothrop, Lee & Shepard, Fall 1995. ALA Best Books for Young Adults, 1996. Visually wild and whirling, Arnold Adoff's new poems are rich in rhymes straight out of rap and in heavy-metal rhythms. Here is valuable reading for people who want to understand teens, and for all teens who want to understand one another. —X. J. Kennedy. *Slow Dance Heart Break Blues* is a treasure to be tasted, savored, shared, and savored yet again. —Nikki Giovanni. Playing with shape and rhythm is nothing new for Adoff, and he uses those techniques to illuminate the thoughts of adolescents in this fast and funky collection. —*School Library Journal*

Adolph, Andrea; Donald L. Vallis, and Anne F. Walker, eds. *bite to eat place: an anthology*

of contemporary food poetry and poetic prose. 187p. pap. $14.95 (0-9640933-1-6). Oakland, CA: Redwood Coast Press, Spring 1995. In this anthology American and Canadian poets use striking food imagery to explore such themes as relationships, eating disorders, illness, and the erotic. —Redwood Coast Press

Afif, Kaissar. Translated by Mansour Ajami, edited by Barbara De Graff Ajami. *And the Word Became Poem.* 141p. pap. $12.00 (0-9626898-3-1). Princeton, NJ: Grindstone Press, Fall 1994. Bilingual edition. These are poems about the complex experience of writing poetry. In the words of Afif, Word becomes Poem, "the drunken tongue of fire." —Grindstone Press

Agosín, Marjorie, ed. *These Are Not Sweet Girls: Poetry by Latin American Women.* 368p. pap. $17.00 (1-877727-38-5). Fredonia, NY: White Pine Press, Fall 1994. Agosín has broken new ground with *These Are Not Sweet Girls.* She has enlarged the poetic canon while creating an international audience for Latin American women's writing. The poems speak to readers in both hemispheres and of both sexes, for they address fundamental human realities that transcend genre and geography. —Barbara Mujica, *Américas*

Agostino, Paul. *The Tourist Heart.* 32p. pap. $5.00 (0-940895-32-3). Chicago, IL: Corner Stone Press Chicago, Fall 1994.

Agüeros, Jack. *Sonnets From the Puerto Rican.* 110p. $20.00 (1-882413-23-7); pap. $12.00 (1-882413-22-9). Brooklyn, NY: Hanging Loose Press, Spring 1996. Agüeros extends the range of poetic possibility in these stunning sonnets from real life. —Lorna Dee Cervantes

Alberti, Rafael. Translated by Christopher Sawyer-Lauçunno. *Concerning the Angels.* 153p. pap. $12.95 (0-87286-297-6). San Francisco, CA: City Lights Books, Fall 1995. First published in Spain in 1929, *Concerning the Angels* is Alberti's masterpiece, at once intensely imaginative and intimately realistic. Alberti is the last surviving member of Spain's "Generation of 1927." —City Lights Books

Alegria, Claribel. Translated by Darwin J. Flakoll. *Thresholds/ Umbrales.* 80p. pap. $10.95 (1-880684-36-5). Willimantic, CT: Curbstone Press, Fall 1996. A lyric meditation, reflecting on her life and her art. —Curbstone Press. Claribel Alegria's work is a continuous feast set out for the hungry soul. —Clarissa Pinkola Estes

Alexander, Kwame. *Just Us: Poems and Counterpoems, 1986–1995.* 92p. pap. $9.95 (1-888018-00-3). Alexandria, VA: Alexander Publishing Group, Fall 1995. A masterful wordsmith, Kwame Alexander is a bad young poet. [Kwame] paints poetic word pictures that inspire, enlighten, and entertain. His words speak to and for a new generation of artists who will definitely make the ancestors proud. —Toni Blackman

Alexander, Meena. *The Shock of Arrival: Reflections on Postcolonial Experience.* 224p. pap. $15.00 (0-89608-545-7). Boston, MA: South End Press, Spring 1996. Meena Alexander has written a fierce new complexity into questions of identity, diaspora, tradition, language, and community. This is a powerful fusion of poetic vision and critical thinking. —Adrienne Rich

Alexander, Robert; Mark Vinz and C.W. Truesdale, eds. *The Party Train: A Collection of North American Prose Poetry.* 353p. pap. $18.95 (0-89823-165-5). Minneapolis, MN: New Rivers Press, Spring 1996. I can't imagine a course on the prose poem or very short fiction not including *The Party Train* on its reading list. —Peter Johnson

Alexander, Will. *Asia & Haiti.* 144p. pap. $11.95 (1-55713-189-9). Los Angeles, CA: Sun & Moon Press, Fall 1995. Two long poems by Los Angeles poet Will Alexander, which, in the broadest sense, are about the cultures, economics, politics, history, and social concerns of the title regions. But Alexander's poetry, densely imagistic and fiercely intelligent, takes these concerns into arpeggios of linguistic realms. Alexander's poetry presents a re-writing of history which is caught up in the vortex of a surrealist vision and in tornadoes of language. —Sun & Moon Press

Alexie, Sherman. *The Summer of Black Widows.* 144p. cloth $22.00 (1-882413-35-0). pap. $13.50 (1-882413-34-2). Brooklyn, NY: Hanging Loose Press, Fall 1996. A young writer who is taking the literary world by storm, [Alexie is] a superb chronicler of the Native American experience. He is a master of language, writing beautifully, unsparingly and straight to the heart. —Chris Faatz, *The Nation*

Alferi, Pierre. Translated by Cole Swensen. *Natural Gaits.* 48p. pap. $10.95 (1-55713-231-3). Los Angeles, CA: Sun & Moon Press, Fall 1995. Dealing with sequence and movement, *Natural Gaits* combines the analytical and scientific with an almost breathless, poetic voice; the poem reads almost as if a scientist were to recite his most recent analyses by playing a long saxophone riff. Alferi constructs a linguistic machine of impacted grammar that drives the poem in absolutely breathtaking directions. —Sun & Moon Press

Allan, Robb. *Full of **it.* 15p. pap. $1.50 Los Angeles, CA: Undulating Bedsheets Productions, Fall 1995.

Allen, Gilbert. *Commandments at Eleven.* 77p. pap. $12.95 (0-914061-46-5). Alexandria, VA: Orchises Press, Fall 1994. Allen's humor is dry, arch, Thurberesque. His religious perspective is clear, yet underplayed. —Orchises Press

Allen, Heather. *Leaving a Shadow.* 80p. pap. $12.00 (1-55659-113-6). Port Townsend, WA: Copper Canyon Press, Fall 1996. These poems are of a profound intimacy. Heather Allen writes out of a fully lived experience of lake and forest, with their light and darkness, silence and sounds, stillness and movement; their deer, crows, owls; their ongoing secret life. And from this authentic and erotic intimacy her lines, images, and stanzas have emerged with the musicality that is inseparable from precision. —Denise Levertov

Allen, Jeffner. *Reverberations: Across the Shimmering Cascadas.* 204p. $44.50 (0-7914-1897-9); pap. $14.95 (0-7914-1898-7). Albany, NY: State University of New York Press, Fall 1994. This is a groundbreaking work of poetry, autobiography, lesbian studies, multicultural writing, feminist philosophy.

—SUNY Press. I like the skillful play of language, the shapes of the words on the page conveying multiple meanings, the reliance on the music of language, the shifting positionalities of the subject in different sections, and the mirrorings of languages. The book is utterly delicious to read. —Rosemary Keefe Curb

Allen, Ron. *I Want My Body Back.* 52p. pap. $10.00 (1-56439-054-3). Roseville, MI: Ridgeway Press, Fall 1996. Hard hitting urban poetry from longtime Detroit street poet and activist Ron Allen. Allen provides a glimpse of the world as it is seen through the eyes of the struggling many. —Ridgeway Press

Allen, Ron, ed. *Brainstorm: An Anthology of Poetry From the Harbor Light Center Salvation Army, Detroit, Michigan.* 18p. pap. $2.50. Detroit, MI: Broadside Press, Spring 1995. The poems in this chapbook are the product of the transformative power of creativity and the individual voice. They were written in order to express the struggle of overcoming addiction. —Christopher Parks

Allen, Tom Morris. *October Leaves: Poems and Prose.* 144p. pap. $9.95 (1-56474-143-5). Santa Barbara, CA: Fithian Press, Fall 1995. From the sublime to the ridiculous, Allen shares his thoughts about life's ponderables, love, and aging. —Fithian Press

Allred, Joanne. *Whetstone.* 24p. pap. $7.00 (1-886226-01-6). Chico, CA: Flume Press, Spring 1996. I admire the range and complexity of these poems, their textured language, the feel and sound of them in my mouth and my inner ear. I want to hang out with a woman this intensely connected to all that is human, and conscious of her presence in the world. —Carole Oles

Alpaugh, David. *Counterpoint.* 96p. pap. $11.95 (0-934257-55-8). Brownsville, OR: Story Line Press, Spring 1995. Winner of the 1994 Nicholas Roerich Poetry Prize. David Alpaugh . . . is a poet of conscience and complete honesty, a poet of vision and intelligence. This, coupled with his wild imaginings and playful wit, makes for an important first book whose craft and sen-sibility will satisfy and delight the reader. —Ruth Daigon

Alurista. *Et Tú . . . Raza?* 72p. pap. $9.00 (0-927534-48-7). Tempe, AZ: Bilingual Press, Fall 1996. A poet with a strong commitment to social issues, Alurista continues to explore racism and other forms of bigotry in *Et Tú . . . Raza?* —Bilingual Press. [His is] a polyphonic voice that is genuinely unique. —*Lector*

Alurista. *Z Eros.* 74p. pap. $8.00 (0-927534-45-2). Tempe, AZ: Bilingual Press, Fall 1995. This is the work of a revolutionary poet. Alurista's style is breathless, electric, and urgent. Moving rapidly between Spanish and English, he introduces readers to a language and a world that exists somewhere between the two cultures and voices. —Bilingual Press. Alurista has established a poetic legacy that mirrors the struggle and the hope of the Chicanos. —Guillermo Rojas, *Chicano Literature*

Alvarez, Julia. *The Other Side: El Otro Lado.* 155p. $18.95 (0-525-93922-9). New York, NY: Dutton, Fall 1995. Tracing a lyrical journey through the landscape of immigrant life, these are direct, reflective, often sensuous poems. Alvarez claims her authority as a poet with this collection. —*Publishers Weekly*

Alvi, Moniza. *A Bowl of Warm Air.* 46p. pap. $11.95 (0-19-282520-8). New York, NY: Oxford University Press, Fall 1996. [Alvi's work] is deceptively simple, disarmingly truthful, full of a vivid and delicate individuality and jouissance. —Linda France, *Poetry Review*

Alvin, Dave. *Any Rough Times Are Now Behind You: Selected Poems and Writings 1979–1995.* 130p. pap. $12.00 (0-884615-09-0). San Diego, CA: Incommunicado Press, Fall 1995. Alvin is peerless when it comes to painting American scenes of extremes, where people are either leaving town or promising never to leave again. Haunting, spellbinding in intensity and sobriety. —*L.A. Weekly*

Amato, Joe. *Symptoms of a Finer Age.* 96p. pap. $12.00 (1-885215-12-6). Woodbridge, CT: Viet Nam Generation/ Burning Cities Press, Spring 1995. Amato proposes a poetry

of discourse: he thinks, talks, and will try to persuade sometimes. The work is alive with intelligence. —Don Byrd

Ammons, A.R. *Brink Road.* 230p. $23.00 (0-393-03958-7). New York, NY: W.W. Norton & Company, Fall 1996. These poems, dating from 1973 to the present, deal with Ammons's lifelong concern with language and mortality; its very name suggesting the sense that we are ever in transition from one state of mind to another, and always on the edge of revelation. —W.W. Norton & Company

Ammons, A.R. *Garbage.* 121p. $17.95 (0-393-03542-5); pap. $9.00 (0-393-31203-8). New York, NY: W.W. Norton & Company, 1993. Winner of the 1993 National Book Award. *Garbage* has a rueful grandeur and characteristically splendid oddity. Over the last 40 years Mr. Ammons has consistently demonstrated the democratic precept that "anything is poetry" and here he playfully takes up—takes on—the subject of trash. —Edward Hirsch, *New York Times Book Review*. [Ammons] is more than good company, he is positively inspiriting. —William Pritchard, *Boston Sunday Globe*

Ammons, A.R. *Sphere: The Form of a Motion.* 80p. pap. $8.95 (0-393-31310-7). New York, NY: W.W. Norton & Company, Spring 1995. Ammons is our Lucretius, swerving and sideswiping his way into the nature of things. —Richard Howard. There wasn't one page of [this long] poem that didn't delight me. —Donald Davie, *New York Review of Books*

Ammons, A.R. *Tape for the Turn of the Year.* 205p. pap. $11.00 (0-393-31204-6). New York, NY: W.W. Norton & Company, Fall 1994. Taking the form of a journal covering the period from December 6, 1963, through January 10, 1964, this long, thin poem was written originally on a roll of adding-machine tape. —W.W. Norton & Company

Andersen, Sam, and Tony Medina, eds. *In Defense of Mumia.* 364p. pap. $14.00 (0-86316-099-9). New York, NY: Writers and Readers Publishing/Harlem River Press, Spring 1996. Winner of the Fire Cracker Alternative Book Award. *In Defense of Mumia* will help to keep the pressure on, to spread the word, and to send a defiant message to the Pennsylvania criminal justice system that the people, nationwide and worldwide, demand justice. —Writers and Readers Publishing

Anderson. *Trust.* pap. $10.00 (0-9639585-1-8). New York, NY: Fly By Night Press, Fall 1994. This collection is essentially about language. But it's not quite 'concrete'. Rather, it experiments with the subtle nuances in that space where language and thought meet and dissolve into the timelessness of desire. —Richard Kostelanetz. Trust this book—translations of screams, gnashings of teeth. Pump these poems into a vein—something to read yourself to sleep by, on your bed of knives and needles. —Bob Holman

Anderson, Alice. *Human Nature.* 87p. $25.00 (0-8147-0632-0); pap. $12.95 (0-8147-0633-9). New York, NY: New York University Press, Fall 1994. *Human Nature* is a collection of poems which explores the redemptive possibilities for an

American girlhood gone wrong. —New York University Press

Anderson, Doug. *The Moon Reflected Fire.* 64p. pap. $9.95 (1-882295-03-X). Farmington, ME: Alice James Books, Fall 1994. Winner of the 1994 Kate Tufts Discovery Award for Poetry. These are trenchant, wrenching poems. With artistry and honesty they perform an inquest into war and its corrosive aftereffects. —James Tate

Anderson, Kath. *An Abbreviated History of Water.* 32p. pap. $6.00 Brockport, NY: State Street Press, Spring 1996. The American Southwest becomes the focus for an extended sequence on Christopher Columbus and the American dream in an arid landscape. —State Street Press

Anderson, Ken. *The Intense Lover: A Suite of Poems.* 96p. pap. $9.00 (1-877978-80-9). Sarasota, FL: Florida Literary Foundation Press/Starbooks, Fall 1995. Few poets write with as much wit and candor. —Jon Hershey. Ken Anderson's contributions to gay culture must not be overlooked. —Jack

Nichols, *TWN News Magazine.* I would be surprised if this book doesn't make its way into the 'Lammys.' —Jesse Monteagudo, *Community Voice*

Anderson, Martha Shelton. *Good Love Gone Bad and Other Rhymes.* 102p. pap. $10.00 (0-934852-64-2). Black Mountain, NC: Lorien House, Spring 1996.

Andersson, Claes. Translated by Rika Lesser. *What Became Words.* 176p. pap. $11.95 (1-55713-302-6). Los Angeles, CA: Sun & Moon Press, Fall 1996. Member of the Finnish Parliament, jazz pianist, literary activist, and Minister of Culture, Claes Andersson is the author of over 17 books of poetry since 1962. His work, selected in this volume, combines colloquial speech, the rhythms of jazz, and the perceptions of psychiatry in an interweaving of the imagination and the everyday. —Sun & Moon Press

Andonov, Nicole. *Portraits Exposed.* 80p. pap. $6.95 (0-9646048-0-9). Brooklyn, NY: Westonian Press, Fall 1995. Striking, witty, twisting reflections on everything from busybodies to white lies that reveal an original energy and joy. —Jason Shinder. With one or two quick strokes of her pen, Nicole Andonov . . . liberates the pure moment of the poem. These poems are a pleasure. —Elaine Equi

Andrea, Joyce Joyce. *PEACE.* 20p. pap. $3.00. New York, NY: Joyce Joyce Andrea, Fall 1995.

Andrews, Bruce. *EX WHY ZEE.* 109p. pap. $10.95 (0-937804-60-6). New York, NY: Roof Books, Spring 1995. These performance texts and scores capture the energy that continues to enliven the new arts scene in dance, theater, music, and poetry. Andrews' work is at the center of these innovations—designed to flood light the impossible, to maximize meaning at the microphone. —Roof Books

Andrus, Pat. *Old Woman of Irish Blood.* 80p. pap. $9.95 (0-940880-59-8). Seattle, WA: Open Hand Publishing, Spring 1996. *Old Woman* resounds as an outcry of reverence, encouraging us to embrace . . . birth as well as growth, death as well as rebirth. —Christianne Balk

Angel, Ralph. *Neither World.* 94p. $15.95 (1-881163-12-1); pap. $9.95 (1-881163-13-X). Oxford, OH: Miami University Press, Fall 1995. Winner of the 1995 James Laughlin Award of the Academy of American Poets. These fiery, trenchant poems illumine the recesses of our labyrinthine consciousness with fierce wit and intelligence. *Neither World* abounds with surprises and delights that defy familiar categories. —James Tate. He eavesdrops on the American psyche and retrieves the somatic residue of speech within the dream-defiled paradise that is Southern California. In the absence of satiation, he makes a haven of longing. I am intoxicated by the fine strangeness of his work. —Alice Fulton. *Neither World* more than fulfills the promise of Ralph Angel's early work. He is now a major voice in poetry. —John Ashbery

Angeline, Mary. *Precise Intrigues.* 72p. pap. $12.00 (0-942996-22-4). Sausalito, CA: Post-Apollo Press, Fall 1994. Angeline's poems seem to be on their way from this world to some other, a dark and fascinating journey. They catch, by little more than a blur of motion, the body's fall into spirit. —Keith Waldrop

Angelou, Maya. *A Brave and Startling Truth.* 32p. $10.00 (0-679-44904-3). New York, NY: Random House, Fall 1995. Read by the poet at the fiftieth anniversary of the founding of the United Nations, San Francisco, 26 June 1995.

Angelou, Maya. *And Still I Rise.* 56p. $12.00 (0-394-50252-3). New York, NY: Random House, reissued Fall 1996. I find it very moving and at times beautiful. It has an innate purity about it, an unquenchable dignity. —M.F.K. Fisher

Apollinaire, Guillaume. Translated by Donald Revell. *Alcools.* 192p. $30.00 (0-8195-2224-4); pap. $15.95 (0-8195-1228-1). Middletown, CT: Wesleyan/ University Press of New England, Fall 1995. Revell buoyantly delivers into English the swift visions and odd, bright beauty of *Alcools* . . . , arguably one of this century's most inventive and influential books of poetry. —*Publishers Weekly*

Aponick, Kathleen. *Near The River's Edge.* 34p. pap. $7.95 Johnstown, OH: Pudding House Publications, Spring 1995.

Appleman, Philip. *New and Selected Poems, 1956–1996.* 280p. $38.00 (1-55728-419-9); pap. $22.00 (1-55728-420-2). Fayetteville, AR: University of Arkansas Press, Fall 1996. A cohesive and substantial collection. His voice is quietly lyrical and deeply rooted in the everyday yet somehow drenched with passion: "we lie in the shelter of blankets / in the summer blood of our loving / and feel the old terror of time / freezing the land." Appleman hasn't exhausted his muse yet. —Patricia Monaghan, *Booklist*

Arbuthnot, Nancy, trans, *Mexico Shining: Songs of the Aztecs.* 120p. $20.00 (0-89410-785-2); pap. $12.00 (0-89410-786-0). Boulder, CO: Three Continents Press/Lynne Rienner Publishers, Fall 1995. Though fragments of Aztec songs translated by William Carlos Williams, Stephen Berg and others have appeared previously, this collection condenses the repetitive chant like songs to their inner sense; lyrical but reflective of the thrust of the entire text of the original. —Three Continents Press

Ardinger, Rick. *Goodbye, Magpie.* 63p. $15.00 (1-881-850-02-1). Boise, ID: Floating Ink Books, 1995. Ardinger intensifies the language of his Northwestern community, blending poetic styles and the Idaho landscape into his own brand of vernacular. —Greg Keeler. It is the hard honesty and the music of these poems that most delights me—that and Rick's wonderful eye for significant blood and bone detail. *Goodbye, Magpie* is an excellent book full of life and the small but so important gestures of love. —Keith Wilson

Armalinsky, Mikhail. *Vplotnuiu (close to).* 92p. pap. $9.00 (0-916201-16-3). Minneapolis, MN: M.I.P Company, Fall 1995. What we have here is a very expressive poet, and one very competent in form. He is capable of innovative rhyme. He experiments in five-line stanzas and in cleverly syncopated sound textures. His [erotic, misogynistic] message is never opaque and is arrestingly expressed. —*World Literature Today*

Armantrout, Rae. *Made to Seem.* 60p. pap. $9.95 (1-55713-220-8). Los Angeles, CA: Sun & Moon Press, Fall 1995. Armantrout takes the everyday jargon of suburbia and plops it down in the surreal-like natural world. —Sun & Moon Press. Paradoxes thrive in the close quarters of her short poems. The formal constraints [she uses] only serve to accentuate these jarring but exhilarating oppositions. —Elaine Equi

Arobateau, Red Jordan. *Laughter of the Witch and Other Known Poems.* 51p. pap. $15.00 (0-934172-40-4). San Jose, CA: Woman in the Moon Publications, Fall 1995. Here is a brave voice worth listening to. —Margaret Busby

Arroyo, Rane. *The Singing Shark.* 83p. pap. $9.00 (0-927534-61-4). Tempe, AZ: Bilingual Press, Fall 1996. Rane Arroyo is a fluid poetic traveler easily crossing borders between Hispanic and Anglo-American life, homo- and heterosexual experience, pop and literary culture. —Martha Collins

Artaud, Antonin. Translated by Clayton Eshleman with Bernard Bador. *Watchfiends and Rack Screams: Works From the Final Period.* 342p. pap. $15.95 (1-878972-18-9). Boston, MA: Exact Change, Fall 1995.

Arthur, Robert P. *Hymn to the Chesapeake.* 88p. pap. $14.95 (1-880016-12-5). Painter, VA: Road Publishers, reissued Spring 1996. The most evocative writing about the Chesapeake since *Beautiful Swimmers.* —David Poyer. [Arthur's work is informed by] passionate knowledge and keen observation. —Annette Silva, the Delaware *News Journal*

Ashbery, John. *And the Stars Were Shining.* 100p. $22.00 (0-374-10500-6); pap. $11.00 (0-374-52434-3). New York, NY: Farrar, Straus and Giroux/ Noonday, Spring 1995. We've come to expect [from Ashbery] the dazzle, the deadpan shifts from speed to languor, the teeming fluidities of tone; a genuine capaciousness of spirit—gifts to thank our lucky stars for. —Linda Gregerson, *The New York Times Book Review.* Ashbery collects words the way a child learns them, as if mesmerized by their strangeness. In his poems they unexpectedly assume new

meanings, in contexts no one's thought of before. —Tom Clark, *San Francisco Chronicle*

Ashbery, John. *Can You Hear, Bird.* 175p. $20.00 (0-374-11831-0). New York, NY: Farrar, Straus and Giroux, Fall 1995. Ashbery has never written as genially, hilariously, and heartbreakingly as he does in these new poems. —Marjorie Perloff

Asher, Elise. *The Visionary Gleam: Texts and Transformations.* 120p. pap. $30.00 (1-878818-33-3). Riverdale-on-Hudson, NY: Sheep Meadow Press, Spring 1995. In this opulent work of exploration and discovery, Asher juxtaposes 47 color plates of her luminous paintings with their sources or parallels in the poems of the great tradition. —Sheep Meadow Press

Atwood, Margaret. *Morning in the Burned House.* 144p. $19.95 (0-395-75591-3); pap. $12.95 (0-395-82521-0). Boston, MA: Houghton Mifflin Company, Fall 1995. Co-winner of the 1996 Trillium Book Award in Canada. In her first poetry collection since 1987 . . . Atwood brings a swift, powerful energy to meditative poems that often begin in domestic settings and broaden into numinous dialogues. —*Publishers Weekly*

Aubert, Alvin. *Harlem Wrestler and Other Poems.* 64p. pap. $10.00 (0-87013-369-1). East Lansing, MI: Michigan State University Press/Lotus Poetry Series, Fall 1995.

Austin, William James. *1 Underworld 2.* 64p. pap. $10.00 (1-884970-00-1). Cambridge, MA: S Press Books, Fall 1994. A first collection of poems from this urban musician and rock lyricist. —S Press Books

Averill, Diane. *Turtle Sky.* 26p. pap. $5.00. Portland, OR: 26 Books, Spring 1995. These poems are about rain forests and their sensous, and endangered, ecology. —26 Books

Axinn, Donald Everett. *The Latest Illusion.* 128p. pap. $12.95 (1-55970-293-2). New York, NY: Arcade Publishing, Spring 1995. Axinn writes with unwavering clarity, an eye for the memorable detail, an ear for the unexpected rhythmic twist. —Jay Parini. Here's what I admire about Donald Axinn's new book: the human facts of our lives, the poet's unflinching gaze, the tongue that reshapes and sings it back to us. —Cornelius Eady

B

Bachar, Jacqueline Miller, ed. *Poetry in the Garden.* 128p. $19.95 (1-886934-07-X). Palos Verdes Peninsula, CA: International Forum, Spring 1996. California women, ten years old to great-grandmothers, total unknowns and established talents, give voice to their special relationships with gardens and garden inhabitants. —International Forum

Bachmann, Ingeborg. Translated by Peter Filkins. *Songs in Flight: The Collected Poems of Ingeborg Bachmann.* 337p. $40.00 (1-56886-009-9); pap. $19.95 (1-56886-010-2). New York, NY: Marsilio Publishers, Spring 1995. Poet, short story writer, novelist, essayist, Ingeborg Bachmann is regarded as one of the half-dozen most important German-language writers of the second half of the twentieth century. English-language readers still don't have enough Bachmann to read, but this volume of eloquent translations is the best of all possible beginnings. —Susan Sontag. This collection brings to an English-speaking audience virtually the entire poetic output of one of the most important post-war European poets, offering the original German and sensitive translations by poet Filkins. —*Publishers Weekly*

Baggett, Rebecca. *Still Life With Children.* 28p. pap. $7.95. Johnstown, OH: Pudding House Publications, Spring 1996. Winner of the 1995 National Looking Glass Poetry Chapbook Competition from Pudding House Publications.

Bailey, Jan. *Paper Clothes.* 52p. (0-9645778-0-1). Greenville, SC: Emrys Press, Spring 1995.

Bailey, R. W. *Silent Sentences.* 71p. $7.95 (1888642-02-5). Nogal, NM: Land-Ship Bookstore Publishers, Fall 1996.

Balakian, Peter. *Dyer's Thistle.* 80p. $20.95 (0-88748-232-5); pap. $11.95 (0-88748-233-3). Pittsburgh, PA: Carnegie Mellon University, Spring 1996. [Balakian's] language is bound inextricably with conscience. [In his work] and the past becomes visible, inscribed into the present, an inheritance both tender and horrifying, but, finally, redemptive in its spiritual resonance. —Carolyn Forché. Like Williams in *Paterson*, Mr. Balakian displays a powerful talent in resurrecting the past, lyrically transforming the story of his heritage into an affirmative history for all survivors. —Shirley Horner, *The New York Times*

Balakian, Peter. *Yad Vashem: Children's Memorial.* 8p. pap. $45.00 (0-916375-26-9). Lewisburg, PA: The Press of Appletree Alley, Fall 1996. One of the most distinguished poets of his generation, Armenian-American Peter Balakian wrote "Yad Vashem" after his visit to the Children's Memorial Holocaust Museum in Jerusalem. Letterpress edition chapbook illustrated by a two-color woodcut by Colleen Shannon. —The Press of Appletree Alley

Balentine-Laurens, Debra. *Shades of Pearl.* 40p. pap. $6.95 (1-56315-040-9). Pittsburgh, PA: Sterling House, Fall 1995.

Balk, Christianne. *Desiring Flight.* 96p. pap. $12.95 (1-55753-062-9). West Lafayette, IN: Purdue University Press, Spring 1995. Winner of the 1995 Verna Emery Poetry Prize. Christianne Balk observes nature with the knowledgeable eye of a trained biologist and writes about it with the skill of a superb poet. Whether she is writing about the natural world, the life of John Muir, or her daughter, she writes with astonishing authority. The poems in *Desiring Flight* are utterly heartbreaking in their sorrow and equally exhilarating in their transcendence. —Andrew Hudgins

Ball, Angela. *Possession.* 96p. pap. $9.95 (0-9639528-6-2). Palmdale, CA: Red Hen Press, Fall 1995. Angela Ball is a poet wise enough to describe love as "a double appetite for seeing." Her poems are suffused by a wary disappointment in romantic excitement, but with the piqued attention that accompanies desire she makes the world, so far as this can be done, the object of her desire. —William Matthews

Ball, Angela. *Quartet.* 61p. pap. $11.95 (0-88748-189-2).

Pittsburgh, PA: Carnegie Mellon University Press, Spring 1995. Four poems, each in the voice of one of the women of the literary Paris of the twenties and thirties: Sylvia Beach, Nora Joyce, Nancy Cunard, and Jean Rhys. —Carnegie Mellon University Press

bandele, ashe. *Absence in the Palms of My Hands.* 128p. pap. $12.00 (0-86316-013-1). New York, NY: Writers and Readers Publishing/Harlem River Press, Fall 1996. *Absence in the Palms of My Hands* is a road map of sorts. In the often mean and isolating landscape of urban America, she charts her losses, acquisitions, and changes in alternately angry and direct, contemplative metaphorical terms. —Writers and Readers Publishing

Baraka, Amiri. Edited by Paul Vangelisti. *Transbluesency: Selected Poems of Amiri Baraka/LeRoi Jones* (1961-1995). 272p. $32.95 (1-56886-013-7); pap. $17.95 (1-56886-014-5). New York, NY: Marsilio Publishers, Fall 1995. An ample selection of works from every period of Baraka's extraordinarily innovative, often controversial struggle as a serious and ideologically committed American artist— from Beat to Black Nationalist to Marxist-Leninist. —Marsilio Publishers

Baraka, Amiri. *Wise, Why's, Y's.* 132p. $29.95 (0-88378-150-6); pap. $12.00 (0-88378-047-X). Chicago, IL: Third World Press, Fall 1995.

Barkan, Stanley H. Translated by Joseph Calabro. *From the Garden of Eden: A Midrash of Origins.* 16p. pap. $3.00 (0-89304-637-X). Merrick, NY: Cross-Cultural Communications, Spring 1995. Bilingual edition, including the English originals and Calabro's Italian translations. —Cross-Cultural Communications

Barkan, Stanley H. *0 Jerusalem.* 48p. $15.00 (0-89304-469-5); pap. (0-89304-470-9). Merrick, NY: Cross-Cultural Communications, Spring 1996.

Barkan, Stanley H. *The Sacrifice: A Midrash on the Akedah.* 20p. pap. $5.00 (0-89304-636-1). Merrick, NY: Cross-Cultural Communications, Fall 1995.

Barkan, Stanley H. Translated by Liotta Saro. *Then & Now.* 10p. pap. $2.00 (0-89304-635-3).

Merrick, NY: Cross-Cultural Communications, Fall 1995. A meeting of an American poet with a Sicilian composer-guitarist in Italy and America, in English and Italian, then & now. —Cross-Cultural Communications

Barkan, Stanley H., and Darrel Bourque, eds. *Cajun Writers.* Boxed set of three books, 48p. ea. $100.00 (0-89304-924-7). Cross-Cultural Communications, Fall 1995. Deluxe boxed set includes: *Jesuis Cadien* by Jean Arceneaux; *Plainsongs* by Darrell Bourque; and *La Grande Pointe* by Beverly Matherne. All are bilingual editions. Art by Terry Clay Girouard and Randall LaBry. Hand-marbled paper, handmade box. —Cross-Cultural Communications. Other deluxe boxed set editions available from Cross-Cultural Communications include: *Native American Poets* and *Yiddish Writers.*

Barnstone, Willis. *The Secret Reader: 501 Sonnets.* 440p. pap. $21.95 (0-87451-660-9). Hanover, NH: University Press of New England, Fall 1995. I am captivated by these sonnets. The free movement of consciousness, the mind operating in the universe . . . [Here] is art and cunning, form and ruthless honesty. —Gerald Stern. A valuable accomplishment . . . a remarkable modernist testament. —Edward Hirsch

Barone, Dennis. *A Matter of Habit.* 22p. pap. $5.00 (0-945112-21-1). Cleveland, OH: Generator Press, Spring 1995. These are short pieces of short story prose poems; collaged fusions of images, ideas, situations, and parts of speech. —Generator Press

Barresi, Dorothy. *The Post-Rapture Diner.* 86p. $24.95 (0-8229-3896-0); pap. $10.95 (0-8229-5581-4). Pittsburgh, PA: University of Pittsburgh Press, Fall 1995. Barresi writes poems that have snap, crackle, and pop, with just the right amount of poetic mystery. Barresi's poetry has wit and pathos. . . . Her metaphors are a delight. —*Library Journal.* What a pleasure to find a poet whose sense of risk and honesty drives her to complicate the emotions and attitudes of her poems rather than to wrap us up a neat little parcel of 'sensitivities.' . . . I'd pay to read or hear her anytime, I'd stand in line. —David Rivard, *Ploughshares*

Barrett, Bettina T. *Sleepdancer.* 80p. pap. $8.95 (1-56474-116-8). Santa Barbara, CA: Fithian Press, Fall 1994. [These poems] follow a high-road landscaped by the subtle images and colors found within light and shadow. Mysticism and reality walk this road together. —Julia Cunningham

Bartel, Robert Paul. *Polarity of the Roman.* pap. 17p. $7.00. Springfield, IL: Bartel, Robert P., Spring 1996.

Barth, Robert L. *Small Arms Fire.* 19p. Edgewood, KY: Robert L. Barth (R.L.B.), Spring 1995.

Barth, Robert L., ed. *Nine Years Later* 77p. pap. $9.95 (0-941150-76-3). Edgewood, KY: Robert L. Barth (R.L.B.), Spring 1995. This anthology shows the range of work that the Robert L. Barth press has published. It provides a look at a group of poets . . . who share a belief in the traditional resources of poetry . . . [and] illuminates the reestablishment of metrical verse as a viable alternative in the composition of contemporary poetry. —Victoria Steele

Basho, Matsuo. Translated by Hiroaki Sato. *Basho's Narrow*

Road: Spring and Autumn Passages. 192p. pap. $15.00 (1-880656-20-5). Berkeley, CA: Stone Bridge Press, Fall 1996. Poems that were written by Mastuo Basho in 1689. Ostensibly a travel diary, the book is rich in allusions to literature and Zen. —Stone Bridge Press. In this remarkable translation we find the elliptical, allusive, suggestive richness of the original. [This is] the most accessible version in English. —Cor van den Heuvel

Bast, Felicity, ed. *The Poetical Cat: An Anthology.* 144p. $20.00 (0-374-23533-3). New York, NY: Farrar, Straus and Giroux, Fall 1995. This is a witty and spirited anthology including poems by W. H. Auden, Charles Baudelaire, Elizabeth Bishop, Robert Graves, Thom Gunn, Issa, and so on. —Farrar, Straus and Giroux

Bathanti, Joseph. *This Metal.* 123p. pap. $10.95 (1-879934-30-2). Laurinburg, NC: St. Andrews College Press, Fall 1996. It is in the struggle to know that these poems generate much of their power, capturing as they do that moment when the story of our lives is "about to catch fire," all of its voices

glittering on the verge of revelation. —Kathryn Stripling Byer

Battaglia, Carol. *Murmurs.* 67p. pap. $12.95 (1-880254-36-0). Long Branch, NJ: Vista Publishing, Spring 1996. An extraordinary collection of original poems and essays encouraging the reader to reach beyond self-imposed boundaries and listen carefully to hear "the murmurs of life." —Vista Publishing

Baudelaire, Charles. Translated by Wallace Fowlie. *Selected Poems From Flowers of Evil.* 54p. pap. $1.00 (0-486-28450-6). Mingola, NY: Dover Publications, Fall 1995. Republication of the English text only from the dual-language edition published by Dover in 1992. —Dover Publications

Bauer, Bill. *Promises in the Dust.* 61p. pap. $10.00 (1-886157-01-4). Kansas City, MO: BkMk Press of the University of Missouri-Kansas City, Fall 1995. Bauer's range is impressive: war, family, nature, the poems brightly or darkly colored with a palette from disparate places. Whether he writes about the Caribbean or a chopper leaving 'Nam, Bauer's the real thing. —Jim McKinley

Baumel, Judith. *NOW.* 64p. $16.95 (1-88163-14-8); pap. $10.95 (1-881163-15-6). Oxford, OH: Miami University Press, Spring 1996. Judith Baumel is one of the most gifted younger poets now writing in this country. [NOW] is a tough and impressive work of art. —Robert Hass

Baumgaertner, Jill Peláez. *Leaving Eden.* 24p. pap. $5.95. Fox River Grove, IL: White Eagle Coffee Store Press, Spring 1995. Winner of the Spring 1994 White Eagle Coffee Store Press Poetry Chapbook Contest. In a voice which is strong and clear, the poet-magician writes of the axis which links myth and memory, creating a new world in which loss—whether psychic or physical—foretells transfiguration. —Martha M. Vertreace

Beard, Henry. *Poetry for Cats: The Definitive Anthology of Distinguished Feline Verse.* $12.95 (0-679435-82-4). New York, NY: Villard Books, Fall 1994.

Beatty, Jan. *Mad River.* 63p. $24.95 (0-8229-3897-9); pap.

$10.95 (0-8229-5570-9). Pittsburgh, PA: University of Pittsburgh Press, Fall 1996. A fresh voice with rough edges, shamelessly bringing sex, fear, compassion, the hurt you feel for others and the self—and the grit and drive of working class lives—into language. —Alicia Ostriker. It is in her keen mental note taking that the real madness—that is, passion—lies. In every poem, she keeps her fury contained but omnipresent, yet she hints of happier possibilities, too. —*Booklist*

Beatty, Jan. *Ravenous.* 28p. pap. $6.00. Brockport, NY: State Street Press, Spring 1995.

Beck, Al. *Sight Lines: Poems and Drawings.* 87p. pap. $6.00 (0-934852-63-4). Black Mountain, NC: Lorien House, Spring 1996. A book of zany poems and illustrations, full of literary puns, Al's forté. —Lorien House

Becker, Anne. *The Transmutation Notebooks: Poems in the Voices of Charles and Emma Darwin.* 99p. pap. $10.00 (0-938572-12-1). Hedgesville, WV: The Bunny and the Crocodile Press/Forest Woods Media, Spring 1996.

Darwin's theories supported by Love? Here is a book of poems with lyricism, intensity, and, rare in the late twentieth century, a fascinating stated premise. In her remarkable *Transmutation Notebooks* poet Anne Becker displays how the courtship and marriage of Charles and Emma Darwin parallels the development of Darwin's evolutionary theory. —Molly Peacock. A richly diverse book that makes this whole tapestry of history and science very accessible. —Maxine Kumin

Becker, Robin. *All-American Girl.* 69p. $24.95 (0-8229-3917-7); pap. $10.95 (0-8229-5580-6). Pittsburgh, PA: University of Pittsburgh Press, Spring 1996. I love Robin Becker's poetry for the place the poems come from: a tough, graceful sensibility. She understands that poetry has the power to deliver us from the burdens of the self. —Bruce Weigl. A lively mix of poems that reflect Becker's sexual and social identity in startling and often magically apt metaphors . . . This is Becker's best work to date. —Maxine Kumin

Bei Dao. Translated by David Hinton with Yanbing Chen. *Landscape Over Zero.* 96p. pap. $9.95 (0-8112-1334-X). New York, NY: New Directions, Fall 1996. Bei Dao's genius and his menace consist in a seamless merging of metaphor and politics: his is a guerrilla battle fought at the level of language. —Nate Johnson, *Chicago Tribune*

Belieu, Erin. *Infanta.* 76p. pap. $12.00 (1-55659-101-2). Port Townsend, WA: Copper Canyon Press, Spring 1995. [In this] brilliant first book, a winner of the prestigious National Poetry Series, Belieu attracts the reader with stunning metaphors, playful language, and engaging titles. Highly recommended. —*Library Journal*. Belieu's poems have a sophisticated urban chic that is both attractive and deceptive. Beneath their verbal glamour, they embody intelligence both sensual and political. —Hayden Carruth.

Belile, Elisabeth A. *Polishing the Bayonet.* 150p. pap. $12.00 (1-884615-05-8). San Diego, CA: Incommunicado Press, Fall 1994. Liz Belile is a witty raging feminist, a cultural activist par excellance, a pure bundle of nerve. Her words tell the modern-woman-story. She's seen a lot and recorded it through passionate sensual ear and focused sensitive eye. —Anne Waldman

Bellen, Martine. *10 Greek Poems.* 16p. pap. $12.50. New York, NY: Dim Gray Bar Press, Spring 1996. Limited letterpress edition.

Ben-Lev, Dina. *Note for a Missing Friend.* 28p. pap. $8.00 (0-9624178-2-3). Tarrytown, NY: Slapering Hol Press, 1991.

Ben-Liv, Dina. *Sober on a Small Plane.* 31p. pap. $6.95 (0-9636545-5-1). Lexington, KY: Wind Publications, Fall 1995. Winner of the Quentin R. Howard Prize, the Wind Publications annual chapbook competition.

Bender, Sheila, and Philip Tobin, eds. *The Poem & the World: An International Anthology, Book III.* 96p. pap. $10.00 (0-9636124-2-5). Seattle, WA: The Poem & the World, Fall 1995. Book III of the ongoing anthology of poetry from Seattle and her sister cities includes poets from Christ-church, New Zealand; Pécs, Hungary; Perugia, Italy; and Seattle. New work from several countries and not just a token poem or two but enough to convey a sense of the present 'ethos' of the place, to remember that there is still a world community of poets attempting to make contact. —Marianne Bluger

Bennett, Bruce. *Bare Bones.* 11p. Edgewood, KY: Robert L. Barth (R.L.B.), Spring 1995.

Bennett, John M.. *Eddy.* 20p. pap. $4.00. Columbus, OH: Luna Bisonte Prods, Fall 1995. A set of 20 linked poems; an autobiography from a multitude of simultaneous perspectives. —Luna Bisonte Prods

Bennett, John M. *Spinal Speech.* 48p. pap. $5.00 (1-57141-13-9). Port Charlotte, FL: Runaway Spoon Press, Spring 1995.

Bennett, John M. *Typewriting in a Swimming Pool.* 20p. pap. $2.00 (0935350527). Columbus, OH: Luna Bisonte Prods, Spring 1995. Poems, drawings, and stories written when the author was 5 to 7 years old. A co-publication with Found Street Books. —Luna Bisonte Prods

Bennett, Paul. *The Sun and What It Says Endlessly.* 24p. pap. $7.95. Johnstown, OH: Pudding House Publications, Spring 1995. Fresh as a roadside market under a July hosedown, these rich, well-grown gardening poems by Dennison University's Poet-In-Residence were seeded, watered, and harvested on his own beautiful hillside. —Pudding House Publications

Berg, Stephen. *Oblivion.* 128p. pap. $12.95 (0-252-06457-7). Champaign, IL: University of Illinois Press, Fall 1995. In *Oblivion,* Berg presents a man searching for glimpses of some unknown salvation, through love—in memory, speculation, fantasy, dream, and the lives of others. —University of Illinois Press

Berger, Bruce. *Facing the Music.* 48p. pap. $10.00 (1-881090-14-0). Lewiston, ID: Confluence Press, Spring 1995. In his first book of poems, Bruce Berger faces the music with keen ears and sharp eyes. Insightful and resonant, these poems vibrate with life, love, and the pursuit of meaning. —Eugenia Zuckerman

Bernard, April. *Psalms.* 72p. pap. $9.00 (0-393-31304-2). New York, NY: W. W. Norton & Company, Spring 1995. Lush, hard, and wonderful. —*Village Voice.* A collection of poems so sharp-edged they could effortlessly elbow their way onto a rush-hour train. —*Boston Globe*

Bernard, Christopher. *The Dilettante of Cruelty: Deserts.* 44p. pap. $5.00 (0-9653587-2-0). San Francisco, CA: Meridien PressWorks, Spring 1996.

Bernstein, Tree. *Journal of the Lingering Fall.* 26p. pap. $4.95 (1-880743-05-1). Boulder, CO: Dead Metaphor Press, Fall 1994. This exquisitely moving and lyrical book speaks without sentimentality of a daughter's final understanding of her mother's life, of a compassion that grows as she experiences her mother's anger and suffering and dying. This is a lovely book. Written in a clear, quiet voice it gives a peaceful dignity to grief. —Lucia Berlin

Berry, Iris. *Two Blocks East of Vine.* 108p. pap. $11.00 (0-884615-00-7). San Diego, CA: Incommunicado Press, Fall 1994. She can capture a scene in twenty words with more clarity and raw emotion than most can in twenty pages. This book will bring the seamier, seedier side of LA right into your lap, and charm the pants off you. —*Carbon 14*

Berry, Wendell. *The Farm.* 10p. $15.00; pap. $10.00. Monterey, KY: Larkspur Press, Fall 1995.

Besserman, Ellen. *Pleadings.* 32p. pap. $5.00 (0-921720-74-2). New Hope, PA: Alpha Beat Press, Spring 1995.

Better, Cathy Drinkwater. *The Moon Tonight: Haiku and Senryu.* 56p. pap. $7.95 (1-879603-20-9). San Diego, CA: Los Hombres Press, Spring 1996.

Bettis, Carl; Sharon Eiker, and Philip Miller. *Cadences of Decline: Images of Utopias & Distopias.* 62p. Lawrence, KS: Wheel of Fire Press, Fall 1995. Transcriptions of poems originally presented orally. —Wheel of Fire Press

Biespiel, David. *Shattering Air.* 69p. $20.00 (1-880238-34-9); pap. $12.50 (1-880238-35-7). Rochester, NY: BOA Editions, Spring 1996. David Biespiel finds his vitality and subtlety in the commonplace as well as the luminous moment, in contemplation as much as verbal action. Indeed, for Biespiel, stillness is an act, thinking a way of allowing the subject to move into the light, and become the light, as if the inwardness of an experience were its substance. —Stanley Plumly

Bilgere, George. *The Going.* 64p. pap. $12.95 (0-8262-0966-1). Columbia, MO: University of Missouri Press, Fall 1994. What impresses me most is the music Mr. Bilgere makes. His ear is exquisitely tuned. —Dabney Stuart

Bishop, Judith. *The Burning Place.* 80p. pap. $8.50 (1-56474-110-9). Santa Barbara, CA: Fithian Press, Fall 1994. Judith Bishop has a natural eye for the intersection of landscape and the settings of the human heart. —Diane Glancy. Anyone who has suffered and chosen a path of transformation and healing, will be touched by these poems. —Elad Levinson

Black, Star. *Double Time.* 64p. pap. $10.00 (1-877593-00-1). Port Washington, NY: Groundwater Press, Fall 1995.

Star Black's patterned sestinas weave a tight web wherein the poet ruminates on the ironies and difficulties of love in a postmodern age. —Marjorie Perloff

Black, Star. *Waterworn.* 91p. pap. $10.00 (09639585-3-4). New York, NY: Fly by Night Press/ A Gathering of the Tribes, Spring 1996. Like a set of etudes, Star Black's sonnet sequence examines the technical problems of increasing difficulty that each day presents us with. Fluently and gracefully, she charts the amazing course of the quotidian. —John Ashbery. Every line of *Waterworn* is opulently right. —Lawrence Joseph

Blaeser, Kim. *Trailing You.* 86p. pap. $10.95 (0-912678-88-7). Greenfield Center, NY: Greenfield Review Press, Spring 1995. Winner of the 1993 North American Writers First Book Award for Poetry. Her poems weave tribal dreams and everyday experiences, intimacy and anger, with astonishing beauty and force. —Louis Owens. *Trailing You* is a new collection of poetry to be read on a starry winter night in the old way when the lodge fire is high and the wolves sing on the hill. —Maurice Kenny

Blair, Farnham. *The Movie Queen and Other Poems.* 58p. pap. $8.95 (0-913006-62-9). Orono, ME: Puckerbrush Press, Spring 1996. Farnham Blair's voice is sure, trustworthy, and generous, yet full of layered irony, ambiguity, and wit. He explores the diversity of intent that results in art, discovering in photographs and paintings those clues which imply the personalities of the artists as well as the elusive ramification of their art. Mostly, though, in the lovely, unpretentious cadences of these poems, we find an insightful acceptance for the fullness of our humanity. —Robert Shetterly

Blake, William. Edited by David and Virgina Erdman. *Blake's Selected Poems.* 96p. pap. $1.00 (0-486-28517-0). Mingola, NY: Dover Publications, Spring 1995.

Blake, William. *William Blake: Selected Poems.* 256p. $6.99 (0-517-12367-3). Avenel, NJ: Gramercy Books, Spring 1995. Including the complete text of the *Songs of Innocence* and *Songs of Experience.* —Gramercy Books

Blanco, Alberto. Edited by Juvenal Acosta. *Dawn of the Senses: Selected Poems.* 240p. pap. $12.95 (0-87286-309-3). San Francisco, CA: City Lights Books, Spring 1996. Alberto Blanco is a dynamic voice in the new poetry of Mexico. This is the first collection of his poetry in English translation. —City Lights Books. Alberto Blanco's deep poetry inhabits both the world and the universe of imagination; these poems shed their own light and fly on their own wings. —Michael McClure

Blevins-Church, Adrian. *The Man Who Went Out for Cigarettes.* 26p. pap. $5.00 (0-9646844-2-X). Treadwell, NY: Bright Hill Press, Spring 1996. Winner of the 1995 Bright Hill Press National Chapbook Competition. Blevin-Church has a strong sense of metaphor [which she uses to express] the struggle of a heart trying to make sense of relationships that have borne odd fruit. —Dan Gribbon, *The Roanoke Times and World News*

Blish, James Banjamin. *With All of Love: Selected Poems.* 208p. $29.95 (0-9631203-1-X). San Francisco, CA: Anamnesis Press, Fall 1995. A limited hardcover collector's edition of only 150 numbered copies. Anyone who enjoys the poetry of Ezra Pound or William Empson will like this book. —Gregory Feeley, *Washington Post Book World*

Blomain, Karen. *The Slap.* 26p. pap. $5.00 (1-879205-40-8). Troy, ME: Nightshade Press, 1992.

Blomain, Karen, ed. *Coalseam: Poems From the Anthracite Region.* 127p. $19.95 (0-940866-54-4). Bronx, NY: University of Scranton Press, Fall 1996. This anthology gathers fourteen voices exploring the Pennsylvania mining experience— the texture of family life, the confluence of ethnic cultures, the brutality and dangers of the mines, and the scars on soul and landscape. —University of Scranton Press

Blue Cloud, Peter. *Clans of Many Nations: Selected Poems 1969-1994.* 166p. pap. $14.00 (1-877727-47-4). Fredonia, NY: White Pine Press, Fall 1995. Blue Cloud's poems are living proof that the power and beauty of the Old Ways cannot be lost. —Gary Snyder. This is a Native writer the world must acknowledge as a major voice. —Maurice Kenny. Peter leads us back to where we poets belong, between Creation and the crushing wheel of modern society. —Jelle Kaspersma

Bluestone, Stephen. *The Laughing Monkeys of Gravity.* 72p. pap. $10.95 (0-86554-452-2). Macon, GA: Mercer University Press, Spring 1995. Stephen Bluestone's poems, haunted by voices from the far and recent past, take us through the difficult passages from melancholy and loss toward love. They are religious poems in the widest and best sense—searching, intelligent, expansive—poems whose achievement is beauty and spiritual wisdom. —Susan Ludvigson. Stephen Bluestone's poems do miraculous things . . . [they] provide what the age never demands but deeply requires. —Donald Hall, *Boston Review*

Blum, Joshua; Bob Holman and Mark Pellington, eds. *The United States of Poetry.* 176p. $29.95 (0-8109-3927-4). New York, NY: Harry N. Abrams, Spring 1996. Combining spectacular images from the breakthrough TV series,

The United States of Poetry "unveils a new nation, conceived in language, and dedicated to the proposition that you don't have to turn off your mind to have a good time," (Bob Holman). The 80 contemporary poems are by poets who run the gamut from renowned Nobel Laureates, to rock 'n' rollers, the Beats, cowboy poets, rappers, former president Jimmy Carter, and others. This book is a feast of language and image, energy and meaning. Here the disparate and unheard voices of our country—pidgin, Spanish, hiphop, Creole, Tagalog, and American Sign Language—speak out and speak for themselves. —Harry N. Abrams

Bobrowski, Johannes. Translated by Ruth and Matthew Mead. *Shadow Lands: Selected Poems.* 208p. pap. $10.95 (0-8112-1276-9). New York, NY: New Directions, Fall 1994. Bobrowski celebrates the historical and mythical figures of Eastern Europe, evoking a world imaginatively reassembled from the pre-Christian gods and heroes of the ancient Prussians. —New Directions. His haunting, mysterious oeuvre abounds with paradox, it is both monolithic and intimate;

concrete, yet seemingly impalpable; consciously post-war, yet timeless. —Jeremy Adler, (London) *Times Literary Supplement*

Bogus, SDiane. *I'm Off to See the Goddamn Wizard, Alright.* 46p. pap. $15.00 (0-934172-00-5). San Jose, CA: Woman in the Moon Publications, Fall 1995. *I'm Off to See the Goddamn Wizard, Alright!* is a visionary collection of rowdy poetry wearing combat boots. —Woman in the Moon Publications

Bogus, SDiane. *Woman in the Moon.* 87p. pap. $20.00 (0-9341-7236-6). San Jose, CA: Woman in the Moon Publications, Fall 1995. These poems cry out with want. [They are] passionate poems dealing with love, sex and need. —Joy Parks, *Motherroot Journal*

Bohnhorst, Ben. *A Service on the Sufficiency of Feeding Finches.* 32p. pap. $6.00 (1-56439-039-X). Detroit, MI: Ridgeway Press, Fall 1994. Bohnhorst writes with a deep sensitivity to life. This is a collection of poems about birds and nature. —Ridgeway Press

Bohnhorst, Ben. *Descent From the Cross: Verses Loosely Ordered in the* *Ancient Form of the Mass.* 30p. (1-56439-048-9). Roseville, MI: Ridgeway Press, Fall 1995.

Boisseau, Michelle. *Understory.* 64p. pap. $10.95 (1-55553-286-1). Boston, MA: Northeastern University Press, Fall 1996. In each poem, Boisseau holds the focus of her imagination until the exact, savory, morally unpredictable vocabulary comes firmly into place. She delivers her poems with silken lines and such honesty of feeling and thought that one is hardly aware of how she is doing it. —Molly Peacock

Boland, Eavan. *An Origin Like Water: Collected Poems 1967-1987.* 250p. $25.00 (0-393-03852-1). New York, NY: W. W. Norton & Company, Fall 1995. Boland has emerged as one of the best poets in Ireland. —Denis Donoghue, *New York Review of Books*

Bond, Bruce. *The Possible.* 32p. pap. $6.00 (1-878851-06-3). Eugene, OR: Silverfish Review Press, Spring 1995. Winner of the 1993 Gerald Cable Chapbook Contest. Bond explores his relationship to the world through four long poems and the short title poem. The work is deeply felt; the language precise and musical. —Silverfish Review Press

Bond, Zane. *Lieutenant From Heaven (Just Another S.O.B.).* 18p. pap. $3.75. Kew Gardens, NY: The Poet Tree, Fall 1994. Zane is the son of Rudy Bond, a well known Hollywood character actor. This is his story of growing up and coming to terms with manic depression. —The Poet Tree

Bonnefoy, Yves. Edited by John Naughton and Anthony Rudolph. *New and Selected Poems.* 216p. $39.00 (0-226-06458-1); pap. $14.95 (0-226-06460-3). Chicago, IL: University of Chicago Press, Fall 1995. Yves Bonnefoy, widely considered the most important and influential French poet since World War II, is the author of six critically acclaimed books of poetry. Spanning four decades, this selection provides a comprehensive overview of his work. Bilingual edition. —University of Chicago Press

Bonomo, Joe. *Vanishings From That Neighborhood.* 39p. pap. $4.75 (0-87338-544-6). Kent, OH: Kent State University Press, Spring 1996. The size

of his world is local and familiar, but that hardly prevents [Bonomo] from achieving, in finely-tuned language, his epiphanies. This is honest and lovely writing. —Stanley Plumly

Bontemps, Arna, ed. *American Negro Poetry, Revised Edition.* 234p. pap. $10.00 (0-8090-1564-1). New York, NY: Farrar, Straus and Giroux/Hill and Wang, Spring 1996. For more than twenty years, Bontemps's anthology has been recognized as a major contribution to our understanding of African-American literature. —Farrar, Straus and Giroux

Bookey, Ted. *Mixty Motions.* 34p. pap. $7.95 (1-879205-56-4). Troy, ME: Nightshade Press, Fall 1995. A slice of Jewish life in the Bronx of the 1930s. —Nightshade Press

Bordao, Rafael. Translated by Louis Bourne. *E Libro de las Interferencios/The Book of Interferences.* 53p. pap. $5.95 (0-9623552-7-5). Brooklyn, NY: Editorial Palmar, Fall 1995. This work differs from Bordao's earlier writing. Here, a delicate sexual touch emerges. —Editorial Palmar

Borrus, Beth. *Fast Divorce Bankruptcy.* 142p. pap. $12.00 (0-884615-08-2). San Diego, CA: Incommunicado Press, Fall 1995. Speaking as one among billions of uprooted American women, on the road, or by it, but certainly not twelve-stepping their way across the continent, this series of short takes on loneliness and unrequited desire are unembellished, bitter and absolutely credible. —Fanny Howe

Boss, Laura. *Reports from the Front.* 64p. $20.00 (0-89304-497-0); pap. $10.00 (0-89304-498-9). Merrick, NY: Cross-Cultural Communications, Fall 1995. I can't think of another poet—male or female—who has written with such terrifying honesty about the sexual terror and dependency of the suddenly-single, middle-aged. Boss seems destined to send us further reports from the front. As a poet-reporter, Boss makes a frighteningly honest foreign correspondent. —Warren Woessner, *Abraxas*

Boston, Bruce. *Sensuous Debris: Selected Poems 1970-1995.* 94p. pap. $6.95 (0-9626708-8-X). Concord, CA: Dark Regions Press, Fall 1995. [Boston is]

probably the most critically acclaimed speculative poet. —Steve Eng, *Anatomy of Wonder.* [He has] a classically lucid style. —John Clute, *The Encyclopedia of Science Fiction*

Bosveld, Jennifer, ed. *The Unitarian Universalist Poets: A Contemporary American Survey.* 208p. pap. $18.95 (0-614-10187-5). Johnstown, OH: Pudding House Publications, Spring 1996. 120 American poets, mostly well-published, aligned with a Unitarian Universalist perspective illustrate the diversity of their style, focus, and lives as poets. —Pudding House Publications

Bottoms, David. *Armored Hearts: Selected & New Poems.* 144p. $25.00 (1-55659-073-3); pap. $14.00 (1-55659-072-5). Port Townsend, WA: Copper Canyon Press, Spring 1995. Bottoms' poems are exceptional for their vigorous narrative, their realistic scenes, and their mythic density. David Bottoms is among the best poets of his generation. —Dave Smith. It is refreshing to read a poet who is not obliquely vague, who tells a story cleanly and convincingly. —Robert W. Hill, *Atlanta Journal-Constitution*

Botts, Gregory. *Clouds, Leaves, Waves: A Painter's Poem.* pap. $12.95 (1-885983-10-7). Chappaqua, NY: Turtle Point Press, Fall 1996. A long poem gathered from the journals and notes of Gregory Botts, a painter who, like Emerson, has been devoted to the American sublime. Highly personal and deeply revealing, this is the poetic record of 10 years of Bott's life. —Turtle Point Press. The grand themes of Bott's paintings are all here, in clear, glowing language, plus meditations on all that makes painting possible—and utterly necessary—at this difficult end of a terrifying century. —Carter Ratcliff. I have for a long time admired Gregory Botts's intense painting of Nature and ideas, and am now convinced he is the rare thing, the painter-poet. —David Shapiro

Boullata, Kamal, ed. *Women of the Fertile Crescent: Modern Poetry by Arab Women.* 264p. pap. $16.00 (0-914478-42-7). Boulder, CO: Three Continents Press/Lynne Rienner Publishers, Fall 1994. This volume is the first collection in English of poems by living poets who are carrying on the Arab woman's thirteen hundred year old tradition of self-expression within the male dominated culture. —Three Continents Press

Bourne, Daniel. *The Household Gods.* 84p. pap. $10.00 (1-880834-13-8). Cleveland, OH: Cleveland State University Poetry Center, Spring 1995. Dan Bourne's poems begin in place—southern Illinois farmland—and branch out into ways of human vulnerability found anywhere. They are alert to the fragile borders between the rational and the irrational, between the order of an open mind and the disorder of a closed one. These are generous, unflinching poems. —Roger Mitchell. With compassionate intelligence, wit and whimsy, Bourne celebrates the 'dark festivities' in his richly textured and memorable first book. —Ron Wallace

Bowman, Catherine. *Rock Farm.* 64p. pap. $12.95 (0-87905-745-9). Layton, UT: Gibbs Smith, Publisher/Peregrine Smith Books, Spring 1996. Bowman's saucy, spicy, frank, unflappable voice is never coy or unsure or too, too delicate. —*Antioch Review.* Bowman [is]

a skilled young poet who seems to manipulate the language with a branding iron in one hand and a bullwhip in the other. —*Ploughshares*

Boyd, Melba. *Letters to Che.* 36p. pap. $7.00 (1-56439-055-1). Roseville, MI: Ridgeway Press, Spring 1996. Beautifully crafted letter poems written to Che Guevara's spirit some 30 years after his assassination. The book concludes with an imaginary letter to the author from Che. —Ridgeway Press

Brackenbury, Rosalind. *The Beautiful Routes of the West.* 79p. pap. $9.00 (1-56474-165-6). Santa Barbara, CA: Fithian Press, Fall 1996. This is easily the best book of poems I've read in a long time. It has a rare kind of "natural imagism" combing the tensile strength of language flawlessly wrought and the sensual rhythms of the natural world. —Bud Navero

Bradley, George. *The Fire Fetched Down.* 72p. $21.00 (0-679-44620-6). New York, NY: Alfred A. Knopf, Spring 1996. *The Fire Fetched Down* earns its promethean title, and helps persuade me that American poetry will go on maintaining itself as a high art even now and in worse days to come. Bradley has the cognitive power, the primal exuberance of language, and the spiritual vision, to develop into the Merrill or Ashbery of his own generation. Everything in *The Fire Fetched Down* will sustain, and reward, many readings. —Harold Bloom

Bradley, John, ed. *Atomic Ghost: Poets Respond to the Nuclear Age.* 330p. pap. $15.95 (1-566689-027-6). Minneapolis, MN: Coffee House Press, Spring 1995. This volume marks the 50th anniversary of the Nuclear Age with poems of protest, prayer, and commemoration by a multitude of international poets. —Coffee House Press. For nearly a half-century, the politicians and historians of the United States and Japan have been unable to deal with the moral aftershocks of Hiroshima. In this volume, undaunted poets have fashioned an epitaph for the atomic age. —Stewart L. Udall, former Secretary of the Interior

Brandi, John. *Heartbeat Geography: Selected & Uncollected Poems 1966-1994.* 247p. pap. $15.00 (1-877727-40-7). Fredonia,

NY: White Pine Press, Spring 1995. I love John Brandi's "pledge to clarity," his politics in the sense of witness, his candor, his delight & heart towards children & friends, his terrific travel details. This book sings with life. —Ann Waldman. Brandi deals with the mysteries of male-female relationships, the loss of innocence, the confrontation with spirituality in the real world, and the complex euphoria of being alive. —*Houston Chronicle*

Brathwaite, Kamau. *Black & Blues.* 69p. pap. $9.95 (0-8112-1313-7). New York, NY: New Directions, Fall 1995. The printed word doesn't rise much closer to singing than in the work of Barbadian troubadour Kamau Brathwaite. [His] voice is as fierce as it is musical. He charges words with unmistakable voltage, and brands them on our tongues. This is just the kind of poetry Williams had in mind when he said that men die for the lack of what is to be found there. —*The Village Voice Literary Supplement*

Brathwaite, Kamau. *Trench Town Rock.* 80p. pap. $10.95 (0-918786-45-2). Barrington, RI: Lost Roads Publishers, Fall 1994. An innovative, incendiary poem by the winner of the Neudstadt International Prize for Literature. —Lost Roads Publishers. *Trench Town Rock*, Kamau Brathwaite's long documentarian song, affords a splay of clips, massed facts and faces. Jimmied lines and real and would-be headlines lament the collapse of postcolonial promise into ongoing predation. —Nathaniel Mackey

Breeden, David. *Building a Boat.* 23p. pap. $6.00 (1-882983-18-1). Greensboro, NC: March Street Press, Spring 1995.

Brennan, Matthew. *Seeing in the Dark.* 56p. pap. $8.00 (0-9635631-1-4). Terre Haute, IN: Hawkhead Press, Spring 1995. Brennan's poems are about the kind of blind insight it takes to perceive one's role in the family, our greatest of fictions. —Richard Flynn. Through a combination of deft lyrical balance and tender, emphatic portraiture, Matthew Brennan has created a poetry which resembles the warm clarity of Dutch interiors. —David Wojahn

Brewer, Gay. *Presently a Beast.* 67p. pap. $8.95 (0-9647127-4-1). Lawrenceville, GA: Coreopsis Books, Spring 1996. In *Presently a Beast,* a brilliantly conceived and carefully crafted collection of poems, Gay Brewer shows us that a single life is actually a series of transformations, from lover to stranger, from body to shadow. These poems offer unflinching views of the lives we live, and they sing of what and who we were, are, will be. —David Citino

Briggs, Everett Francis. *Across the Bridge: Selected Poems.* 365p. pap. $14.95 (0-9615976-4-X). Sykesville, MD: Apostrophe Publishing, Fall 1996. This anthology includes poems on an admixture of themes, most of them in English, some in Japanese dress. —Apostrophe Publishing

Brock, James. *The Sunshine Mine Disaster.* 82p. pap. $12.95 (0-89301-181-9). Moscow, ID: University of Idaho Press, Fall 1995. Brock combines original poetry with various historical documents surrounding the 1972 Idaho silver mine explosion . . . American poetry could use a lot more of what *The Sunshine Mine Disaster* has. —*Choice*

Brock, Van K. *Unspeakable Strangers: Descents Into the Dark Self, Ascents Into the Light.* 110p. pap. $12.00 (0-938078-42-9). Tallahassee, FL: Anhinga Press, Spring 1996. Poems and an essay about the holocaust. I like even what I would call their moral earnestness and the at times-coolness with which it's delivered. —Donald Justice. These are very bold and powerful poems about [of course] practically the most difficult theme in the world. I read them with increasing admiration for [their] mastery of imagery and control. But mainly I am impressed by the pervasive music, the requiem sound. —William Styron

Brock-Broido, Lucie. *The Master Letters.* 84p. $20.00 (0-679-44174-3); pap. (0-679-76599-9) (avail. 4/97). New York, NY: Alfred A. Knopf, Fall 1995. Lucie Brock-Broido pays homage to Emily Dickinson by investigating the lair of the secret self where bliss and blighted hope reside and the fierce yet playful drama of salvation is acted out. Lucie Brock-Broido reclaims for

American poetry a Baroque voice that is arresting, 'unbridled,' aphoristic, beautiful. —Herbert Leibowitz

Brodey, Jim. Edited by Clark Coolidge. *Heart of the Breath: Poems, 1979-1992.* 381p. pap. $15.95 (0-9638433-7-0). West Stockbridge, MA: Hard Press, Spring 1996. This volume comprises the last major series by Brodey, a contemporary of Ted Berrigan and Frank O'Hara, who died of AIDS in 1993. It is full of humor, vitality, and wry, uncompromising vision. —Hard Press. His zigzag is unearthly, sometimes. Not just word/nerve/combinations, but flowing structures to amaze the gloom of lower Manhattan. The discipline inherent in Kerouac's locomotive meditations (which look so easy when read), is fed-back to him, but in mad overdubbing stanzas. Brodey's [work] is a flying horse of wild crab language served up by a poet already well-versed in how a poem walks. —Ted Berrigan

Brodsky, Joseph. *So Forth.* 132p. $18.00 (0-374-26641-7). New York, NY: Farrar, Straus and Giroux, Spring 1996. Joseph Brodsky's last volume of poems in English, *So Forth*, represents eight years of masterful self-translation from the Russian, as well as a by now substantial body of work written directly in English. —Farrar, Straus and Giroux

Brodsky, Louis Daniel. *Disappearing in Mississippi Latitudes: Volume Two of a A Mississippi Trilogy.* 121p. $18.95 (1-877770-80-9); pap. $12.50 (1-877770-81-7). St. Louis, MO: Time Being Books, Fall 1994. Brodsky's verse is steeped in the sensuous brew of the North Mississippi country, and the mixture of ingredients—what he finds there, what it tells him about himself—makes for memorable poems. —Louis D. Rubin, Jr.

Brodsky, Louis Daniel. *Paper-Whites for Lady Jane: Poems of a Midlife Love Affair.* 74p. $18.95 (1-877770-95-7); pap. $12.50 (1-877770-96-5). St. Louis, MO: Time Being Books, Fall 1995. This sequel to *Forever, for Now: Poems for a Later Love* depicts the second year of a romance between two middle-aged lovers, who have started over. —Time Being Books

Bromley, Anne C. *Scenes From the Light Years.* 75p. pap. $11.95

(0-88748-197-3). Pittsburgh, PA: Carnegie Mellon University Press, Spring 1995.

Bronk, William. Selected by Henry Weinfield. *Selected Poems.* 96p. pap. $8.95 (0-8112-1314-5). New York, NY: New Directions, Fall 1995. They are poems I would like to have written, which I say without envy, as one does in the face of a transient perfection. —Hayden Carruth, *New York Times Book Review*

Brontë, Emily. Edited by Peter Washington. *Poems.* 256p. $12.50 (0-679-44725-3). New York, NY: Alfred A. Knopf/ Everyman's Library Pocket Poets, Spring 1996.

Brooks, Dorothy Howe. *Simple Fracture.* 22p. pap. $3.75. Kew Gardens, NY: New Spirit Press, Spring 1995. Winner of the New Spirit Press Quarterly Chapbook Contest. A woman coming to terms with motherhood, femininity, her sons in the service; these are poems about the art of letting go. —New Spirit Press

Brosman, Catharine Savage. *Passages.* 60p. $16.95 (0-8071-2049-9); pap. $9.95 (0-8071-

2050-2). Baton Rouge, LA: Louisiana State University Press, Spring 1996. Brosman's language succeeds in being at once traditional and modern, temporal and intemporal. Her poems evoke and translate Nature as well as the motions of the body, the heart, and the mind. —Jean-Claude Renard

Broughton, James. *Little Sermons of the Big Joy.* 24p. pap. $7.00 (1-882827-05-8). Philadelphia, PA: Insight to Riot Press, Fall 1994. These 24 12-line poems turn the conventional notion of the "sermon" on its head, being celebrations of the great spirit of Joy at the center of the Universe. Broughton was a leading figure in the San Francisco literary and arts renaissance of the 50's, 60's, and 70's and remains a well-known name to afficionados of experimental cinema. —Insight to Riot Press

Broughton, T. Alan. *In the Country of Elegies.* 114p. pap. $11.95 (0-88748-198-1). Pittsburgh, PA: Carnegie Mellon University Press, Spring 1995.

Broumas, Olga and T Begley. *Helen Groves.* 36p. $75.00; pap. $55.00. Tucson, AZ: Kore

Press, Fall 1994. A collaborative act which yields the intensely lyrical pitch of one hypnotically incantatory voice, this is a series of poems which returns us to the traditions of Greek poets Sappho and Odysseaus Elytis. —Kore Press. The language is mystical, quizzical, sensual, wrestling the lower deities of melancholy, violence, incest, and suicide with Hellenistic candor and redemption. —Jane Miller

Broumas, Olga, and T Begley. *Sappho's Gymnasium.* 190p. pap. $12.00 (1-55659-071-7). Port Townsend, WA: Copper Canyon Press, Fall 1994. *Sappho's Gymnasium* is a collaborative spiritual experiment, a series of chants or prayers, a quest for wholeness, the attempt to join two voices in spiritual identity. The effect of the poems resembles that of verbal wind chimes ringing bells in 175 different pages of moods that range from sexy to despondent, from damaged to repaired. —*Voice Literary Supplement*

Brown, Bill. *The Art of Dying.* 64p. $20.00 (1-885912-07-2); pap. $12.00 (1-885912-04-8). Abingdon, VA: Sow's Ear Press, Fall 1996. In this third book,

Bill Brown's elegiac lyrical poems focus on the death of his mother. —Sow's Ear Press

Brown, Dee. *Beyond What You See.* 54p. pap. $9.95 (1-55618-197-7). Lawrenceville, VA: Brunswick Publishing, Spring 1995.

Brown, Rosellen. *Cora Fry's Pillow Book.* 179p. $15.00 (0-374-14402-8). New York, NY: Farrar, Straus and Giroux, Spring 1995. Full of humor, truth, anger, and tenderness, Rosellen Brown has given us a novel stripped down to essences in the vivid evocations of a country woman's life in this remarkable set of poems. —May Sarton

Brown, Tim W. *Starstruck.* 29p. pap. $8.00. Chicago, IL: Contemporary Arts Publishing, Spring 1996.

Browning, Elizabeth Barrett. *Elizabeth Barrett Browning: Selected Poems.* 224p. $6.99 (0-517-12366-5). Avenel, NJ: Gramercy Books, Spring 1995. Included in this volume is the complete *Sonnets from the Portuguese* as well as sections from *Casa Guidi Windows* and *Aurora Lee.* —Gramercy Books

Browning, Elizabeth Barrett. Edited by Julia Markus and William S. Peterson. *Sonnets from the Portuguese: Illuminated by the Brownings' Love Letters.* 93p. $22.00 (0-88001-451-2). Hopewell, NJ: Ecco Press, Spring 1996. It is time to take a fresh look at these remarkable poems. They contain the deepest and at times the darkest thoughts of a woman of genius, in grave health, who finds in middle life, not the death she waits for, but the love she never expected. —Julia Markus

Brox, Jane; Dzvinia Orlowsky and Martha Rhodes, eds. *The Four Way Reader #1.* 220p. pap. $14.95 (1-884-800-00-9). Marshfield, MA: Four Way Books, Spring 1996. An anthology featuring poetry by Indran Amirthanayagam, Robin Becker and others; and short fiction by Peter Josyph, Kate Walbert and others. —Four Way Books

Bruchac, Joseph, ed. *Returning the Gift: Poetry and Prose From the First North American Native Writers' Festival.* 370p. $45.00 (0-8165-1376-7); pap. $19.95 (0-8165-1486-0). Tucson, AZ: University of Arizona Press, Fall 1994. The anthology includes works from Native Americans from every corner of the continent, representing a wide range of tribal affiliations, languages, and cultures. —University of Arizona Press

Brunk, Juanita. *Brief Landing on the Earth's Surface.* 66p. $17.95 (0-299-15200-6); pap. $10.95 (0-299-15204-9). Madison, WI: University of Wisconsin Press, Fall 1996. Brunk's poetry has a delicate verbal grace and ease, and even more importantly all the right sort of literary and human ambitions. It is sensitive, attentive to urgent emotional matters, and approaches experience with a rich sense of whimsy, a genuine and idiosyncratic concern. —C. K. Williams

Bryan, Sharon. *Flying Blind.* 66p. $20.95 (0-9641151-6-6); pap. $12.95 (0-9641151-7-4). Louisville, KY: Sarabande Books, Fall 1996. It's a brilliant book. It's smart as hell, this book, and very sad, I think: behind the brainy and considering voice-in-the poems is real woundedness, real and interesting experience. It's felt thinking. I admire it enormously. —Frederick Busch. We're all flying blind through life, Sharon Bryan's poetry suggests, relying on the shaky information that language and our senses send back to us. As with all good poetry, Bryan's work is shot through with paradox. —*The Salt Lake Tribune*. [These] poems set off sparks in the mind. —Small Press

Bryant, William Cullen, ed. *The Library of World Poetry.* 912p. $12.99 (0-517-11892-0). Avenel, NJ: Gramercy Books, Spring 1995. This comprehensive collection of the greatest poems in the English language was selected by Bryant toward the end of the 19th century. As it is organized according to subject matter, the reader is able to see how a subject has been handled over a period of more than five hundred years. —Gramercy Books

Bryner, Jeanne. *Breathless.* 36p. pap. $4.75 (0-87338-533-0). Kent, OH: Kent State University Press, Fall 1995. "Our story is how we did not break / and run—no matter how close / the lightning gouged," writes Jeanne Bryner. In *Breathless*, Bryner offers an unflinching and urgent view of those who care and those they care

for—an exchange which is recreated in the gritty yet luminous life of these poems which compel us to care as well. —Maxine Scates

Buckley, Christopher, and Christopher Merrill, eds. *What Will Suffice: Contemporary American Poets on the Art of Poetry.* 200p. pap. $17.95 (0-87905-692-4). Layton, UT: Gibbs Smith, Publisher/ Peregrine Smith Books, Fall 1995. A poem is a moral and mythic construct, revealing something about his or her vision of the world. Nowhere is that vision more on display than in an ars poetica, which is where a poet takes stock, writing down his or her articles of faith. An ars poetica is also a barometer for the cultural climate of one's times, and what the "reading" contained in this book suggest about post-Cold War America is that there are countless ways to interpret and transform our experiences. —Christopher Merrill

Bugeja, Michael J. *The Visionary.* 64p. pap. $10.00 (0-914061-50-X). Alexandria, VA: Orchises Press, Fall 1995. *The Visionary* recreates the disquiet and eventual joy within a couple's relationship as they adopt a child. Characteristically, Bugeja never loses touch with the particulars of this situation as he explores a wide spectrum of emotions in social and religious terms. The book is both a narrative and a collection of superb individual poems. —Orchises Press

Bukowski, Charles. *Betting on the Muse: Poems & Stories.* 402p. $27.50 (1-57423-002-6); pap. $15.00 (1-57423-001-8). Santa Rosa, CA: Black Sparrow Press, Fall 1996. In these new poems and stories (representing only a portion of the rich store of manuscripts he left behind), Bukowski, the erstwhile street brawler, battles on until his last breath, punching away at hypocrisy and fakery to lay bare essential truths. As death stares him in the face, he looks back over a lifetime of struggling to survive and refuses to give up or make concessions, except to death itself. —Black Sparrow Press

Bull, Arthur. *Twenty-Five Scores.* 25p. pap. $3.00 (1-57141-006-6). Port Charlotte, FL: Runaway Spoon Press, Spring 1995. Zen-like meditation texts. —Runaway Spoon Press

Burnham, Deborah. *Anna and the Steel Mill.* 75p. $16.50 (0-89672-345-3). Lubbock, TX: Texas Tech University Press, Spring 1995. *Anna and the Steel Mill* is a work of great range and maturity. Whether Deborah Burnham is writing of the immigrant experience, the music of city life, or her own daughter, her work is full of grace, beauty and magic. —Jim Daniels

Burns, Christopher, ed. *The Seashell Anthology of Great Poetry.* 352p. $25.00 (0-517-20011-2). Avenel, NJ: Park Lane Press, Fall 1996. "Like a seashell, a poem resonates to the beating of your heart," writes Christopher Burns. He has gathered poems that emphasize this personal aspect of poetry, organizing them by subject. Poets as diverse as Alfred Lord Tennyson, Sara Teasdale, and Gary Snyder, for example, echo the themes and images of "Western Wind." Robert Browning and Richard Wilbur talk about the way men look at women. Walt Whitman and Allen Ginsberg describe the America each has found. —Park Lane Press

Burns, Michael. *The Secret Names.* 64p. pap. $12.95 (0-8262-

0947-5). Columbia, MO: University of Missouri Press, Fall 1994. The poems in *The Secret Names* are dignified, deephearted, mysterious, and true. —David Baker

Burns, Ralph. *Swamp Candles.* 65p. pap. $10.95 (0-87745-539-2). Iowa City, IA: University of Iowa Press, Spring 1996. These poems combine emotional and intellectual depth with great melodic beauty. They shine with ferocious clarity. —Pam Durban. In *Swamp Candles* Ralph Burns fuses the two major strands in American poetry. His spare images dazzle us with their precision, while his colloquial voice moves us with its vital rhythms and deep emotions. —Maura Stanton

Burnshaw, Stanley, ed. *The Poem Itself.* 384p. pap. $22.00 (1-55728-328-1). Fayetteville, AR: University of Arkansas Press, Spring 1995. Now in its eighth printing, this classic work contains over 150 French, Spanish, German, Italian, Portuguese, and Russian poems presented in the original languages and brilliantly illuminated by English commentary. —University of Arkansas Press.

This book represents an exciting and radical departure in the art of translation. —John Ciardi

Burr, Gray. *Afterlives.* 80p. pap. $9.00 (1-880286-25-4). Canton, CT: Singular Speech Press, Spring 1996. [Levin's work] is clear and cool . . . graphic and humane, [leading us to] some new sphere of quickening speculation. —Harry Levin

Burritt, Mary. *Arias.* 96p. $24.95 (0-8263-1696-4); pap. $9.95 (0-8263-1697-2). Albuquerque, NM: University of New Mexico Press, Fall 1995. *Arias* is an anachronism, modernist and romantic in a postmodern age. It also has the universal appeal of lyric and romantic literature, evoking and celebrating basic emotions and experiences: fear, anger, love, death, sorrow, and joy. —University of New Mexico Press

Burrus, Harry. *Cartouche.* 220p. pap. $17.95 (0-941749-33-9). Houston, TX: Black Tie Press, Fall 1995. There's a vision in these poems, of language under pressure slowly tearing, of trying to speak in skin that's out of reach, of passing furious through. —John M. Bennett, *Laft*

Burt, John. *Work Without Hope.* 93p. $16.95 (0-8018-5371-0). Baltimore, MD: Johns Hopkins University Press, Spring 1996. These poems aspire to record something of what Wordsworth called "the sad music of humanity," that ability to endure the limitations of the world—and the folly of one's own desires and ambitions in it—until one arrives, beyond disappointment or defeat, at a kind of lucid and reflective acceptance of experience. —Johns Hopkins University Press

Bush, Casey. *Blessings of Madness.* 26p. pap. $5.00. Portland, OR: 26 Books, Fall 1994. The manic imagery and inventive humor of these poems cause the reader to question ordinary definitions of both perception and sanity. —26 Books

Bushman-Carlton, Marilyn. *On Keeping Things Small.* 60p. pap. $10.95 (1-56085-080-9). Salt Lake City, UT: Signature Books, Fall 1995. Written from the heart, these poems validate the sanctity of dailiness and the dignity of womaness. —Sally Smith. Bushman-Carlton writes with wonder, love, and not a little wit. —Leslie Norris

Buys, Matt. *The Nietzsche Itinerary.* 32p. pap. $6.00. Niagara Falls, NY: Slipstream Publications, Spring 1996. Matt Buys bases this collection of poetry on his experiences during a three-year stay in Latin America when he survived by living in two dollar rooms and eating one cent bananas. He traveled from one war zone to the next, working as a reporter and teaching. —Slipstream Publications

Byrne, Edward. *Words Spoken, Words Unspoken.* 62p. pap. $10.00 (0-9627300-1-7). Valparaiso, IN: Chimney Hill Press, Fall 1995. The world of Edward Byrne's poems is our own world viewed through the wrong end of a telescope: curiously small and urgent. But the minuteness of scope is deceptive. In Byrne's poetry particulars explode into universality as through the action of a zoom lens. —John Ashbery. Byrne's poems are sinewy yet delicate, clear yet atmospheric, the precise character of their effect is unpredictable, but they are always moving, always engaging. —Mark Strand

Byron, (George Gordon, Lord Byron). *Lord Byron: Selected Poems.* 256p. $7.99 (0-517-11832-7). Avenel, NJ: Gramercy Books, Fall 1994. This collection contains a selection of Byron's best shorter lyric works, one of his major longer poems, *The Vision of Judgment*, as well as generous excerpts from *Childe Harold's Pilgrimage* and *Don Juan.* —Gramercy Books

Byrum, John. *Text Blocks.* 18p. pap. $5.00 (1-57141-004-X). Port Charlotte, FL: Runaway Spoon Press, Spring 1995. Appropriated texts combined with notes to create a lyrosophical poem that ends with the word, "yond." —Runaway Spoon Press

Byrum, John. *Text Blocks, Drawn.* 24p. pap. $5.00 (1-57141-10-4). Port Charlotte, FL: Runaway Spoon Press, Spring 1995. An abstract-expressionist verbo-visual companion to Byrum's *Text Blocks.* —Runaway Spoon Press

C

Cabral de Melo Neto, João. Edited by Djelal Kadir. *Selected Poetry, 1937-1990.* 224p. $25.00 (0-8195-2217-1); pap. $14.95 (0-8195-2231-7). Middletown, CT: Wesleyan University Press of New England, Fall 1994. Bilingual edition. These poems are marked by a captivating use of simple language. The translations are remarkably true to the spirit of the originals. —*The New York Times Book Review*

Cafagña, Marcus. *The Broken World.* 80p. pap. $10.95 (0-252-06550-6). Champaign, IL: University of Illinois Press, Fall 1996. Marcus Cafagña is a poet who will not turn away from what he sees—ordinary people struggling against, and sometimes breaking on, the wheel of their fate. *The Broken World* is a deeply humane and accomplished first book— probing, watchful, compassionate, and necessary. —Edward Hirsch. I challenge anyone to be unmoved by *The Broken World.* —Jim Daniels

Calbert, Cathleen. *My Summer as a Bride.* 32p. pap. $5.00. West

Chester, PA: Riverstone Press, Fall 1995. Winner of the 1995 Riverstone Poetry Chapbook Award. There is the stoicism of beauty in her poems, poems which have the resonance of rather formal or at least rather tough-minded utterance. —Richard Howard, *American Poet*

Callahan, Laura. *On This Day.* 55p. pap. $7.95. Santa Clara, CA: Joe Miller's Company, Fall 1995. Laura Callahan's poetry, enhanced by the innovative graphic design of Joe Miller, evokes images from the ordinary to the surreal, and transforms the commonplace into the sublime. —Joe Miller's Company

Cameron, Norman. Edited by Warren Hope. *The Complete Poems of Norman Cameron.* 82p. (0-941150-40-2). Edgewood, KY: Robert L. Barth (R.L.B.), Spring 1995. James Reeves [described Cameron as] "a poet's poet." People who read poetry because they derive pleasure from it, because it is an important and integral part of their lives, like Cameron's poems . . . Auden, Robert Graves and Dylan Thomas are among those who admired

Cameron's work. His brief, witty, neat, and unrhetorical products of introspection are a pleasure to read. —Warren Hope

Camner, Howard. *Brutal Delicacies.* 544p. $10.00. Ormond Beach, FL: Camelot Publishing Company, Fall 1996.

Camner, Howard. *Jammed Zipper.* 96p. $5.00. Ormond Beach, FL: Camelot Books, Fall 1994.

Campo, Rafael. *What the Boly Told.* 132p. $35.95 (0-8223-1733-8); pap. $12.95 (0-8223-1742-7). Durham, NC: Duke University Press, Spring 1996. Campo's background and concerns—he writes out of his identity and experience as a gay Cuban American physician—make for a rich field of investigations, and his best work is both passionate and formally accomplished. —Mark Doty. Campo is one of the most interesting and— I can think of no better word—*valuable* poets of his generation. The news he has to tell is the news we need, and his talent is equal to his message. —Richard Howard

Canavan, Rosemary. *The Island: Irish Poems.* 116p. pap. $10.95

(0-934257-56-6). Brownsville, OR: Story Line Press, Fall 1994. [Canavan's] lyric voice is strong and sure, almost lilting, certainly musical, and provides a metrical spine that can hold up any subject. This is both promising and fulfilling work. —Pat Monaghan, *Booklist*

Carbó, Nick. *El Grupo Mc-Donald's.* 77p. pap. $10.95 (1-882688-08-2). Chicago, IL: Tia Chucha Press, Spring 1996. North Americans have almost managed to forget the long and complex history we share with Filipinos. Yet repressed knowledge has a way of returning— sometimes as poetry. Nick Carbó's understated narratives present small moments of life in this most Americanized of Asian nations; moments into which history has been gently folded. —Susan Tichy. Carbo's forte is the ironic twist in narrative and dramatic incident and the telling juxtaposition of details and characters. —E. San Juan, Jr.

Carbó, Nick, ed. *Returning a Borrowed Tongue: An Anthology of Filipino and Filipino American Poetry.* 238p. pap. $14.95 (1-56689-043-8). Minneapolis, MN: Coffee House Press, Spring

1996. A necessary addition to our rich Asian American canon. It is an exciting tapestry of Filipino American poets from all walks of life. —Marilyn Chin

Cariño, Maria Luisa. *In the Garden of Three Islands.* 128p. pap. $11.95 (1-55921-117-2). Wakefield, RI: Asphodel Press/Moyer Bell, Fall 1995. This first collection to be published in the U.S. introduces American readers to a quite remarkable poet from the Philippines. Written in an English of singular resonance, of lyric richness informed by history, by legend, by political awareness, and everywhere by a deep perception, it is deserving of a wide, enthusiastic readership. —Ralph J. Mills, Jr. Cariño's language is light, always maintaining that sense of wonder and awe that we feel as children. —*National Book Review* (The Philippines)

Carlson, Barbara Siegel. *Between This Quivering.* 34p. pap. $5.50 (0-9647127-5-X). Lawrenceville, GA: Coreopsis Books, Fall 1996. "Who can be lost?" Barbara Carlson asks in one poem, and "I forget which way is home," she says in another. It is between these two poles that *Between This Quivering* finds its emotional ground and its unique voice. Here is a vision potentially shattering and defeated which finds victory, finds its way home, in the originality and force of its language, that is, in its poetry. —Richard Jackson

Carper, Thomas. *From Nature.* 80p. $16.95 (0-8018-5208-0). Baltimore, MD: Johns Hopkins University Press, Fall 1995. The poems in Thomas Carper's newest collection start at the beginning—childhood—and move from the concrete to the more abstract problem of presenting reality through artistic expression. —Johns Hopkins University Press. A superb technician, Carper manages demanding form[s] with ease. —*Kennebec*

Carr, M. L. *Enough Is Enough.* 158p. pap. $12.95. Southboro, MA: M. L. Enterprises, Fall 1995. A book of poems dedicated to every person who has known the horrors of discrimination, racism, sexism or anti-Semitism. —M. L. Enterprises

Carruth, Hayden. *Scrambled Eggs & Whiskey: Poems 1991-1995.*

110p. $25.00 (1-55659-109-8); pap. $14.00 (1-55659-110-1). Port Townsend, WA: Copper Canyon Press, Spring 1996. Hayden Carruth writes free verse so invisibly artful that under its spell we are not in the presence of a poem, but of the world. —Galway Kinnell. [He is] a part of our country's poetic treasure. —Adrienne Rich. These poems demonstrate that Carruth is still at the top of his form. Recommended for all poetry collections. —*Library Journal*

Carson, Anne. *Glass, Irony and God.* 176p. pap. $14.00 (0-8112-1302-1). New York, NY: New Directions, Fall 1995. Anne Carson's poems are narratives as beguiling as good short stories without relinquishing any of the intensity or decisive imagery of a good poem. She commands a depth of field and a richness of emotion not often seen in contemporary verse. —Guy Davenport

Carson, Anne. *Plainwater: Essays and Poetry.* 260p. $23.00 (0-679-43178-0). New York, NY: Alfred A. Knopf, Fall 1995. Despite her fastidious, ornately post-modern style, Carson finds her subject matter in classicism. The fruits of this unique, difficult combination are strikingly displayed in this selection of her published work. —*Publishers Weekly*

Carter, Jimmy. *Always a Reckoning.* $18.00 (0-812924-34-7). New York, NY: Times Books, Spring 1995. In this moving, wide-ranging, and intensely personal collection of poems, President Jimmy Carter opens to us his very private and reflective world. *Always a Reckoning* is sparked with wry and sometimes bitter humor, warmed with tenderness, and glowing with an intense and passionate caring that is born of an awareness both political and sensual. —Times Books

Casey, Michael. *Millrat.* 25p. pap. $8.00 (0-938566-72-5). Easthampton, MA: Adastra Press, Spring 1996. Seventeen poems in the voices of textile mill workers, set in northeastern Massachusetts, one of the cradles of the factory system during the industrial revolution. The poems are as stark as a row of brick factories. Limited edition, hand-set and hand-sewn.

Castan, Fran. *The Widow's Quilt.* 64p. pap. $12.00 (1-886435-04-9). Sag Harbor, NY: Canio's Editions, Fall 1996. A restrained but impassioned, moving work. We have never seen the Vietnam tragedy through such eyes, with such grief, rage, clarity. —Robin Morgan. Fran Castan's poems greet and challenge us with with a keen urgency, absolute sincerity, and a simplicity that defines eloquence. —Philip Appleman. This is good writing. —Robert Bly

Castillo, Ana. *My Father Was a Toltec and Selected Poems, 1973-1988.* 158p. $18.95 (0-393-03718-5); pap. $12.00 (0-393-31354-9). New York, NY: W.W. Norton & Company, Spring 1995. Ana Castillo has a reputation as one of the country's most powerful novelists, but she began her literary career as a poet of passion and uncompromising commitment. This collection brings back into print the best of her early work. —W.W. Norton & Company. Ana Castillo's use of Spanish, Chicago street lingo and English in *My Father Was a Toltec* is exciting and— forerunners notwithstanding— absolutely new. —Margaret Randall, *Women's Review of Books*

Catlin, Alan. *Self Annihilation With Shopping Bag Ladies*. 20p. pap. $2.25. Los Angeles, CA: Undulating Bedsheets Productions, Spring 1996. Distant fires hovering as demons trapped in a storm cellar try to bite each other's heads off. —Undulating Bedsheets

Catlin, Alan. *Shelley and the Romantics: Prose Poems*. 20p. pap. $7.00 (0-938566-64-4). Easthampton, MA: Adastra Press, Fall 1994. Handset, letterpress, hand-sewn edition. [This work] accomplishes the astounding feat of adding fresh perspectives to great art while covertly developing into art itself. —M.A. Rossi, *Collages & Bricolages*

Cavafy, Constantine. Edited by Edmund Keeley. *The Essential Cavafy*. 70p. $16.00 (0-88001-426-1); pap. $10.00 (0-88001-516-0). Hopewell, NJ: Ecco Press, Fall 1995. The major poems are all here [and] Keeley's introduction is comprehensive and useful. If you have never encountered Cavafy's quiet eroticism, and his exaltation of beauty and memory against the wry backdrop of his historical events, [*The Essential Cavafy*] is a good place to start.

If you are already an admirer of Cavafy's work, this volume is easily packed and travels lightly. —*Harvard Review*

Cavalieri, Grace. *Migrations*. 70p. pap. $15.00 (0-964253-70-4). Pensacola, FL: Vision Library Publications, Fall 1995. The prevailing metaphor of *Migrations* is motherhood, the prevailing mood is loss. We are each the mother, each the child. —Vision Library International. In *Migrations* Cavalieri presents a series of poems in which speakers come as close as the far reaches of the body, as if they are themselves being born . . . —Shelby Stephenson, *The Pilot*

Celan, Paul. Translated by Pierre Joris. *Breathturn*. 272p. pap. $12.95 (1-55713-218-6). Los Angeles, CA: Sun & Moon Press.

Cendrars, Blaise. Translated by Bertrand Mathieu. *Christmas at the Four Corners of the Earth*. 65p. $16.95 (1-880238-16-0). Rochester, NY: BOA Editions, Fall 1994. The 12 trans-realist prose sketches in *Christmas At The Four Corners of The Earth* take the reader to Paris, Rio de Janeiro, Bahia, Rotterdam,

China, New Mexico, New Zealand, the Ardennes Forest, and the south Atlantic ocean. —BOA Editions

Centolella, Thomas. *Lights & Mysteries.* 118p. pap. $12.00 (1-55659-106-3). Port Townsend, WA: Copper Canyon Press, Fall 1995. Thomas Centolella is a true walker in the city, richly responsive to the wide range of survivors, misfits, and wounded heroes that make up our common landscape. —Carl Dennis. This is an exciting book—so much passion, compassion, humor, zest for living, sadness, and big questions. The amplitude of Centolella's forms allows for a rare synthesis of meditative discourse and lyrical sensibility. —Denise Levertov

Chadwick, Irene. *Dawn Pearl.* 48p. pap. $9.50 (0-9642725-0-4). Modesto, CA: Ietje Kooi Press, Fall 1995. Readers should expect the new, the fresh, the about-to-be. *Dawn Pearl* is very new indeed, a sparkler, a red-haired baby born with a dimple, a smile, diamond rings on five ringers, already happy and humming what might be Bach. —Lee Nicholson

Chalmer, Judith. *Out of History's Junk Jar: Poems of a Mixed Inheritance.* 100p. $18.95 (1-56809-016-1); pap. $12.50 (1-56809-017-X). St. Louis, MO: Time Being Books, Fall 1995. This is a sure and powerful first book. These somehow beautiful poems are the searchlight Chalmer carries into the dark of her life, and the intersections of lost personal and political history. —Linda McCarriston

Chandler, Janet Carncross. Edited by Shirley Coe. *Time for Love: Assisted Living Viewed by One of the Very Old.* 120p. pap. $9.00 (0-918949-91-2). Watsonville, CA: Papier-Mache Press, Spring 1996. This is Chandler's last book, written when she was 85 years old. A touching and human book from beginning to end. —*Poet's Fantasy.* Old age and a consequent awareness of death are the themes, but the poet is a relentless exponent of life, of the adventure of sapient human awareness. —Bill Hotchkiss. These poems are a celebration of age . . . gifts from a genuine survivor. —Mark Doty

Chappell, Fred. *Spring Garden.* 157p. $24.95 (0-8071-1948-

2); pap. $14.95 (0-8071-1949-0). Baton Rouge, LA: Louisiana State University Press, Fall 1995 Among the most notable qualities of his poetry are its carefully crafted variety of forms, its fine storytelling and creation of character, its humor, and its serious moral intent. Chappell's poems reveal both enormous erudition and a profound commitment to what he has called folk art. —John Lang, *The Oxford Companion to Twentieth Century Poetry*. Finally, a book that isn't big or expensive at all, without a single picture, but packed with satisfaction. It is just great fun. —*Fayetteville Observer Times*

Chase, Naomi Feigelson. *The Judge's Daughter*. 29p. pap. $10.00 (1-882329-07-4). Truro, MA: Garden Street Press, Spring 1996. The power of this chapbook comes from its images and the truth it tells us about the power of art to save lives. —Samuel J. Keyser, *Harvard Review*

Chatfield, Hale. *Vox*. 62p. pap. $13.00 (0-9628478-5-2). Hiram, OH: North Star Press, Fall 1995.

Chaucer, Geoffrey. *Selected Canterbury Tales*. 135p. pap. $1.00 (0-486-28241-4). Mineola, NY: Dover Publications, Fall 1994.

Chavis, William Muse. *Designs/Lines*. 72p. pap. $8.00 (0-940713-10-1). Detroit, MI: Broadside Press, Fall 1995. Not only is this a book of poems, but it is also filled with various drawings, doodles and designs. A wonderful work. —*National Entertainment Plus Magazine*

Chelnik, Peter. *Eternity Road*. 186p. pap. $12.00 (0-964-2708-2-X). New York, NY: Peter Chelnik, Spring 1996. Peter Chelnik is a lonesome cowboy in New York City. His quest for truth and salvation make him a truly American poet. He believes folks should travel eternity road with heart and passion, always heading west. —Little Sky Press. *Eternity Road* is fierce, political and sassy. —Flo Kennedy

Cherry, Kelly. *Lovers and Agnostics*. 67p. pap. $11.95 (0-88748-208-2). Pittsburgh, PA: Carnegie Mellon University Press/ Classic Contemporary Series, Fall 1995.

Child, Abigail. *Scatter Matrix.* 79p. pap. $9.95 (0-937804-63-0). New York, NY: Roof Books, Fall 1996. Abigail Child is out to help us "Demythologize habit." "Dissenting conscience/ to support sunbeam/ sufferance/ and permeable/ genres/ in their breathing life/ morphic and unfashionable." Master of the precise torquing variable line, this clear-ended *listener* speaks to us more plainly than her ways let on. Read her aloud and listen to *her.* —Jackson Mac Low

Childers, Joanne. *Moving Mother Out.* 96p. pap. $7.95 (1-877978-35-3). Sarasota, FL: Florida Literary Foundation Press, Fall 1994. Poems about people you will recognize because there is something of them in all of us. In their complexity, vitality, eagerness, and passion they will engage you in their human dramas. —Florida Literary Foundation Press

Chipasula, Stella and Frank, eds. *The Heinemann Book of African Women's Poetry.* 256p. pap. $10.95 (0-435-90680-1). Portsmouth, NH: Heinemann—Boynton/Cook Publishers, Spring 1995. This anthology offers an extensive selection of poetry by women all over the African continent. The poems address love, motherhood, death, colonial domination and human dignity. They employ a variety of styles from the conversational to the didactic. —Heinemann—Boynton/Cook Publishers

Chirodea, Doru. *Nonathambia.* 26p. pap. $3.00 (1-57141-14-7). Port Charlotte, FL: Runaway Spoon Press, Spring 1995. These are rawly visceral idiol-inguistic poems. —Runaway Spoon Press

Chmielarz, Sharon. *Stranger in Her House.* 28p. pap. $3.95 (0-9641986-4-9). Duluth, MN: Poetry Harbor, Spring 1995. *Stranger in Her House* is an emotional diary of a mother's death. The poems observe a life and its consequences with deeply felt sentiment that eschews sentimentality. —Mary Smith, *Minnesota Literature*

Christopher, Georgia. *The Butterfly Hotline.* 25p. pap. $6.00. Dallas, TX: HaSk, Spring 1995. *The Butterfly Hotline* is a memorial chapbook of surprising poems by the distinguished Miltonist who died in 1994. —HaSk

Christopher, Nicholas. *5 Degrees and Other Poems.* 112p. $22.95 (0-670-85341-0); pap. $12.95 (0-14-058718-7). New York, NY: Penguin Books, Spring 1995. I have read Nicholas Christopher's *5 Degrees* with great pleasure and a sense of wonder: he has transcended his previous work and broken through into his own sphere. —Harold Bloom

Chrystos. *Fugitive Colors.* 69p. pap. $10.00 (1-880834-11-1). Cleveland, OH: Cleveland State University Poetry Center, Spring 1995. Winner of the 1994 Audre Lorde Poetry Competition. These poems burn incandescently hot, in the flames of desire and anger. —Minnie Bruce Pratt. Chrystos' words are made sharp by the living traditions of her people and the edgy rythms of urban life. Both draw us in to hear her stories of passion and injustice. —Jewelle Gomez

Chute, Robert. *Woodshed on the Moon: Thoreau Poems.* 48p. pap. $9.95 (1-879205-10-6). Troy, ME: Nightshade Press, Spring 1995. *Woodshed on the Moon* enters into the mind, language and spirit of Thoreau. It is a book to re-read and savor. —X. J. Kennedy

Ciolli, Vivina. *Bitter Larder.* 20p. pap. $3.75. Kew Gardens, NY: New Spirit Press, Fall 1994. Winner of the New Spirit Press Quarterly Chapbook Contest. A book of poems about the men in the poet's life: father, husband, son, lovers; about lost joys and found courage. —New Spirit Press

Clabon, George D. *The Gathering.* 60p. pap. $10.00 (0-9635690-7-4). Minneapolis, MN: TA Publications, Fall 1995. George D. Clabon bases his writing on his life as a Black man in America. He uses poetry to call up our history and present his vision for the future. —Ginny Knight

Claman, Elizabeth, ed. *Writing Our Way Out of the Dark: An Anthology by Child Abuse Survivors.* 288p. pap. $16.95 (0-9638992-2-8). Eugene, OR: Queen of Swords Press, Fall 1995. This moving collection transforms the tragedy of childhood abuse into a triumph of the human spirit. —Wendy Maltz

Clampitt, Amy. *A Silence Opens.* $20.00 (0-679-42997-2); pap.

$13.00 (0-679-75022-3). New York, NY: Alfred A. Knopf, Spring 1994. [In Clampitt's work we find] a brilliant exactitude in seeing and hearing, a luxuriant use of language, and an ability to discover the hidden unities connecting experience and knowledge. —Alfred Corn, *Boston Globe*. From *The Kingfisher* onward, Clampitt has created a distinguished body of work praised for linguistic invention and delight, imaginative originality, and metaphysical depth. With *A Silence Opens*, she has given us an exquisitely sensitive exploration of where and how the mysterious intersects with the ordinary. —Robert Hosmer, *The Southern Review*

Clark, Suzanne U. *Weather of the House*. 36p. pap. $6.00 (1-885912-01-3). Abingdon, VA: Sow's Ear Press, Fall 1994. That much-abused word "original" can be truthfully applied to Suzanne Clark's work. Her poems have force and skill, and often a shocking wisdom. —Josephine Jacobsen

Clark, Tom. *Like Real People*. 240p. $25.00 (0-87685-985-6); pap. $13.50 (0-87685-984-8); sig. $35.00 (0-87685-986-

4). Santa Rosa, CA: Black Sparrow Press, Fall 1995. By turns wry and moving in tone, these poems frame autobiographical reflections with haunting lyric and elegiac meditations. The themes of Clark's autobiographical poems—loss of youthful hopes, coming-to-terms with aging—meld into a larger view of personal and public history. —Black Sparrow Press

Clary, Killarney. *By Common Salt*. 62p. $22.95 (0-932440-73-8); pap. $12.95 (0-932440-74-6). Oberlin, OH: Oberlin College Press, Spring 1996. Attempting to find a still point from which she might engage the violence and mystery of the contemporary landscape, this poet is brought to face the dangers which come disguised as comfort or steadiness. Through details of the moment, fragments of dream, and confrontations with devastating loss, she celebrates the unknown. —Oberlin College Press

Clewell, David. *Now We're Getting Somewhere*. 96p. $17.95 (0-299-14410-0); pap. $10.95 (0-299-14414-3). Madison, WI: University of Wisconsin Press, Fall 1994. Winner of the Felix

Pollak Prize in Poetry. His wit and energy seem inexhaustible, and he reminds us that the world is, too. —Henry Taylor

Clift, Elayne. *Demons Dancing In My Head: Collected Poems 1985-1995.* 110p. pap. $8.95 (0-9634827-2-6). Potomac, MD: OGN Publications, Spring 1995. This woman has a wonderful imagination, and her poems are filled with color, bounce, and satisfying images. —*Dusty Dog Review*

Clifton, Lucille. *The Terrible Stories.* 72p. $20.00 (1-880238-36-5); pap. $12.50 (1-880238-37-3). Rochester, NY: BOA Editions, Fall 1996. Employing brilliantly honed language, stunning images and sharp rhythms, Clifton's poetry addresses the whole of human experience. Hers is a poetry passionate and wise, ranging from the personal to the biblical to the mystical, not afraid to rage or whisper. —BOA Editions

Climenhaga, Joel. *Blues for Present Inhabitants of the Earth.* 56p. pap. $5.00. Tarkio, MO: Shadow Press, Fall 1994. 22 poems written by the author in his late teens and early twen-

ties, between 1940 and 1947. —Shadow Press

Climenhaga, Joel. *Bottom of the Spittoon.* 56p. pap. $5.00. Tarkio, MO: Shadow Press, Fall 1994. Comprised of 16 pieces of writing of fugitive and experimental form. —Shadow Press

Climenhaga, Joel. *Nothing Can Stop the Words.* 56p. pap. $5.00. Tarkio, MO: Shadow Press, Fall 1994. 16 pieces of writing in alternate forms, different beats, and experimental approaches. —Shadow Press

Climenhaga, Joel. *Sad Dreams of the Lonely Divorcee and 24 Other Poems.* 56p. pap. $5.00. Tarkio, MO: Shadow Press, Fall 1994. 25 poems written while the author was in his late teens and early twenties, between 1939 and 1946. —Shadow Press

Climenhaga, Joel. *The Yellow Breasts of Lena and 30 Other Poems.* 56p. pap. $5.00. Tarkio, MO: Shadow Press, Fall 1994. Comprised of 31 poems written when the author was in his twenties, between 1943 and 1945. —Shadow Press

Coffey, Michael. *Elemenopy*. 104p. pap. $10.95 (1-55713-240-2). Los Angeles, CA: Sun & Moon Press, Spring 1996. Poet Michael Coffey created *Elemenopy* in order to represent a procession of struggles and outcomes in his relationship to language. The first section, "Loving," contains playful poems that delight in the promise of poetic form and lyric utterance. "Javajazyk," the concluding section, invents a language in which to tell a love story. —Sun & Moon Press

Cohen, Betty, ed. *Poets at Work: Contemporary Poets—Lives, Poems, Process*. 291p. pap. $15.00 (0-9647047-0-6). Buffalo, NY: Just Buffalo Literary Center, Fall 1995. This multicultural anthology brings together the lives, poems, and processes of twenty-four of America's brightest writers including Robert Creeley, Ron Padgett, and Lucille Clifton. —Just Buffalo Literary Center

Cole, Henri. *The Look of Things*. 80p. $20.00 (0-679-43352-X); pap. $13.00 (0-679-76593-X). New York, NY: Alfred A. Knopf, Fall 1995. In this book the burning-glass of anguish and lament is held mercifully under the gentling moonlight of form. The suffering of AIDS victims are distanced by 'stories' brushed on the page like French Impressionist paintings. Pity and terror once more join hands with beauty and grace. —Mona Van Duyn

Cole, James. *A Brave Passenger*. 63p. pap. $10.00 (1-881119-43-2). Amherst, MA: Pyncheon House, Spring 1995. James Cole writes with a clarity and precision that is rare and refreshing. In each quietly articulated poem he draws his reader on as into an unexpected sunlit clearing. He has produced a memorable book. —William Jay Smith

Cole, Norma. *Contrafact*. 112p. pap. $11.00 (0-937013-54-4). Elmwood, CT: Potes & Poets Press, Spring 1996. Norma Cole's work is beautiful— yes, with sharp edges— musically exact—poetry's curious happiness—and deep as the ocean of language, where it laughs, shadows and overwhelms. —Robin Blaser

Coleman, Horace. *In the Grass*. 88p. pap. $12.00 (1-885215-17-7). Woodbridge, CT: Viet

Nam Generation/Burning Cities Press, Fall 1995. Horace Coleman's *In the Grass* is a book of darkness and revelation. Here are poems filled with ammunition that penetrate not flesh but soul. Coleman's memories of Vietnam are not war stories—instead they capture moments when blackness is the battlefield. This is a book for careful readers. —E. Ethelbert Miller

Coles, Nicholas, and Peter Oresick, eds. *For a Living: The Poetry of Work.* 432p. $44.95 (0-252-02122-3); pap. $18.95 (0-252-06410-0). Champaign, IL: University of Illinois Press, Spring 1995. In this companion volume to their anthology *Working Classics*, Nicholas Coles and Peter Oresick present poems written in the 1980s and 1990s that address the nature and culture of nonindustrial work—white collar, domestic, clerical, technical, managerial, or professional. —Univeristy of Illinois Press. This collection may exert even wider appeal than its twice-reprinted predecessor, not only because of the diversity of occupations represented but also because of the immediacy and aural clarity of the selections. —*Booklist*

Collier, Michael. *The Neighbor.* 72p. $20.00 (0-226-11358-2); pap. $9.95 (0-226-11359-0). Chicago, IL: University of Chicago Press, Fall 1994. The dark splendor of this collection is the burden of its witnessing, the quiet courage of a speaker who will not turn away from what he sees and remembers. How are we changed by what we come to know—sometimes unwittingly—about each other? *The Neighbor* is a book of transforming and compassionate answers. —Edward Hirsch

Collier, Michael, ed. *The Wesleyan Tradition: Four Decades of American Poetry.* 316p. pap. $14.95 (0-8195-1229-X). Middletown, CT: Wesleyan/University Press of New England, Fall 1993. "Wesleyan's characteristic independence in scooping up unfound poets and publishing them well—and in sustaining the ongoing publication of established writers like David Ignatow and James Tate—is shown to advantage in this anthology of work drawn from books issued over 34 years." —*Publishers Weekly*

Collins, Billy. *The Art of Drowning.* 95p. $24.95 (0-8229-3893-6); pap. $10.95 (0-8229-

5567-9). Pittsburgh, PA: University of Pittsburgh Press, Spring 1996. Billy Collins is an American original—a metaphysical poet with a funny bone and a sly, questioning intelligence. He is an ironist of the void, and his poems—witty, playful, and beautifully turned—bump up against the deepest human mysteries. —Edward Hirsch. Mr. Collins is funny without being silly, moving without being silly, and brainy without being silly. If only he were silly, we should know how to place him. But he is merely— merely!—funny, moving, brainy. —Richard Howard

Collins, Judy. *Squall Line.* 60p. pap. $8.50 (0-936563-17-6). Bellingham, WA: The Signpost Press, Fall 1995. Again and again in Judy Collins' poetry, one finds words that rise from the depths like monoliths of stone into the wild eddies of syntax: "the silken nucleal tent, the lover, the tangled boughs, a fresh confluence." Then comes the shiver of recognition. —James Bertolino

Condini, Ned. *Quartettsatz.* 66p. pap. $7.00 (1-884419-06-2). West Lafayette, IN: Bordighera, Fall 1996. Ned Condini's poetry unexpectedly combines the compressed lyricism of Italian modernism with the democratic tone of contemporary American verse. "Exiled by choice, he coined / a language all his own," writes Condini. Yes, his blend of two literatures has created a fresh and serious idiom entirely his own. —Dana Gioia

Conforti, Gerard J. *Now That the Night Ends.* 92p. pap. $10.00 (0-944676-40-5). Gualala, CA: AHA Books, Fall 1996. Gerard John Conforti, who is also an excellent haiku poet, has been able to adapt the tanka in such a way as to transform his feelings of love into poems of simple beauty. Though he is certainly not the first to use this strict form in English, he has demonstrated a facility with it rarely seen before. —Cor van den Heuvel

Congdon, Kirby. *Poem for Early Morning.* 8p. pap. $1.00. Key West, FL: Cycle Press, Spring 1996. Produced for The Heritage House Museum Robert Frost Celebration, 1996. —Cycle Press

Congdon, Kirby. *Rowboats*. 8p. pap. $1.00. Key West, FL: Cycle Press, Spring 1995. Produced for The Heritage House Museum Robert Frost Celebration, 26 March 1995. —Cycle Press

Connellan, Leo. *Provincetown*. 78p. pap. $11.00 (1-880684-29-2). Willimantic, CT: Curbstone Press, Fall 1995. It's vintage Connellan: brave, angry, intense, relentless. Time has only sharpened his sword and stoked his fire. —Martha Smith, *Small Press Magazine*

Connor-Bey, Brenda. *Thoughts of an Everyday Woman: An Unfinished Urban Folktale*. 100p. pap. $14.95 (0-940738-16-3). Bronx, NY: Blind Beggar Press, Fall 1995. Connor-Bey's writing is grounded in the Black American experience and in the history of her family. —Blind Beggar Press

Conoley, Gillian. *Beckon*. 80p. $20.95 (0-88748-218-X); pap. $11.95 (0-88748-219-8). Pittsburgh, PA: Carnegie Mellon University, Spring 1996. These remarkable poems help us to see ourselves *as* ourselves in all of our glorious tatters and tiaras. Always highly shrewd and richly sensual. Gillian Conoley's poems stand with the very finest and most moving in all of contemporary poetry. —David St. John

Conti, Edmund. *The Ed C. Scrolls*. 43p. pap. $3.00 (1-57141-011-2). Port Charlotte, FL: Runaway Spoon Press, Fall 1995. Light verse on the scriptures and related matters. —Runaway Spoon Press

Conway, Jeffery. *Blood Poisoning*. 28p. pap. $7.00. New York, NY: Cold Calm Press, Fall 1995. In his confessional sestinas and his quiet slice-of-life epiphanies, Conway [uses] the simplest and most straightforward poetic gestures. For Conway clarity equals truth; he shuns affectation and embellishment in favor of flatness . . . so real, so sexy. Conway makes his own kind of music—both profound and matter-of-fact, both beautiful and bland. —David Trinidad

Cook, Geoffrey. *A Cleveland Poetry Retrospective 1964–1971: The Heart of the Beast*. 30p. pap. $4.50. Hiram, OH: Hiram Poetry Review. These poems will remind you of what we were like when we equated a city with the world. —Hiram Poetry Review

Cooley, Nicole. *Resurrection.* 79p. $19.95 (0-8071-2058-8); pap. $10.95 (0-8071-2059-6). Baton Rouge, LA: Louisiana State University Press, Spring 1996. Winner of the 1995 Walt Whitman Award from the Academy of American Poets. *Resurrection*'s cumulative power comes from its erotic, passionate, repressed, frightening, and ecstatic qualities. —Cynthia Macdonald. Occasionally, a collection of poetry comes along so intense and gripping that you want to shout the news and dive in again and again. Such is Nicole Cooley's *Resurrection.* —*The Charlotte Observer*

Coolidge, Clark. *For Kurt Cobain.* 12p. pap. $5.00 (0-935724-72-9). Great Barrington, MA: The Figures, Spring 1995.

Coolidge, Clark. *The Crystal Text.* 156p. pap. $11.95 (1-55713-230-5). Los Angeles, CA: Sun & Moon Press, Fall 1995. The occasion for this poetic meditation is a colorless quartz crystal sitting upon the writer's desk. The crystal is as still and irreducible as a death's head in St. Jerome's study or Cezanne's studio. But what would the crystal reveal, if it could speak? How might the issue of its presence be brought into language? The poet of *The Crystal Text,* by means of a rare stamina of attention and listening vulnerability, seeks to become the medium of the crystal's transmissions. —Sun & Moon Press. In a world where people are cut off from the mystical cosmic and sublime aesthetic everythings, the works of Clark Coolidge provide for us the beauty of some of the interstitial stuff that might weave the world back together. —Bernadette Mayer

Copioli, Rosita. Translated by Renata Treitel. *The Blazing Lights of the Sun.* 144p. pap. $11.95 (1-55713-195-3). Los Angeles, CA: Sun & Moon Press, Spring 1996. Working from the idea of the "beautiful" in Lucretius onward, Copioli explores the myths of origin and concepts of the infinite. —Sun & Moon Press

Corbett, William. *New & Selected Poems.* 256p. pap. $18.75 (0-944072-54-2). Cambridge, MA: Zoland Books, Fall 1995. Corbett swings. His confiding, bemused, and warmly observant poems flow, soar, and stride with hardly a mark of punctuation. That's how perfect his meter is, how musical his word choice, how clear his ideas. —*Booklist*

Corbin, Harold. *Northering: New and Collected Poems.* 180p. $25.00 (0-9648611-9-4). New York, NY: The Stinehour Press, Fall 1995. Written by self described amateur poet Harold Corbin, these poems come out of his kinetic connection with books and teaching and usually happy and useful life. He assigned the work to family and friends but it well deserves a far larger audience. —The Stinehour Press

Cording, Robert. *Heavy Grace.* 68p. pap. $9.95 (1-882295-09-9). Farmington, ME: Alice James Books, Spring 1996. The quotidian is the subject of Robert Cording's luminous third collection of poems. These quiet lyrics reveal the steady gaze of a man determined to confront his mortal fears. Cording's stern poems offer a measure of solace, a kind of grace—a way to live in the now. —Christopher Merrill

Corey, Del. *Bloodline Poems.* 56p. pap. $5.00 (1-56439-043-8).

Detroit, MI: Ridgeway Press, Spring 1995.

Cornish, Sam. *Cross a Parted Sea.* 128p. pap. $11.95 (0-944072-71-2). Cambridge, MA: Zoland Books, Fall 1996. Sam Cornish has an insistent commitment to statement understood by feeling, experience, history, memory. —Amiri Baraka

Cortez, Jayne. *Somewhere in Advance of Nowhere.* 124p. pap. $12.99 (1-85242-422-2). New York, NY: Serpent's Tail/High Risk Books, Fall 1996. Jayne Cortez is an energy, a nourishment, a Black Nation song. —Gwendolyn Brooks. *Somewhere in Advance of Nowhere* follows the footprints left by ecstatic dancers on sands that are drenched with the vital fluids of revolution, love and hope. —Walter Mosley. Cortez writes verse that's frank and urban. These poems range from the overtly political . . . to the streetwise sensuality of Cortez's rhythmic, percussive efforts. —*Publishers Weekly*

Cory, Jean-Jacques. *Exhaustive Combinations-2.* 26p. pap. $5.00 (1-57141-022-8). Port Charlotte, FL: Runaway Spoon

Press, Spring 1996. A permutation poem using just five words over and over. —Runaway Spoon Press

Coss, Clare, ed. *The Arc of Love: An Anthology of Lesbian Love Poems.* 240p. $20.00 (0-684-81446-3). New York, NY: Scribner, Spring 1996. This beautiful and power-bestowing gift tells in gorgeous detail what we women do, feel, dream, think and say—in bed, before bed, after bed—when we love! —Ronnie Gilbert. A book that represents the enormity of love, the tragedy and amazingness of it, the deviance, beauty, and passion. —Jacqueline Woodson

Costley, Bill. *Siciliconia.* 46p. Bayonne, NJ: The Beehive Press, Spring 1995.

Cousineau, Phil, ed. *Prayers at 3 A.M.: Poems, Songs, Chants and Prayers for the Middle of the Night.* 240p. pap. $12.00 (0-06-251200-5). San Francisco, CA: HarperCollins/HarperSanFrancisco, Fall 1995. A source of inspiration for the nighthawk at the allnight diner, an insomniac's guide to the dark night of the soul, or a beguiling companion to sit alongside the warm brandy on the bedstand. Includes sections from Borges, Rich, Gandhi, O'Hara, Brontë, Rumi, Olds, St. John of the Cross, Beethoven, Dillard, and many more. —HarperCollins

Cowing, Sue, ed. *Fire in the Sea: An Anthology of Poetry and Art.* 152p. $29.95 (0-8248-1649-8). Honolulu, HI: University of Hawai'i Press, Fall 1996. This collection contains work by poets from many Pacific lands—Hawai'i, Samoa, Tahiti, Papua New Guinea, Fiji, and New Zealand, among others—as well as from Europe, Asia, and the Americas. Ranging from the thirteenth century to the twentieth, from the widely read to the lesser known, the poems were gathered especially but not exclusively for young readers. Selected works of art from the collections of the Honolulu Academy of Arts accompany the poems. —University of Hawai'i Press

Creighton, Dean, ed. *Cattle Bones & Coke Machines: An Anthology of Poems Examining the Impact of Humanity on the Earth's Energy Systems.* 38p. pap. $10.00. Maple City, MI: Smiling Dog Press. Here are thirty plus poets and an editor doing something in the face of ugly iron environmental destruction. —Michael Basinski, *Small Press Review*

Crews, Stella, ed. *The Oak Park Bards: A Poetry Excursion at Oak Park High School.* 10p. pap. $2.50. Detroit, MI: Broadside Press, Spring 1995.

Crow, Barbara. *Coming Up for Light and Air.* 72p. pap. $7.95 (0-89823-159-0). Minneapolis, MN: New Rivers Press, Spring 1995. This handsome book is beautifully and appropriately designed for Crow's modest and profound voice. Reading it is the adventure of entering another life described with grave and mysterious eloquence. —*Choice*

Crow, Mary. *I Have Tasted the Apple.* 71p. pap. $12.50 (1-880238-33-0). Rochester, NY: BOA Editions, Spring 1996. *I Have Tasted the Apple* has a big feel to it; basic and metaphysical, these poems are informed by a mature lyricism. —Yusef Komunyakaa

Crunk, T. *Living in the Resurrection.* 64p. $16.00 (0-300-06525-6); pap. $9.00 (0-300-06526-4). New Haven, CT: Yale University Press, Fall 1995. *Living in the Resurrection,* winner of the 1994 Yale Series of Younger Poets competition, is about the tensions between allegiance to the history and traditions of the author's birthplace in western Kentucky and a longing for a more expansive life beyond the confines of that dying culture. —Yale University Press. Here is that rare phenomenon, a writer of instinctive formal vision. —James Dickey

Cummings, E. E. Edited by Richard Kostelanetz. *AnOther Cummings.* 288p. $25.00 (0-87140-157-6). New York, NY: Liveright Publishing, Spring 1996. An eye-opening selection of Cummings's more avantegarde poetry and prose. —Liveright Publishing

Cummings, E. E. *Tulips & Chimneys.* 188p. pap. $13.00 (0-87140-165-7). New York, NY: Liveright Publishing, Fall 1996. Only now can the reader see this collection in its author's own arrangement of the contents. A manuscript that no publisher was willing to take a chance on in the early 1920's, *Tulips & Chimneys* clearly reveals the conservatism of the American literary scene just after World War I. —Richard S. Kennedy

Cumpián, Carlos. *Armadillo Charm.* 80p. pap. $10.95 (1-882688-09-0). Chicago, IL: Tia Chucha Press, Spring 1996. Carlos Cumpián writes poems brimming with Chicano life, full of anger, humor and irony. The explosive energy of these poems flows into a vision of justice, gleaming from the page. —Martin Espada

Curtiss, A. B. *Children of the Gods.* 88p. $18.95 (0-932529-57-7). Escondido, CA: Oldcastle Publisher, Fall 1994. *Children of the Gods* is the fictional journal of a man who writes in the ancient language of poetry about his vision of the creation of the Earth. Suggesting that we are all children of the Gods searching for our lost and mythic selves, Curtiss writes with the simple wisdom of the earnest storyteller. —Oldcastle Publishing

Cutler, Bruce. *The Massacre at Sand Creek: Narrative Voices.* 264p. $19.95 (0-8061-2730-9). Norman, OK: University of Oklahoma Press, Spring 1995.

Cutler [portrays] the murder of almost 200 Cheyenne men, women, and children. Their voices have been re-created like a lyrical vision. —*Library Journal*

Cypser, Cora E. *Wandering in the Wilderness.* 150p. pap. $8.00 (0-9625774-1-3). Katonah, NY: Kim Pathways, Fall 1995. These poems explore the wilderness of our society, touching on abortion, evolution, prisons, and ecology. —Kim Pathways

D

D'Alosio, Geoffrey Piper. *Triptych.* 11p. pap. $2.00 Portland, OR: Ahistorical Productions, Fall 1995. *Triptych* employs historical anecdotes, the scientific method and the poetic imagination in its condemnation of the current state of humanity. —Ahistorical Productions

Daigon, Ruth. *About a Year.* 22p. pap. $3.00 Pleasant Hill, CA: Small Poetry Press, Spring 1996.

Daigon, Ruth. *Between One Future and the Next.* 116p. $12.00 (0-918949-67-X); pap. $8.00 (0-918949-66-1). Watsonville, CA: Papier-Mache Press, March 1995. [Daigon is] interested in shapes of memory and distances between loved ones, in how a woman's life is to be observed. These poems trace moments in the midst of the rough-hewn immigrant family life in Manitoba "when the sun honeyed/the earth and things came/softly to order." —Frank Allen, *Library Journal.* [Her] poems are acts of noticing, exaltation and love. —*Publisher's Weekly.* [Her] work is a long drink of cold crystalline spring water. It is clear without being shallow; direct without simplification. —Marge Piercy. Daigon's poems stop me in my tracks. I have to move my eyes away from the page because the pain is too real, the love is too destructible, the sight of the words too wrenching. —June Owens, *Iowa Woman*

Dalachinsky, Steven. *One Thin Line.* 8p. pap. $1.00 Brooklyn, NY: Pinched Nerves Press, Spring 1995. Wise and quiet poems inspired by the Beats. —Pinched Nerves Press.

Dalachinsky, Steven. *People/Places.* 46p. pap. Bayonne, NJ: Beehive Press, Spring 1995.

Dalton, Roque. Translated by Jonathan Cohen, et. al. Edited by Hardie St. Martin. *Small Hours of the Night: Selected Poems.* 243p. pap. $14.95 (1-880684-35-7). Willimantic, CT: Curbstone Press, Fall 1996. This is the most comprehensive and scholarly collection of Dalton's poetry available in English. —*Publishers Weekly*

Dana, Robert. *Hello, Stranger: Beach Poems.* 64p. $14.95 (0-938078-46-1); pap: $9.95 (0-938078-43-7). Tallahassee, FL: Anhinga Press, Spring 1996. To begin at a margin and make oneself at home there has been Robert Dana's central method all along, as this fine collection of beach poems amply demonstrates. We're not born knowing how to love the world; we're born squalling. *Hello, Stranger* reminds us how much we can teach ourselves by strict attention and imagination. —William Matthews. A Dana poem seems not crafted but improvised. Yet it is about as "effortless" as a jazz solo that brings to bear years of experience. You hold your breath as the poem takes place. —Edward Brunner. *Des Moines Register*

Daniels, Jim. *Niagara Falls.* 39p. pap. $7.00 (0-938566-63-6). Easthampton, MA: Adastra Press, Fall 1994. A *Small Press Review* Pick of the Month, October 1994. A 700 line poem of three interwoven narratives: growing up Catholic in Detroit, a honeymoon to Niagara Falls, and a pilgrimage to Assisi, Italy. Letterpress edition also available. —Adastra Press

Daniels, Jim, ed. *Letters to America: Contemporary American Poetry on Race.* 230p. pap. $19.95 (0-8143-2542-4). Detroit, MI: Wayne State University Press, Spring 1996. *Letters to America* explores this country's shameful history of intolerance, but the poets do it in many different ways. . . . This is a vital anthology. —*The Bloomsbury Review.* As tough and important as its subject, this book does more than collect the probings of several dozen American poets on their nation's nightmare—it calls into question the purpose of poetry. If poetry exists to make us feel safe and erudite and well-mannered, then the book fails utterly. If

poetry exists to speak soul-to-soul of the heart's pain and the body's vivid longing and the soul's singular purity, then it succeeds completely. —*Booklist*

Dante Alighieri. Translated by Harry Duncan. *I Come to That Point on the Wheel/Io son venuto al punto de la rosa.* 12p. pap. $15.00 Omaha, NE: Bradypress, Fall 1995. Limited letterpress edition.

Dante Alighieri. Translated by John Ciardi. *The Divine Comedy: Inferno.* 298p. $15.50 (0-679-60209-7). New York, NY: Random House/Modern Library Editions, Spring 1996. A spectacular achievement. A text with the clarity and sobriety of a first-rate prose translation which at the same time suggests the run and rhythm of the great original. —Archibald MacLeish

Dante Alighieri. Translated by John Ciardi. *The Divine Comedy: Paradiso.* 368p. $15.50 (0-679-60211-9). New York, NY: Random House/Modern Library Editions, Spring 1996.

Dante Alighieri. Translated by John Ciardi. *The Divine Comedy: Purgatorio.* 368p. $15.50 (0-

679-60210-0). New York, NY: Random House/Modern Library Editions, Spring 1996.

Dante Alighieri. Translated by Robert Pinsky. *The Inferno of Dante: A New Verse Translation.* 427p. $35.00 (0-374-17674-4). New York, NY: Farrar, Straus and Giroux, Spring 1995. One hell of a poem. —Richard Howard. This translation is wonderfully alert to Dante's strange blend of fierceness and sympathy, clear-eyed lucidity and heart-stopping wonder. With Michael Mazur's stunning monotypes, this is now the premier modern text for English-language readers. —Stephen Greenblatt. Pinsky's voice is nearly irresistible when rounding out the grotesqueries of Dante's Hell: his versions of the ninth and final circle bring the bizarre terror of the fiery pit to life. Plainspoken yet elegant, this *Inferno* sustains a tactile succession of images. —*Publishers Weekly*

Darr, Ann. *Flying the Zuni Mountains.* 136p. pap. $10.00 (0-938572-08-3). Hedgesville, WV: The Bunny and the Crocodile Press/Forest Woods Media, Fall 1994. These poems recount the poet's experience as a Women's Airforce Service Pilot during World War II. Darr discusses how women flyers were dismissed before the end of the war and were denied Veteran's status until 33 years later. —The Bunny and the Crocodile Press. A serious delight; a truly important and moving book. —Ruth Whitman

Darr, Ann, ed. *Hungary as We Are: An Anthology of Washington Area Poets.* 346p. pap. $17.95 (0-931846-48-X). Washington, DC: Washington Writers' Publishing House, Fall 1995. As E. Ethelbert Miller states in his foreword, "When one speaks of hunger, one speaks of space, a space that can be physical, emotional, or Spiritual, the empty space in one's stomach or heart." Defining this empty space in its broadest sense, the more than 120 poets, all living within a 60-mile radius of the Capitol, write eloquently and variously about food, love, home, sex, dreams, time and spirituality. —Washington Writers' Publishing House

Darwish, Mahmud. Translated by Ben Bennani. *Psalms.* 75p. $22.00 (0-89410-761-5); pap. $12.00 (0-89410-762-3).

Boulder, CO: Three Continents Press/Lynne Rienner Publishers, Fall 1994. Ben Bennani's translations of Darwish give me a thrill. I am very moved by these poems; they make a beautiful book. —James Tate. [Darwish] is one of the most widely acclaimed poets writing in Arabic today. —*Nimrod.* [His is] the foremost poetic voice of the Palestinian struggle. —*The Harper Collins World Reader*

Daughtry, Philip. *Celtic Blood: Selected Poems 1968–1994.* 104p. $20.00 (1-883197-05-8); pap. $9.95 (1-883197-05-8). Cullowhee, NC: New Native Press, Fall 1995. This is a powerful book that mingles bardic language, mythological imagination, and the American landscape. Philip Daughtry may be the best synthesis of ancient Celt and purely modern American writing in English today. —Robert Bly

Davenport, Guy, trans. *7 Greeks.* 256p. pap. $16.95 (0-8112-1288-2). New York, NY: New Directions, Spring 1995. The most complete collection of its sort ever to appear in one volume, *7 Greeks* includes the works of poets and philoso-

phers who lived from the eighth to the third centuries B.C., including Archilochos, Sappho, Alkman, Herakleitos, Diogenes, Anakreon, and Herondas. —New Directions

David, Gary. *Tierra Zia.* 40p. pap. $8.00 (1-878888-19-6). Winston, OR: nine muses books, Fall 1996. Earth spots and petroglyphs in the southwest speak their ancient truths into the atomic age. —nine muses books

Davis, Cortney. *The Body Flute.* 24p. pap. $8.00 (0-938566-66-0). Easthampton, MA: Adastra Press, Fall 1994. Poems about nursing by a nurse. —Adastra Press. [Here is] primal sympathy and insight. —*Café Edition*

Davis, Cortney, and Judy Schaefer, eds. *Between the Heartbeats: Poetry and Prose by Nurses.* 240p. $27.95 (0-87745-516-3); pap. $14.95 (0-87745-517-1). Iowa City, IA: University of Iowa Press, Fall 1995. A striking, often beautiful collection which brings to speech what occurs between the caring and the cared for— moments at the edges of life when, for most of us, even crucial communication seems beyond the reach of words. Coming now, *Between the Heartbeats* seems a particularly important book, breaking as it does the silence of women and men who live the essentials behind the health care debate. —Honor Moore

Davis, Jon. *Scrimmage of Appetite*. 102p. $24.95 (1-884836-11-9); pap. $12.95 (1-884836-12-7). Akron, OH: University of Akron Press, Fall 1995. *Scrimmage of Appetite* is brilliantly said, resplendent with wisdom, a triumph and pure pleasure, beautiful and heartening. —William Kittredge

Davis, Roswita. *Assorted Lives*. 70p. pap. $14.95 (0-9632687-5-9). Mystic Island, NJ: Pen-Rose Publishing Company, Fall 1995. From her European and American background, Davis discusses the vagaries of modern life, providing us with tough answers, insight, and compassion. —Penrose Publishing

Davison, Peter. *The Poems of Peter Davison, 1957–1995*. 314p. $25.00 (0-679-44180-8). New York, NY: Alfred A. Knopf, Spring 1995. Peter Davison's quiet, deep poems are among the best being written. Any

thoughtful reader will be moved by his clear, unpretentious writing, his imaginative participation in life, his passionate balance. —James Dickey

de Andrade, Eugénio. Translated by Alexis Levitin. *Solar Matter/Matéia Solar*. 120p. pap. $12.95 (0-936609-34-6). Fort Bragg, CA: QED Press, Spring 1996. It is sheer delight to come across the poems of Eugénio de Andrade again in Alexis Levitin's sensitive and lyrical translations. These are poems about aging and dying and above all about the intensity of love, a burden and a joy, which does not diminish with age in the least but grows ever more profound. —C.W. Truesdale

De Angelis, Milo. Translated by Lawrence Venuti. *Finite Intuition: Selected Poetry and Prose*. 258p. pap. $11.95 (1-55713-068-X). Los Angeles, CA: Sun & Moon Press, Fall 1995. The work of this major Italian poet is a series of stunning poetic researches that draws on classical literature, existential phenomenology, and psychoanalysis, but rethinks them according to the new conceptions of subjectivity and language that underlie the variety of poststructuralisms in French and Italian culture. —Lawrence Venuti

Deanovich, Connie. *Watusi Titanic.* 76p. pap. $12.00 (0-943221-24-2). New York, NY: Timken Publishers, Spring 1996. Metaphysical comedian and Chicago Imagist, Connie Deanorich writes poetry that captures the imagery of American culture with extravagance and humor. —Timken Publishers. The secret is out: this book is a great find. —Elaine Equi

Deisler, Guillermo. *Everything I Do Is Poetry.* 28p. pap. $5.00 (0-945112-22-X). Cleveland, OH: Generator Press, Fall 1996. A work of visual poetry by an internationally recognized poet, engraver, and editor who died on October 21, 1995. —Generator Press

Delgado, Joseph. *Storms of a Soul.* 40p. pap. $5.50 (0-9646866-0-0). North Bergen, NJ: Enchanted Quill Press, Spring 1995. These poems celebrate the poets victory over depression through his acceptance of himself and his own voice. —Enchanted Quill Press

Deluy, Henri. Translated by Guy Bennett. *Carnal Love.* 136p. pap. $11.95 (1-55713-272-0). Los Angeles, CA: Sun & Moon Press, Spring 1996. One of the most noted of French poets writing today, Henri Deluy explores the various aspects of love: the love of love, of gestures, of smells, of the activities of the body, of the taste of food and alcohol, of the sea, of the ebb and flow of politics, of voluptuousness itself. These and others serve as subjects for Deluy's greatest loves: the love of writing, of the order and disorders of poetry, of the flavor of words. —Sun & Moon Press

Deming, Alison. *Girls in the Jungle: What Does It Take for a Woman to Survive as an Artist?* 26p. pap. $10.00 Tucson, AZ: Kore Press, Spring 1995.

DeNicola, Deborah. *Where Divinity Begins.* 67p. pap. $9.95 (1-882295-02-1). Farmington, ME: Alice James Books, Fall 1994. *Where Divinity Begins* is clearly poetry written out of necessity. There is nothing trivial here, nothing settled easily. Deborah DeNicola has an uncanny instinct to locate her poems at the heart of our human commerce. —Bruce Weigl

Deppe, Theodore. *The Wanderer King.* 70p. pap. $9.95 (1-882295-08-0). Farmington, ME: Alice James Books, Spring 1996. In these elegant and searing poems, Deppe gives voice to the full complexity of human character, creating a world that is charged . . . with cinematic vividness and stunning eloquence. —Betsy Sholl. Deppe mediates his subjects with a Chekhovian eye and heart in these extraordinary poems. —Stephen Dunn

di Suvero, Victor. *Naked Heart.* 80p. pap. $12.00 (0-938631-28-4). Tesuque, NM: Pennywhistle Press, Fall 1996. Victor di Suvero's poetry expresses his strong and ongoing interest in daily life. His contention that poetry can be found *just about everywhere* is demonstrated in this latest collection. —Pennywhistle Press

di Suvero, Victor, and Jeanie C. Williams, eds. *Sextet I: Six Powerful American Voices.* 226p. pap. $17.50 (0-938631-27-6). Tesuque, NM: Pennywhistle Press, Fall 1996. An anthology of poetry comprised of six chapbooks by new and established voices alike . . . including Kim Addonizio, Thomas

Fitzsimmons, Harry Lawton, Annamaria Napolitano, Doren Robbins and Ruth Stone. —Pennywhistle Press

Dickey, William. *The Education of Desire.* 69p. $25.00 (0-8195-2235-X); pap. $11.95 (0-8195-2236-8). Middletown, CT: Wesleyan/University Press of New England, Fall 1996. This posthumous collection shows the full range of Dickey's abilities, from the complex, wide-ranging diction of the opening series to the utter simplicity of its poignant closing lyric. —Jane Hirshfield. Here is one of the most fully textured and searing voices of our time. These poems, diverse in method and music, issue a passionate challenge to mortality and to loss of feeling and memory. Read them for your life's sake, whoever you are. —Adrienne Rich

Dickinson, Emily. *Emily Dickinson: Selected Poems.* 255p. pap. $8.00 (0-517-09129-1). Avenel, NJ: Park Lane Press, Spring 1996.

Dickinson, Emily. *Poems.* 172p. pap. $6.00 (1-57062-099-7). Boston, MA: Shambhala Publications/Shambhala Pocket

Classics, Fall 1995. Also available in a boxed set with editions of Whitman, Thoreau and Emerson: *Four American Classics*, $24.00 (1-57062-126-8). The more than one hundred poems presented here are some of Dickinson's finest works. Unlike other editions of her work, the poems reprinted here are reconstructions based on original manuscripts. —Shambhala Publications

Dickinson, Emily. Edited by Joyce Carol Oates. *The Essential Dickinson.* 94p. $18.00 (0-88001-494-6). Hopewell, NJ: Ecco Press, Fall 1996.

Dienstfrey, Patricia. *The Woman Without Experiences.* 144p. pap. $12.00 (0-932716-37-7). Berkeley, CA: Kelsey St. Press, Fall 1995. Dienstfrey writes movingly and with astonishing freshness of a woman's passage from childhood to motherhood, navigating through poetry, philosophy, literature and intimate relationships. Dienstfrey carves out and then animates a rarefied space where desire and expression and memory intermingle. —*Publishers Weekly*

Digges, Deborah. *Rough Music.* 80p. $20.00 (0-679-44176-X).

New York, NY: Alfred A. Knopf, Fall 1995. Deborah Digges's rough new music is bold and fractious, spilling over with ardor and grief. Everything in the path of her rapturous attention is swept up into a poetry we've never heard before, lifted and burnished to a wild splendor. *Rough Music* is a fierce, headlong book, so exhilarating that even its darkest notes shine with a strange joy. —Mark Doty

Digges, Deborah. *Vesper Sparrows.* 51p. pap. $11.95 (0-88748-228-7). Pittsburgh, PA: Carnegie Mellon University Press/Classic Contemporary Series, Fall 1996.

Dillard, Annie. *Mornings Like This: Found Poems.* 75p. $20.00 (0-06-017155-3). New York, NY: HarperCollins Publishers, Fall 1995. Annie Dillard has gone through old nonfiction books, often books on unusual or bizarre topics, found passages that intrigue or amuse her, and rearranged and edited them into found poems. —HarperCollins

DiPalma, Ray. *Motion of the Cypher.* 99p. pap. $10.95 (0-937804-61-4). New York, NY:

Roof Books, Spring 1995. Ray DiPalma's taut and tightly patterned new collection of poems "fosters," in the words of the title poem, "the once organized/ imperfect/outside/that was the model/of center." For DiPalma, opposites must confront one another, and so "outside" becomes "inside," "sprawl" becomes "pattern," "impulse" becomes "order." —Marjorie Perloff. Self-conscious, musical, meditative, the poetry of Ray DiPalma is spare but polysemic, elemental but baroque. —Tom Becket, *Poetry Briefs*

DiPalma, Ray. *Provocations.* 101p. pap. $11.00 (0-937013-55-2). Elmwood, CT: Potes & Poets Press, Spring 1995.

Dischell, Stuart. *Evenings & Avenues.* 74p. pap. $14.95 (0-14-058766-7). New York, NY: Penguin Books, Fall 1996. There is a poetic soul in these poems which has chosen to regard as closely as it can a world which is resolutely unpoetic; the tensions Dischell enacts and the resolutions he accomplishes in his work are engaging and often delightful. —C.K. Williams. [Dischell is] a serious comedian of the hu-

man spirit. —David St. John, *The Boston Review*

Dittberner-Jax, Norita. *What They Always Were.* 76p. pap. $7.95 (0-89823-160-4). Minneapolis, MN: New Rivers Press, Spring 1995. These are the poems of a woman who has learned that ordinariness is the stuff of most lives and that a poet's difficult task is to illuminate that ordinariness without distorting it. —*The Minneapolis Star Tribune*

Dixon, Melvin. *Love's Instruments.* 80p. pap. $10.95 (1-882688-07-4). Chicago, IL: Tia Chucha Press, Fall 1995. Eloquent, cosmopolitan, acute, at home in Harlem or Dakar, Paris or Provincetown, or on a back porch "down home," Melvin Dixon wrote poems of a lyrical complexity, an intellectual forth-rightness, imbued with a love of language which mirrored his love of the physical world. He was an adept at the erotics of compassion. We are fortunate to have this last book—even as we mourn its author. —Marilyn Hacker

Djanikian, Gregory. *About Distance.* 86p. pap. $11.95 (0-88748-187-6). Pittsburgh, PA:

Carnegie Mellon University Press, Spring 1995.

Dlugos, Tim. Edited by David Trinidad. *Powerless: Selected Poems 1973–1990.* 150p. pap. $12.99 (1-85242-407-9). New York, NY: Serpent's Tail/High Risk Books, Fall 1996. A stunning retrospective of the work of Tim Dlugos—one of the finest post-New York school poets to be published in the '70s and '80s. Dlugos died of AIDS as he was writing his strongest work—poems about the disease itself, which are included in this collection. —Serpent's Tail. This is a poetry of extraordinary speed and energy that fuses fact and fantasy, dream and documentary. —Marjorie Perloff

Dobyns, Stephen. *Common Carnage.* 132p. pap. $14.95 (0-14-058748-9). New York, NY: Penguin Books, Spring 1996. In this collection, Dobyns addresses the conundrum, "How hard to love the world; we must love the world." The spiritual intermixed with the bawdy, the courageous with the cowardly. *Common Carnage* rejects the decorous to map the complexity, the common carnage of our lives. —Penguin

Books. Questions, informed with irony and always with wit, dominate Dobyns' ninth book. —*Publishers Weekly.*

Doctorovich, Fabio. Translated by John M. Bennett. *Bribage Cartooniano.* 52p. pap. $9.00 (093535042X). Columbus, OH: Luna Bisonte Prods, Fall 1994. A bilingual edition of innovative poetry by an Argentine poet, which includes textual and visual computer-aided manipulations, and introductions by John M. Bennett and Enrique Blanchard. A co-edition with Ediciones Nuevo Milenio, Buenos Aires. —Luna Bisonte Prods

Dolin, Sharon. *Climbing Mount Sinai.* 17p. $25.00; pap. $10.00. New York, NY: Dim Gray Bar Press, Spring 1996. Stunningly original. —*American Book Review*

Dolin, Sharon. *Heart Work.* 86p. pap. $12.95 (1-878818-42-2). Riverdale-on-Hudson, NY: Sheep Meadow Press, Fall 1995. The poems in this outstanding first collection are notable for their clarity, audacity, and depth—compelling in their dramatic urgency and emotional power. For Dolin the sacred and the quotidian share the same cup, and the literary sits comfortably at the table of everyday life. —Phillis Levin. Sharon Dolin is without question a poet whose work will help to define the resources and determinants of her generation. —Robert Creeley

Dolly. *From Sad Beginnings to Happy Endings*. 214p. pap. $14.95 (1-56550-028-8). Santa Rosa, CA: Vision Books International, Fall 1995.

Domina, Lynn. *Corporal Works*. 79p. pap. $11.95 (1-884800-03-3). Marshfield, MA: Four Way Books, Spring 1995. [Here] is the voice of someone who is passionately engaged with her subject matter and passionately engaged with language. These are carefully crafted, deeply moving poems. —Stephen Dobyns

Donahue, Joseph. *World Well Broken*. 56p. pap. $9.95 (1-883689-22-8). Jersey City, NJ: Talisman House Publishers, Spring 1995. Ultimately, Donahue's writing occupies a strange threshold between the particular and the universal, the quotidian and the sacred, the experienced and the

transfigured—that threshold where the poetic best thrives. —Leonard Schwartz

Donne, John. Edited by Peter Washington. *Poems and Prose*. 256p. $10.95 (0-679-44467-X). New York, NY: Knopf, Alfred A./Everyman's Library Pocket Poets, Fall 1995.

Donney, Gene D. *A Few Mental Notes: Poems of Celebration, Mystery and Complaint*. 84p. pap. $14.95 (1-56715-056-X). Boca Raton, FL: Relative Publishing, Fall 1996. Ordinary people, ordinary circumstances, and ordinary emotions are explored through the author's relativistic looking glass. Many of the works intersect at the juncture of science and spirituality. —Relative Publishing

Dooley, David. *The Revenge by Love*. 56p. pap. $11.95 (1-885266-06-5). Brownsville, OR: Story Line Press, Fall 1995. The love and marriage of Georgia O'Keeffe and Alfred Stieglitz has become the stuff of legend due, in great part, to Stieglitz's powerfully sensual portraits of O'Keeffe. Much has been written about their relationship, but rarely as succinctly and perceptively as in Dooley's poems. This new book includes a witty and lyrical series about the celebrated couple, most written from O'Keeffe's perspective. —Donna Seaman, *Booklist*. David Dooley is one of the best new poets I've come across in a long time. —Helen Vendler, *National Public Radio*

Dorbin, Sanford. *Never Enough Light: New and Selected Poems 1966–1994.* 206p. pap. $14.00 (0-9627891-7-8). Bedford, NH: Igneus Press, Fall 1995. Dorbin's language smells of love, dope, jazz and jizzum. You won't find these words in dictionaries. He lives in language, which he remakes and undoes and turns inside out. His world is your world. Here's poetry that will stay, and stay. —Barry B. Powell

Doris, Stacy. *Kildare.* 99p. pap. $9.95 (0-937804-59-2). New York, NY: Roof Books, Fall 1994. A tantalizing wacky, ideolectical treat for ears & what minds 'em. Here you will find (amidst arctic uncles on rollerblades, basketball-sized yokes, the world's largest crackerjack, and cameo appearances by a contortionist & a nurse sorceress), the brain of

Dr. Kildare's network archrival, Ben Casey, in the textual body of all those enduring charms upon which Stacy Doris lays new & resounding claim. For those looking for the direction of poetry, *Kildare* is ready & on call, bubbling and singing with voices fresh and tonic. —Charles Bernstein

Dorsett, Robert. *Threshold.* 18p. pap. $3.00 Las Cruces, NM: Whole Notes Press, Fall 1995. Robert Dorsett's first collection of poems demonstrates his unusual ear and eye for perceptions of art, people, places, and the natural world. —Whole Notes Press

Doty, Mark. *Atlantis.* 103p. $22.00 (0-06-055362-6); pap. $11.00 (0-06-095106-0). New York, NY: HarperColllins/ HarperPerennial, Fall 1995. In *Atlantis*, Doty claims the mythical lost island as his own: a fading paradise whose memory he must keep alive at the same time he is forced to renounce its hold on him. Atlantis recedes, just as the lives of those Doty loves continue to be extinguished by the ravages of AIDS. Doty's struggle is to reconcile, even celebrate, the evanescence of our earthly connections—and to understand how we can love more at the very moment we must consent to let go. —HarperCollins. Mark Doty has written a book that is ferocious, luminous, and important. —Mary Oliver. [Doty] confronts with a jeweler's exactitude sorrowful emotions. [This is] a sad, frank, meticulous book. —Frank Allen, *Library Journal*

Doucet, John. *A Local Habitation and a Name: Poems From the Lafourche Country.* 24p. pap. $8.00 (1-884725-12-0). Tibodaux, LA: Blue Heron Press, Fall 1995. In attempting a lyrical history of Lafourche Parish, Doucet suggests how, through poetry, we can connect with the people and landscape of our origins. —Grady Ballenger, *Louisiana Literature*

Doud, Patrick. *The Man in Green.* 64p. pap. $10.00. Lawrence, KS: First Intensity Press, Fall 1996. At the heart of the quotidian world lurks the dream. These eerie poems trace a tangled path toward the mysterious man in green. —First Intensity Press. The language is elegant and spare, and suits its business. —Theodore Enslin

Dove, Rita. *Mother Love.* 88p. $17.95 (0-393-03808-4); pap. $10.00 (0-393-31444-8). New York, NY: W.W. Norton & Company, Spring 1995. *Mother Love* calls upon the ancient Greek myth of Demeter and Persephone to examine the tenacity of love between mother and daughter. —W.W. Norton & Company. Dove's is a brilliant mind that seeks for itself the widest possible play, an ever-expanding range of reference, the most acute distinctions, and the most subtle shadings of meaning. —Arnold Rampersad, *Callaloo*. This volume shows Dove—Pulitzer Prize winner, novelist, and 1993–95 U.S. Poet Laureate—at the height of her poetic powers. —*Publishers Weekly*

Dove, Rita. *The Darker Face of the Earth: Completely Revised Second Edition of the Verse Play.* 164p. pap. $12.00 (1-885266-19-7). Brownsville, OR: Story Line Press, Fall 1996. Poet Laureate Dove has done an amazing thing . . . her placement of the tale of Oedipus within the context of slavery and its open secret of miscegenation is brilliant, potent, and repercussive. —*Booklist* (starred review).

Dove has created a drama in which black and white Americans are bound together not only by the chains of history, and not only by the necessity of sharing this land, but by ties of blood and passion as well. —*Detroit Free Press*

Drake, Barbara. *Space Before A:* 26p. pap. $5.00. Portland, OR: 26 Books, Spring 1996.

Drey, James. *Bigbang.* 28p. pap. $3.95 (0-9641986-7-3). Duluth, MN: Poetry Harbor, Fall 1995. Drey looks at real life with a bright eye, finding humor and mystery. It's a fresh, intelligent collection! —Gail Rixen, *Lake Region Review*

du Bouchet, André. Translated by David Mus. *Where Heat Looms.* 144p. pap. $12.95 (1-55713-238-0). Los Angeles, CA: Sun & Moon Press, Spring 1996. Born in 1924, André du Bouchet is one of the last great modern French poets whose work remains largely untranslated. *Where Heat Looms* is an investigation of light and that which is associated with it: fire, white, wind, sky, air, sun, and flame. In this brilliantly lyrical collection, du Bouchet delights

in the natural world while probing linguistically all he sees. —Sun & Moon Press

Duemer, Joseph. *Static.* 70p. pap. (0-937669-57-1). Seattle, WA: Owl Creek Press, Fall 1996. The poems are so rich with intelligent thought that their lively, lyrical surfaces might seem anomalous in a lesser poet. —William Matthews. Joe Duemers is a fresh voice and a resonant one. —Robert Dana.

Duemer, Joseph, and Jim Simmerman, eds. *Dog Music: Poetry About Dogs.* 274p. $16.95 (0-312-13964-0). New York: NY: St. Martin's Press, Spring 1996. *Dog Music* should certainly be the number one Christmas present for dog lovers, not just in 1995 but ever after. It's a vital, living book of poems, many of almost unbearable beauty—a book that in more than a hundred voices expresses the deep, often unspoken feelings we have about dogs and they about us. —Elizabeth Marshall Thomas

Duffy, Carol Ann, ed. Illustrated by Trisha Rafferty. *Stopping for Death: Poems of Death and Loss.* 134p. $14.95 (0-8050-4717-

4). New York, NY: Henry Holt and Company Books for Young Readers, Spring 1996. A fine, imported anthology of simple but sophisticated poems about the mystery, grief, fear, and occasional gallows humor that surround death. —*Kirkus Reviews*

Duhamel, Denise. *Girl Soldier.* 61p. pap. $13.00 (1-882329-05-8). Truro, MA: Garden Street Press, Spring 1996. With humor and insight, Denise Duhamel's third full-length collection probes the uneasy relationship of women to their bodies. —Colette Inez, *Indiana Review.* Denise Duhamel writes wonderful poems, poems full of pognant detail, poems that are breezy and clever, poems that make you laugh as they eat away at your heart. —David Trinidad, *Los Angeles Reader*

Duhamel, Denise. *How the Sky Fell.* 36p. pap. $6.00 (1-888219-02-5). Long Beach, CA: Pearl Editions, Spring 1996. Winner of the 1995 Pearl Chapbook Prize. The setting for these fairy tales is a media-mad, pop-culture-crazed civilization dotted with smashed psyches and busted

hearts . . . a piquant, cracking and sparking little book about America in the *fin de millennium.* —Suzanne Lummis. If there is a better young poet than Denise Duhamel in the USA, don't tell me. I can't take it, I can barely take her! —Bill Knott

Duhamel, Denise. *The Woman With Two Vaginas.* 85p. pap. $9.95 (0-9634000-6-1). Anchorage, AK: Salmon Run Press, Spring 1995. In wildly feminist adaptations of Eskimo myths, Denise Duhamel explores issues of gender identity and sexuality in poems so basic to human psychology and anatomy that readers cannot help but be returned to their own wild and basic urges. Here the poet Denise Duhamel, a talented, hip, young, white woman, carries on, sensuously, with shocking directness, the poetry of the self in the context of the ancient wisdoms of the North. —Molly Peacock. Riotously humorous, thoroughly engaging. I couldn't put it down. —Cleanth Brooks

Dunn, Stephen. *Loosestrife.* 96p. $19.00 (0-393-03982-X). New York, NY: W.W. Norton & Company, Fall 1996. Stephen

Dunn's subject has never been the large issue, the political or the abstract. What is at stake in his poetry is more immediate and more essential: how to live the one life we're given with integrity, with humor and exuberance and, yes, grace. —Judith Kitchen, *Georgia Review.* The poetry of Stephen Dunn helps make the landscape of all our lives more livable—quietly, unobtrusively, he has taken his place among our major, indispensable poets. —*Miami Herald*

Durand, Marcella. *Lapsus Linguae.* 8p. pap. $5.00. Brooklyn, NY: Situations, Fall 1995. Experimental poetry concerned with structure— visual, architectural, aural. Much of it deals with the perception of space: public and private, inner and outer, as well as with the process of writing and language—how words work. —Marcella Durand

Durcan, Paul. *A Snail in My Prime: New and Selected Poems.* 288p. pap. $14.95 (0-14-058720-9). New York, NY: Penguin Books, Fall 1995. Durcan can, like Orpheus, charm the birds from the trees; he is that kind of poet.

—Derek Mahon. For him, poetry is storytelling and his stories are told in a direct fashion that makes them totally accessible. Paul Durcan's poetry sings, it moves the reader with its bareness. —Roger McGough. *The Sunday Tribune.* One of the most original and distinctive Irish writers alive. The work of Durcan is unlike that of any other poet writing in English today. This is a landmark book. —Dermot Bolger, *The Sunday Independent*

E

Eady, Cornelius. *You Don't Miss Your Water.* 36p. $20.00 (0-8050-3667-9); pap. $12.00 (0-8050-3668-7). New York, NY: Henry Holt and Company, Spring 1995. A poet sits at the bedside of his dying father, remembering, closer to this man in death than he ever was in life. Each poem links the poet to his father, and in each the poet uses his rich imagination to reach out to this hard and absent man. —Henry Holt and Company. Eady's new book is alive with passionate irony, with joy of language, and with unsentimental grief. —Sharon Olds. This is a poet of great energy and resourcefulness. —*The New York Times Book Review*

Early, Gerald. *How the War in the Streets Is Won: Poems on the Quest of Love and Faith.* 118p. $18.95 (1-56809-003-X); pap. $12.50 (1-56809-004-8). St. Louis, MO: Time Being Books, Spring 1995. Early's cultural critiques, reminiscences, and tributes to friends and family killed by bullets and drugs are all intensely introspective and strongly percussive. His lamentations are searingly beautiful, as full of escalating drama as sermons, and his humor is quick and sharp. —*Booklist*

Edelberg, Cynthia Dubin, ed. *Scars: American Poetry in the Face of Violence.* 214p. pap. $24.95 (0-8173-0787-7). Tuscaloosa, AL: University of Alabama Press, Fall 1995. This collection dramatizes an urgency and compassion within contemporary poetry. These poets come together in their desire to explore ways of telling truths that are also ways of responding to such realities. —University of Alabama Press

Edelstein, Carol. *The World Is Round.* 72p. pap. $12.00 (0-941895-09-2). Amherst, MA: Amherst Writers & Artists Press, Fall 1994. There is an underlying joyous affirmation in [this] poetry—a celebration of life lived solidly in this world, . . . infused with mystery, full of intimations. —Pat Schneider. Edelstein crafts images so fresh and orginal I find myself returning to them again and again thinking I must have imagined how good they really are. —*Feminist Bookstore News*

Edwards, Melvin, with the poetry of Jayne Cortez. *Fragments: Sculpture and Drawings From the "Lynch Fragment" Series.* 32p. pap. (0-9608062-7-X). New York, NY: Bola Press, Fall 1994. The "Lynch Fragments" initiated my artistic participation in the Civil Rights struggle through sculpture. . . . Visual artists have often related positively to the sensibilities of poetry. The poetic response to the "Lynch Fragments" over the past twenty-four years by Jayne Cortez has given both corroboration and inspiration to the development of these works. The poems included in this volume are unique and dynamic expressions on the subject. —Melvin Edwards

Ehrhart, W. D. *Mostly Nothing Happens.* 20p. pap. $8.00 (0-938566-71-7). Easthampton, MA: Adastra Press, Fall 1996. In a meditation on our decaying cities, the author uses his own experiences in Vietnam and Philadelphia as a metaphor of white urban life. Limited edition with hand-set type and hand-sewn binding. —Adastra Press

Ehrmann, Max. *The Desiderata of Faith.* 64p. $12.00 (0-517-70331-9). New York, NY: Crown Publishers, Spring 1996.

Ehrmann, Max. *The Desiderata of Love.* 64p. $12.00 (0-517-70078-6). New York, NY: Crown Publishers, Spring 1995.

Eiker, Sharon, and Carl Bettis. *The Peasant and the Pedant.* 58p. pap. Lawrence, KS: Wheel of Fire Press, Fall 1994. Transcriptions of poems originally presented orally. —Wheel of Fire Press

Eiland, Sarah Kimberly. *Portraits: A Face for Every Mask.* 76p. pap. $12.95 (1-880254-33-6).

Long Branch, NJ: Vista Publishing, Spring 1996. A remarkable collection written by a survivor of child abuse, who has transformed shame into personal triumph. —Vista Publishing

Elizabeth, Martha. *The Return of Pleasure.* 52p. $20.00 (1-881090-21-3); pap. $10.00 (1-881090-20-5). Lewiston, ID: Confluence Press, Fall 1996. Winner of the Montana Arts Council's First Book Award. Elizabeth's poems are vivid, smart, and passionate—indeed a pleasure. —William Kittredge

Elkin, Lillian. *Generations.* 55p. $10.00. New York, NY: Cardinal Press, Fall 1995. By vivid metaphor, ironic juxtaposition, and telling images, Elkin levels the great and famous and immortalizes the homely and familiar. The reader who opens this volume will be quietly dazzled. —Ruth Ann Lief

Elledge, Jim. *Earth as It Is.* 26p. pap. $4.00 (0-912592-38-9). Ashland, OH: Ashland Poetry Press, Fall 1994. These poems celebrate the earth through a finely wrought, taut verse, and a

wide range of experience.
—Ashland Poetry Press

Elledge, Jim. *Into the Arms of the Universe.* 24p. pap. $8.00 (0-932616-51-8). Balton, MD: New Poets Series, Spring 1995. First annual winner of the NPS/Stonewall Series Chapbook Award for best manuscript on a gay, lesbian, or bisexual theme. —New Poets Series

Elovic, Barbara. *Time Out.* 30p. pap. $8.00. Brooklyn, NY: Amity Street Press, Spring 1996. Barbara Elovic's deeply felt and finely crafted poems show that family is still the great American subject. —Katha Pollitt. The poems in *Time Out* have hard emotional and intellectual work to do; they propose to repair a frayed link between a daughter and her dying father. The poems are so accurate they not only succeed, but also come to embody something of the blessing they strove so carefully to invoke. —William Matthews

Elovic, Barbara; Steve Fried, Molly McQuade, and Stephanie Rauschenbusch, eds. *Father Poems.* 40p. pap. $5.00 (1074-9047). Brooklyn, NY: Poetlink, Spring 1995.

Poems about fathers by 25 contemporary authors, including Nina Cassian, Julia Kardorf, Enid Dame, and D. Nurkse. —Poetlink

Elsberg, John. *O F F S E T S.* 70p. pap. $12.00 (0-9637483-5-1). St. Augustine, FL: Kings Estate Press, Fall 1994. Illustrations by Wayne Hogan. John Elsberg is a poet of paths and convergences, matrixes and mazes. *OFFSETS* is masterful, a must read. —Maurice Watson, Jr.

Elsberg, John. *The Randomness of E.* 8p. $12.00; pap. $4.00. Jackson, MS: Semiquasi Press, Spring 1995. A revisioning of Genesis and a fine verbo-visual poem. Words fall down the long yellow pages, disorienting sense, giving one the feeling of being a co-creator at the Creation. —W.B. Keckler, *Logo-Crit*

Éluard, Paul. Translated by Lloyd Alexander and Cicely Buckley. *Ombres et Soleil/Shadows and Sun: Selected Writings 1913-1952.* 368p. pap. $24.95 (0-9617481-7-6). Durham, NH: Oyster River Press, Fall 1995. Poems and prose inspired by Éluard's collaboration with artists Picasso, Chagall and others. Illustrated bilingual edition. —Oyster River Press

Elyshevitz, Alan. *The Splinter in Passion's Paw.* 18p. pap. $3.75. Kew Gardens, NY: New Spirit Press, Spring 1995. Winner of the New Spirit Press Quarterly Chapbook Contest.

Embree, Bruce. *Beneath the Chickenshit Mormon Sun.* 28p. pap. $12.00. Boise, ID: Limberlost Press, Spring 1995. Letterpress edition.

Engels, John. *Big Water.* 96p. $22.95 (1-55821-357-0); pap. $16.95 (1-55821-358-9). New York, NY: Lyons & Burford Publishers, Spring 1995. This has the makings of a crossover hit; a book of marvelous poetry about fly-fishing and fishers. Engels's clean, direct free verse reveals the world of the fly fisher's rivers to be a locus of passion and solitude, of spiritual yearning and revelation, of companionship and loss. —*Booklist.* Few have looked at the natural world with the intelligence and perception of John Engels. *Big Water* is as accessible to the lover of poetry as it is to the fly fisherman. —*Rochester Post-Bulletin*

Engler, Robert Klein. *Shoreline.* 70p. pap. $10.00 (0-944300-13-8). Chicago, IL: Alphabeta Press, Spring 1995. A long poem by an award winning Chicago poet. —Alphabeta Press

Epstein, Daniel Mark. *The Boy in the Well and Other Poems.* 75p. $19.95 (0-87951-587-2); pap. $13.95 (0-87951-597-X). New York, NY: The Overlook Press, Fall 1995. Daniel Mark Epstein's sixth book of poetry gathers the intimate lyrics, inquisitive odes and powerful narrative poems of a decade, works that transform autobiography into living legend recreated in vital American language. —The Overlook Press. Epstein has a vision as tortured and powerful as early Robert Lowell. —Donald Hall, *National Review.* His style is forceful, in Browingesque interlocked harshness, in the ruggedly mimetic, in the anti-lyrical. He may become one of the best poets of the century. —Paul Ramsey, *Sewanee Review*

Equi, Elaine. *Decoy.* 84p. pap. $11.95 (1-56689-026-8). Minneapolis, MN: Coffee House Press, Fall 1994. *Decoy* moves upon you gradually with postludes of gentleness . . . then agile maneuvers that seize you unaware. —Barbara Guest. Equi creates her poems with fragmentary lines artfully arranged on the page to create an image, or the image of an image, in her reader's mind. —*The Nation*

Erb, Elke. *Mountains in Berlin.* 96p. pap. $8.00 (1-886224-06-4). Providence, RI: Burning Deck, Fall 1995. Short, enigmatic poem-narratives that leave readers with the impression that the world is a far stranger place than we ever understood. —Mark Wallace, *Washington Review.* Mordant and funny. —Eliot Weinberger, *American Poet*

Espada, Martín. *Imagine the Angels of Bread.* 107p. $18.95 (0-393-03916-1). New York, NY: W.W. Norton & Company, Spring 1996. Martín Espada is well on his way to becoming *the* Latino poet of his generation. —Earl Shorris

Espada, Martín. *Trumpets From the Islands of Their Eviction.* 100p. pap. $8.00 (0-927534-51-7). Tempe, AZ: Bilingual Press, Fall 1995. Sometimes Espada writes with wit, sometimes

with more than a hint of the music of the islands, but always, his poems press forward with an unrelenting search for justice. —*The Texas Review.* Martín Espada defines political poetry for the turn of the century. —*The Nation*

Estes, Angie. *The Uses of Passion.* 64p. pap. $9.95 (0-87905-684-3). Layton, UT: Gibbs Smith Publishers/Peregrine Smith Books, Fall 1995. An unusually distinctive first volume. —Robert Pinsky. A luminous, beautiful debut. The pages nearly tremble with light—with intelligence and tenderness. —Carole Maso

Evans, Stacey Lyn. *Real Soul Food and Other Poetic Recipes.* 92p. pap. $9.95 (1-888018-01-1). Alexandria, VA: Alexander Publishing Group, Fall 1995. This first collection by Stacey Evans is filled with joy and happiness. Much of the work is uplifting—yes, even those words she directs towards men. This is a tasty, finger-licking book, something like greens, ribs and potato salad. —E. Ethelbert Miller

Everett, Graham. *Minus Green Plus: New and Selected Poems.*

40p. pap. $7.00 (0-935252-52-5). Sound Beach, NY: Street Press/Breeze, Fall 1995.

Evers, Larry, and Ofelia Zepeda, eds. *Home Places: Contemporary Native American Writing From Sun Tracks.* 97p. $19.95 (0-8165-1521-2); pap. $9.95 (0-8165-1522-0). Tucson, AZ: University of Arizona Press, Fall 1995. The creative wellspring of American Indian culture is well represented in this anthology, a compilation of stories, songs, poems, and other writings taken from twenty-five years of Sun Tracks: An American Indian Literary Series. —University of Arizona Press

Evetts, Dee, ed. *A Small Umbrella.* 26p. pap. $3.00. New York, NY: Spring Street Haiku Group, Spring 1995.

F

Faiz, Ahmed Faiz. Translated by Agha Shahid Ali. *The Rebel's Silhouette: Selected Poems.* 128p. pap. $14.95 (0-87023-975-9). Amherst, MA: University of Massachusetts Press, Fall 1995.

Revised bilingual edition in Urdu and English by a leading poet of the South Asian subcontinent. —University of Massachusetts Press

Falk, Pat. *In the Shape of a Woman.* 68p. pap. $12.00 (1-886435-02-2). Sag Harbor, NY: Canio's Editions, Fall 1995.

Falleder, Arnold. *William Said.* 28p. pap. $5.00 (0-945112-19-X). Cleveland, OH: Generator Press, Fall 1994. A gentle, loving precision radiates through and informs each of the poems in this cycle about the life of William. —Generator Press

Fandel, John. *On Poetry and Prayer: The Eighth Morning.* 136p. pap. $5.95 (0-88028-159-6). Cincinnati, OH: Forward Movement Publications, Spring 1995. To those who are poets or academics or mystics, a word of warning: this book may be dangerous to your orientation. Its argument is not linear but multilayered. —Forward Movement Publications

Fanthorpe, U.A. *Safe as Houses.* 70p. pap. $10.00 (1-885266-26-X). Brownsville, OR: Story Line Press, Spring 1996. U.A.

Fanthorpe is one of England's best, most popular and prolific poets. —Story Line Press. She is a national treasure. *Safe as Houses* is a unique pleasure to be savoured for its truth, disconcerting obliqueness, and even more disconserting directness. —Liz Lochhead, *Poetry Book Society Bulletin, (U.K.)*

Farawell, Martin Jude. *Genesis.* 20p. pap. $4.95. Kew Gardens, NY: New Spirit Press, Fall 1994. Winner of the New Spirit Press Quarterly Chapbook Contest. Insightful images of the fall of mankind. —New Spirit Press

Fargas, Laura. Edited by Dr. Walt McDonald. *An Animal of the Sixth Day.* 79p. $17.95 (0-89672-360-7). Lubbock, TX: Texas Tech University Press, Spring 1996. 1996 Winner of the Texas Tech University Press First Book Competition. There is an abiding, loving seriousness to Laura Fargas' poems. They are wise and beautiful and very much her own. —James Tate. Laura Fargas' poems are a delight to read. But they are too dark to quite delight. They are what's dark about delight. Is that joy? They are written out of some

unaccountable joy. The pain running through them, the ache, is borne simply, happily. —Li-Young Lee

Farley, Blanche Flanders, and Janice Townley Moore, eds. *Like a Summer Peach: Sunbright Poems and Old Southern Recipes.* 64p. $14.95 (0-918949-89-0). Watsonville, CA: Papier-Mache Press, October 1996. This collection blends poems that evoke memories of food and love with savory, primarily southern, recipes. The poems impart both humorous and serious emotional ties with food: family tensions are expressed during a breakfast of waffles; a woman prepares a familiar stew while estranged from her lover, the memory of a father is evoked by a bowl of raspberries and cream. Cover and interior art are from Deidre Scherer, the popular fiber artist. —Papier-Mache Press. From the region of soul food comes this wonderful book of food for the soul—poetry to nourish the spirit, recipes to please the palate. A gourmet feast of literary delight. —Pat Conroy

Farr, Sidney Saylor. *Headwaters.* 88p. pap. $5.95 (0-936015-58-6). Blacksburg, VA: Pocahontas

Press, Spring 1995. Sidney Saylor Farr, editor of *Appalachian Heritage*, writes about her native mountains in this collection. —Pocahontas Press. Sidney Saylor Farr is one of Applachia's treasures. —Allison Thorpe, *Iowa Women*

Fay, Nancy, and Judith Rafaela, eds. *Written With a Spoon: A Poet's Cookbook.* 200p. pap. $18.00 (0-9644196-2-9). Santa Fe, NM: Sherman Asher Publishing, Spring 1996. As a poet of the palate and a gastronome, I know this tome will become well known. —Ned Laventall. An eclectic collection of poems about food by 64 poets, paired with recipes—a melting pot of frijoles, matzo balls, pastas and brownies. —*The Fresno Bee*

Featherstone, Simon, ed. *War Poetry: An Introductory Reader.* 287p. pap. $15.95 (0-415-09570-0). New York, NY: Routledge, Fall 1995. *War Poetry* is a new anthology of the poetry of the two world wars. Challenging the dominance of English officer poets in the canon of war poetry, it reveals a diversity of voices, many of which have not, until now, been heard. The anthology was collected with the student in

mind but will make fascinating reading for any poetry lover. —Routledge

Feinstein, Robert. *Oyster's Last Stand.* 94p. pap. $10.00 (0-914061-44-1). Alexandria, VA: Orchises Press, Fall 1994. Light verse on a variety of domestic situations, on aging, and on the modern world. Illustrated by Trygre Olson. —Orchises Press

Feldman, Irving. *The Life and Letters.* 104p. $26.00 (0-226-24067-3); pap. $11.95 (0-226-24068-1). Chicago, IL: University of Chicago Press, Fall 1994. In poems whose subjects range from theme parks to late-night radio, the aftermath of the Holocaust to television, *The Life and Letters* represents a celebrated poet-scholar at the height of his art. —University of Chicago Press. This book is astonishing in its range of language and invention, and utterly enthralling in its combination of irreverent humor, linguistic play, and deadly insight. —Alan Shapiro

Feng, Anita. *Internal Strategies.* 86p. $24.95 (1-884836-13-5); pap. $12.95 (1-884836-14-3). Akron, OH: University of

Akron Press, Fall 1995. In *Internal Strategies*, Anita Feng tells the story of her husband, Xiao Ge Feng, who was born at the outset of communist rule in Beijing, China, and who grew up through succeeding waves of patriotic fervor, disillusionment, and disaster. *Internal Strategies* goes beyond a narrative of one man's struggle into a profound discussion of issues of cultural and personal identity. —University of Akron Press. This is the poetry of necessity, drawn from a searing yet gentle vision of human tragedy and nobility. Anita Feng's poems articulate quiet courage, humility, subtlety and authentic grace in this seamless book. —Sam Hamill

Fenton, James. *Out of Danger.* 104p. pap. $10.00 (0-374-52437-8). New York, NY: Farrar, Straus and Giroux/Noonday, Fall 1994. The poems in *Out of Danger*, British poet James Fenton's acclaimed second collection, renew and amplify the qualities of unflinching observation and freewheeling verbal play that gained his first collection, *Children in Exile*, distinction. —Farrar, Straus and Giroux. This is a wonderful book.

—Anthony Thwaite, *The Sunday Telegraph* (London)

Ferlinghetti, Lawrence. *Pictures of the Gone World.* pap. $6.95 (0-87286-303-4). San Francisco, CA: City Lights Books, Spring 1995. An expanded edition with 18 new poems to celebrate the 40th year of this popular classic. —City Lights Books

Ferlinghetti, Lawrence, ed. *City Lights Pocket Poets Anthology.* 259p. $18.95 (0-87286-311-5). San Francisco, CA: City Lights Books, Spring 1996. This comprehensive selection from the influential City Lights Pocket Poets Series is a landmark retrospective, celebrating 40 years of publishing and cultural history. —City Lights. [This is] a who's who of post World War II American modernism, as well as their foreign counterparts. —*Booklist*. This collection makes an essential statement and is recommended for all poetry collections. —*Library Journal*

Ferrini, Vincent. *The Magi Image.* 135p. pap. $10.00 (0-9627891-8-6). Bedford, NH: Igneus Press, Fall 1995.

Fields, Leslie Leyland. *The Water Under Fish.* 56p. pap. $4.95 (0-916155-28-5). Parkdale, OR: Trout Creek Press, Fall 1994.

Fink, Robert A. *The Tongues of Men and of Angels.* 63p. $16.50 (0-89672-341-0). Lubbock, TX: Texas Tech University Press, Spring 1995. The title of Robert Fink's collection, *The Tongues of Men and of Angels,* gets it right: this is language with its feet on the ground and its eyes on transcendence. —Steven Cramer. Robert Fink powerfully juxtaposes the story of the Apostle Paul with his own—the frightening and touching story of a Vietnam vet who comes home and sets about trying to live a normal family life, remembering what he doesn't want to remember. —Andrew Hudgins. These poems are sinewy, pervasively energetic from opening line to emphatic conclusion. —*Texas Review*

Fink, Sid. *Taxi Poet.* 24p. pap. $5.00. Port Townsend, WA: Sagittarius Press, Spring 1996. Designed and printed by the author. Handset, hand-sewn and printed on a hand-crafted Vandercook letterpress. —Sagittarius Press

Finkelstein, Caroline. *Germany.* 64p. pap. $11.95 (0-88748-193-0). Pittsburgh, PA: Carnegie Mellon University Press, Spring 1995. Caroline Finkelstein fixes . . . utterly and unerringly the identifying images that make [the people in her poems] palpably real, revealing all one needs to know about their conflicts, besetting character traits, historical and psychological confines. —Joseph Parisi, *Booklist.* Finkelstein's poetry is deeply sensuous, not only in horror's antipathy but in love of beautiful language. In the volatile lyrics, calm is cherished because it is precarious; power rises from the hellfire underneath. —Donald Hall, *Boston Review*

Finnell, Dennis. *Beloved Beast.* 88p. pap. $11.95 (0-8203-1708-X). Athens, GA: University of Georgia Press, Spring 1995.

Firmat, Gustavo Pérez. *Bilingual Blues: Poems, 1981-1994.* 128p. pap. $8.00 (0-927534-47-9). Tempe, AZ: Bilingual Press, Fall 1995. Firmat writes with wicked humor and candor, handling Spanish and English with seamless assurance. —Bilingual Press. [He] personifies the pilgrimage from the baroque Cuban spirit to the straightforward American mind. —Ilan Stavans

Fiscus, Sheila. *Bogart in Paradise.* 38p. pap. $6.95 (1-56315-041-7). Pittsburgh, PA: Sterling House, Spring 1996.

Fishman, Charles. *Nineteenth-Century Rain.* 22p. pap. (1-885346-012). Winterville, GA: Whistle Press, Spring 1995.

Fishman, Charles. *The Firewalkers.* 118p. pap. $12.00 (1-888105-03-8). Greensboro, NC: Avisson Press, Spring 1996. These poems of recuperative memory and redemption are written out of the wounded landscape of the body and its mortality—blood speaking—the world in its passing. The elements become figural here: water, air, fire, the earth, in a language of mystery and desire. *The Firewalkers* is a work of great poignancy and breadth. —Carolyn Forché

Fitts, Christopher A.P. *Bad Ass Dogs Don't Do Ballet.* 89p. pap. $9.95 (0-9635689-6-5). Alexandria, VA: Storm Grove Press, Fall 1994.

Fitzmaurice, Gabriel. *The Village Sings.* 82p. pap. $9.00 (1-885266-29-4). Brownsville, OR: Story Line Press, Spring 1996. Fitzmaurice writes about the way things are—mundane and plainly beautiful—and the way people are—informed by that something often called the spirit. —*Booklist*

FitzPatrick, Kevin. *Rush Hour.* 84p. pap. $9.00 (0-935697-08-X). St. Paul, MN: Midwest Villages and Voices, Fall 1996. Kevin FitzPatrick evokes the daily life of a city and its myriad people. His ability to elevate ordinary life resonates throughout *Rush Hour*, and his capacity for connecting with the dispossessed shows him to be, above all, a poet with heart. —Ethna McKiernan. A fine literary craftsman. —*Minneapolis Tribune*

Flook, Maria. *Reckless Wedding.* 65p. pap. $11.95 (0-88748-226-0). Pittsburgh, PA: Carnegie Mellon University Press/ Classic Contemporary Series, Fall 1996. This poet has the power to see unexpected resemblances—a wonderfully unsettling mix of sexual contamination and back-attic mustiness. —*New York Times*

Flynn, Keith. *The Book of Monsters.* 70p. pap. $12.00 (1-889276-

01-4). Asheville, NC: Animal Sounds, Spring 1996. Keith Flynn is dungareed griot, hinge-hipped healer, a world rover with a heart where his pen should be. He's a blues growler, a soul surgeon, a lover of momentum. He is deft and delicate, fiery and unerring. In these pages, he sees through to the bones of lovers and warriors, strangers and fools. According to his gritty gospel, we are all the monsters. And with this book he has given us language—jolting, tender, as dependable as pulse. —Patricia Smith, *The Boston Globe*

Flynn, Keith. *The Talking Drum.* 73p. pap. $12.00 (1-889276-00-6). Asheville, NC: Animal Sounds, Spring 1996. Poems from the lyricist and lead singer for the nationally acclaimed rock band The Crystal Zoo. —Animal Sounds

Flythe, Starkey, Jr. *Paying the Anesthesiologist.* 52p. pap. $10.00. Greenville, SC: Ninety-Six Press, Spring 1996. *Paying the Anesthesiologist* is a remarkably witty, emotionally resonant collection of poems by the winner of the 1989 Iowa Award for Short Fiction. —Ninety-Six Press

Fogel, Alice B. *I Love This Dark World.* 96p. pap. $11.95 (0-944072-64-X). Cambridge, MA: Zoland Books, Spring 1996. Rural in setting but urbane in tone, familial yet metaphysical, Fogel's poems embrace paradox with flashes of insight triggered by juxtaposition. Listen very closely to them; what they tell you just may keep you awake at night. —Steven Cramer

Follett, C.B. *Gathering the Mountains.* 44p. pap. $7.00 (1-880575-16-7). Somerset, CA: Hot Pepper Press, Spring 1995.

Foo, Josephine. *Endou: Poems, Prose, and a Little Beagle Story.* 64p. pap. $12.00 (0-918786-46-0). Barrington, RI: Lost Roads Publishers. A first book from this tender, adroit poet and prose writer. —Lost Roads Publishers

Ford, Deborah. *Hourly Saints.* 40p. pap. $6.00 (1-880286-31-9). Canton, CT: Singular Speech Press, Fall 1995. Ford combines two qualities I don't see often in contemporary verse—ruthless compression and fierce honesty. —Dana Gioia

Ford, Victoria. *Rain Psalm.* 28p. pap. $5.95 (0-9651210-0-3). Seattle, WA: Rose Alley Press, Spring 1996. Victoria Ford's poems are at once modest and courageous, cut clean and sure without malice or intrusive ego. I welcome her poems like a good neighbor. —Sam Hamill. Her poems of the earth are generous in both their observation and their reverence. —Pattiann Rogers

Fossa, John A. *Poems, and Other Poems.* 72p. $12.95 (0-944957-78-1). New York, NY: Rivercross Publishing, Spring 1996. These poems, garnished by the author's drawings, use common experiences to seek deeper insights, virtually all upbeat and sometimes self-depracatingly humorous. —Rivercross Publishing

Foster, Ed. *All Acts Are Simply Acts.* 111p. Boulder, CO: Rodent Press, Spring 1995. A collection of poems and prose pieces by the editor of the journal *Talisman.* —Rodent Press

Foster, Sesshu. *City Terrace Field Manual.* 176p. pap. $12.95 (1-885030-19-3). New York, NY: Kaya Production, Fall 1996. *City Terrace Field Manual* takes you through the physical and psychological landscapes of an inter-ethnic working-class barrio in East Los Angeles. With rage, compassion, and a patient humor, these brawling, streetwise prose poems push the boundaries of narrative form, language, and poetry. Haunted by L.A.'s explosive history, Foster's "field manual" relentlessly details the violence and moments of transcendence that accompany the breakdown of urban industrial culture. —Kaya Production. Sesshu Foster is dangerous, ese! The way a poet should be. —Luis J. Rodríguez. This stuff is crackling! —Wanda Coleman

Foster, Thomas E., and Elizabeth C. Guthrie, eds. *A Year in Poetry: A Treasury of Classic and Modern Verses for Every Date on the Calendar.* 485p. $25.00 (0-517-70008-5). New York, NY: Crown Publishers, Fall 1995. Poets of whatever century are made contemporaries of us and each other, with Corbière and Thomas More cheek by jowl; and Horace as present-day as this year's Easter or the

Fourth of July. —Richard Wilbur

Fox, David. *A Compass at the North Pole.* 48p. pap. $6.00. Plainsboro, NJ: David Fox, Spring 1995.

Frances, Dee. *In the Mid of Night.* 130p. pap. $9.95 (0-9635341-7-3). St. Louis, MO: DDDD Publications, Fall 1994. Issues of personal growth and self-esteem are dealt with in these poems. —DDDD Publications

Frances, Dee. *Poet in Motion.* 180p. pap. $7.95 (1-885519-02-8). St. Louis, MO: DDDD Publications, Fall 1996. In this new collection, Dee Frances helps us to understand that with every opinion we formulate, we change: personhood itself is shaped by ideas. —DDDD Publications

Franklin, Walt, ed. *The Flutes of Power: Poetics of the Wild.* 39p. pap. $5.00 (0-945215-14-9). Rexville, NY: Great Elm Press, Spring 1995.

Frantz III, William F. *Writings From a Nam Mind.* 71p. pap. $7.95 (1-879183-28-5). Bristol, IN: Bristol Banner Books, Fall 1995.

Fraser, Kathleen. *Wing.* 16p. pap. $75.00 (0-9632085-7-8). Mill Valley, CA: Em Press, Fall 1995. Limited letterpress edition, numbered and signed. —Em Press

Fraser, Meg. *Keep to the Left of Grizzlies.* 96p. pap. $8.95 (1-56474-096-X). Santa Barbara, CA: Fithian Press, Fall 1994. Unexpected diction, transformative use of natural imagery, uncanny syntax— Fraser's work is at that queer threshold between inner and outer worlds and is for that reason rich and exciting. —*Small Press*

Fraser, Sanford. *14th Street.* 24p. pap. $4.00. New York, NY: The New School Chapbook Series, Fall 1995. Sanford Fraser is gifted with the ability to contain in each quirky pentameter line all his wit and compassion and insight. —Pearl London

Freeman, John P. *Illusion on the Louisiana Side.* 60p. pap. $9.00. Albion, CA: Pygmy Forest Press, Spring 1996. Modern, semi-formal verse dedicated to loving relationships and life in the rural south, with an intense and intimate insight into people, animals and landscape. —Pygmy Forest Press

Freeman, Keller Cushing. *Walking Like a Waterspider.* 52p. pap. $10.00. Greenville, SC: Ninety-Six Press, Fall 1996. *Walking Like a Waterspider* is an elegant first collection by a poet whose work has appeared in *Carolina Quarterly, Kenyon Review*, and *Radcliffe Quarterly.* —Ninety-Six Press

Friebert, Stuart. *Funeral Pie.* 64p. pap. $11.95 (1-884800-07-6). Marshfield, MA: Four Way Books, Spring 1996. Winner of the 1995 Four Way Books Award. [I] celebrate the sharp sense of humor in this book. You expect dessert and get a duel, or vice versa— either way, you'll probably want seconds. —Heather McHugh

Friebert, Stuart, and David Young, eds. *Models of the Universe: An Anthology of the Prose Poem.* 320p. pap. $25.00 (0-932440-69-X). Oberlin, OH: Oberlin College Press, Fall 1995. From its beginnings, with Aloysius Bertrand and Charles Baudelaire, to the present day, the prose poem has been something of a renegade and a deliberate freak, a resource for expressiveness and invention that combines the unpredictable and the subver-

sive. Drawing on the prose poem's chronological development and on its polylingual and multicultural manifestations, this book assembles the best examples that can be found. —Oberlin College Press

Fried, Michael. *To the Center of the Earth.* 68p. $18.00 (0-374-27829-6). New York, NY: Farrar, Straus and Giroux, Fall 1994. What gives the heart of Fried's poetry its real power is his stylized use of natural speech, his ability to be both colloquial and direct, whilst projecting a voice that is passionate and vulnerable. —David Cooke, *Agenda*

Friedman, Ed. *Mao & Matisse.* 96p. $20.00 (1-882413-21-0); pap. $12.00 (1-882413-20-2). Brooklyn, NY: Hanging Loose Press, Fall 1995. These poems are a gift simply because they are so generous in scope, depth and ear/voice/heart/emotion. —Jim Carroll. These are New York School poems— zany, in an unhurried but ebullient line: they're genial (full of genies) and happy. "There's no adequate explanation for happiness," Ed says in a poem, and happiness is the light in this book—a curiously rare light in contemporary poetry. Ergo revolutionary? —Alice Notley

Friedman, Howard. *Angels and Stardust.* 48p. pap $8.50 (1-55618-149-3). Lawrenceville, VA: Brunswick Publishing, Fall 1995. A collection of poems depicting a world which is dark, bleak, sometimes frightening, but always compassionate. —Brunswick Publishing

Friedman, Michael, and Duncan Hannah. *Arts & Letters.* 40p. pap. $10.00. Great Barrington, MA: The Figures, Fall 1996. A limited edition collaboration between poet Michael Friedman and artist Duncan Hannah in which 16 new prose poems by Friedman are paired with 16 new drawings by Hannah. —The Figures. Friedman's generally immaculate snaps and subtle caresses are formal, private, and discrete. Only apparently perverse, he hangs giddy frames on the undeniable, ancient and delapidated barn door of just language. —Stephen Rodefer

Frost, Carol. *Venus and Don Juan.* 72p. pap. $11.95 (0-8101-5063-8). Evanston, IL: Northwestern University Press/ Triquarterly Books, Fall 1996.

Frost has an uncanny ability to dissociate from and observe emotion . . . transforming her observations into shimmering and haunting images. Her poems are subtle examinations of psychological states through a kind of metaphoric transcription. —*Library Journal*

Frost, Celestine. *I Gathered My Ear From the Green Field.* 105p. (0-9651401-0-5). Harrisburg, PA: Logodaedalus Press, Spring 1996. An inquiry into the origins of lyric thought. The drawings and the photograph which accompany the poems are not illustrations but are an integral part of that thinking. —Logodaedalus Press

Frost, Richard. *Neighbor Blood.* 71p. $20.95 (0-9641151-4-X); pap. $12.95 (0-9641151-5-8). Louisville, KY: Sarabande Books, Fall 1996. Richard Frost has a rich range and a good ear. He is a lively storyteller, sardonic and compassionate as he invites the reader back into his childhood— vivid, exacting and loving as he testifies to the grown-up world he inhabits. —Maxine Kumin

Frost, Robert. Edited by Jeffrey Meyers. *Early Frost: The First Three Books.* 200p. pap. $14.00

(0-88001-447-4). Hopewell, NJ: Ecco Press, Spring 1996. With an illuminating introduction and explanatory notes by Frost's biographer, Jeffrey Meyers, this volume includes many of Frost's best and most beloved poems. —Ecco Press

Frost, Robert. Edited by Richard Poirier and Mark Richardson. *Robert Frost: Collected Poems, Prose, and Plays.* 1036p. $35.00 (1-883011-06-X). New York, NY: The Library of America, Fall 1995. Here, based on extensive research into Frost's manuscripts and published work, is the first authoritative and truly comprehensive collection of his writings, bringing together all the book-length collections, a generous selection of uncollected poems (many of which are printed here for the first time), all of Frost's dramatic writing, and the most extensive gathering of his prose writings ever published. —The Library of America

Frost, Robert. *Robert Frost: Selected Poems.* 224p. pap. $8.00 (0-517-20017-1). Avenel, NJ: Park Lane Press, Spring 1996.

Fulker, Tina. Edited by Richard Peabody. *Loose Change.* 32p.

pap. Free for postage ($.78). Arlington, VA: Bogg Publications, Fall 1996. A representative selection of the poems and short prose of the British poet, who died in 1992. —Bogg Publications. Her poetry is exceptionally airy, immaterial as thistledown, always vague and always winning, as she discusses within herself the possibilities of an inevitable loss. —*Dusty Dog Reviews.* She is one of the leading forces in a whole new generation of poets. —*Poetry For People*

Fulton, Alice. *Dance Script With Electric Ballerina.* 88p. pap. $12.95 (0-252-06576-X). Champaign, IL: University of Illinois Press, Fall 1996. *Dance Script with Electric Ballerina,* Fulton's critically acclaimed first book, is now considered a classic of contemporary poetry. It won the 1982 Associated Writing Programs Award in poetry. Alice Fulton's writing has been characterized by *The New Yorker* as "electrifying," and the poet herself, according to *Publisher's Weekly,* "may be Dickinson's postmodern heir." —University of Illinois Press. Fulton's distinct voice marks her as a poet to watch. —*Library Journal.* Delightful, energetic poems, alive with the exhilaration of creation. —Stephen C. Behrendt, *Prairie Schooner*

Fulton, Alice. *Sensual Math.* 128p. $17.95 (0-393-03750-9). New York, NY: W.W. Norton & Company, Spring 1995. [Fulton is] one of the finest young poets in the country. —David Barker, *Poetry.* She is an ambitious, powerful poet. —Eavan Boland, *Partisan Review*

Funk, Allison. *Living at the Epicenter.* 56p. pap. $10.95 (1-55553-247-0). Boston, MA: Northeastern University Press, Fall 1995. Winner of the 1995 Morse Poetry Prize. Images from the natural world are rarely far from these poems; the volume is richer for it. [A major theme is the desire] for reunification between earthly and human forces. Through earthquake, flood, or even the slow kiss of erosion, power and meaning are traded back and forth between men and women, rock and water. —Sonia Sanchez

Gabis, Rita. *The Wild Field.* 62p. pap. $9.95 (1-882295-01-3). Farmington, ME: Alice James Books, Fall 1994. These are often beautiful poems. They make much of dailiness and its icons—wings and petals and a man's shirt. But they are never easy poems: they make claims upon their own experience, they make claims upon our attention. —Eavan Boland

Gale, Kate. *Blue Air.* 64p. pap. $7.95 (0-9639528-5-1). Palmdale, CA: Red Hen Press, Fall 1995. This book claims as its territory the indefinite spaces separating us: the ground where we move together and apart, the long curve desire describes and follows. I think the secret of Harper's strength is this: from the middle of all loss, all bewilderment, her poems aspire to the condition of dancing. —Angela Ball, *Mississippi Review*

Gale, Kate. *Where Crows and Men Collide.* 72p. pap. $7.95 (0-9639528-4-6). Palmdale, CA: Red Hen Press, Fall 1995.

I urge you to read this book. Kate Gale has a dream of justice and a wry sense of how hard it is to obtain. She confronts the wrongs of sex, of gender, of husbands and lovers, and sees how easily we confuse our desires with what is right. She enters the garden of language and returns whole, humming. —Benjamin Saltman

Gale, Vi, ed. *The Prescott Street Reader*. 171p. pap. $20.00 (0-915986-26-4). Portland, OR: Prescott Street Press, Spring 1995. For twenty years Vi Gale's Prescott Street Press has quietly published remarkable books of both literary and artistic merit. These books are lovely to look at and a delight to read. This stunning new collection gathers the work of forty-one of the fine writers and translators who have been associated with the press. It demonstrates once again that good literature thrives when there are good small presses. —Brian Booth

Galvin, James. *Lethal Frequencies*. 64p. pap. $11.00 (1-55659-069-5). Port Townsend, WA: Copper Canyon Press, Spring 1995. Prominent chronicler of the West, Galvin employs a spare style to depict the tough landscapes of his Wyoming home and his unsentimental affection for the people who live there. —*Publishers Weekly*. Galvin's style is characterized by the strikingly direct statement, often at the beginning or toward the end of a poem, the literary equivalent of the pre-emptive strike. [He] has a voice and a world, perhaps the two most difficult things to achieve in poetry. —*The Nation*

Ganick, Peter. *Silence*. 16p. pap. $5.00 (1-57141-019-8). Port Charlotte, FL: Runaway Spoon Press, Spring 1996. This is minimalist poetry contrasting numeric sequences with chains of disconnecting words. —Runaway Spoon Press

Garcia, Albert. *Rainshadow*. 64p. pap. $9.95 (0-914278-68-1). Providence, RI: Copper Beech Press, Spring 1996. Out of the details of the common life, Albert Garcia manages to focus for us those moments that make us most human. This is the highest kind of poetry. —David Bottoms

Garcia, Carlos Ernesto. Translated by Elizabeth Gamble Miller. *Even Rage Will Rot*. 48p.

pap. $7.50 (0-89304-163-7).
Merrick, NY: Cross-Cultural
Communications, Spring 1995.
In his poems the experiences and
emotions of the years in El Sal-
vador and in his travels in Eu-
rope are evoked. The poet's sense
of irony and compassion perme-
ates the substance of his poetry,
which often carries the burden of
the tragic, even the macabre,
expressed with crafted restraint.
—EGM, *New Orleans Review*

Garland, Max. *The Postal Confess-
ions.* 120p. pap. $10.95 (087-
023-982-1). Amherst, MA:
University of Massachusetts
Press, Fall 1995. Max Garland,
winner of the Juniper Prize,
shows a lyrical determination
to deal with history through
the lives, minds, and emotions
of ordinary people "stricken
with time." In poems about
baptism, bowling, Greek god-
desses, and the hydrogen
bomb, Garland seems to say
that knowledge and even revelation might come from anywhere. —University of Massachusetts Press. These poems
bear the mark of the expert.
—*Kliatt*

Gaspar, Frank X. *Mass for the
Grace of a Happy Death.* 80p.
pap. $10.00 (0-938078-38-0).

Tallahassee, FL: Anhinga Press,
Fall 1995. These poems make
an extended song, sometimes a
wail, sometimes a hymn of
quiet thanksgiving. We need
this ceremony for reconcilia-
tion of our fragile and violent
humanity with the devine impulse of beauty. —Joy Harjo

Gehman, Pleasant. *Señorita Sin.*
140p. pap. $11.00 (0-
9627013-9-4). San Diego, CA:
Incommunicado Press, Fall
1994. Trashy yet noble, her
work is proof that, with a little
eyeliner, this is indeed the best
of all possible worlds. —Lisa
Buscani. Gehman writes like a
woman possessed with passion
for her subjects and a truly
remarkable memory for the
funny, sick, sad, bizarre stuff
she's seen in her varied career.
—Libby Molyneaux, *L.A.
Weekly.* Smart, funny, and liter-
ate. —*Austin Chronicle*

Gentry, Jane. *A Garden in Kentucky.* 74p. $17.95 (0-8071-
2002-2); pap. $9.95 (0-8071-
2003-0). Baton Rouge, LA:
Louisiana University Press, Fall
1995. Jane Gentry evokes, in
images as haunting as the Kentucky landscape, a garden
thriving with the flowers of
memory, a physical world that

reflects the realm of transcendence. —Louisiana State University Press

George, Alice Rose. *Ceiling of the World.* 71p. $20.00 (1-881471-12-8); pap. $10.95 (1-881471-13-6). New York, NY: Spuyten Duyvil, Spring 1996. Alice Rose George's poems have an exquisite lightness of being: they *rise* before our eyes, slip free the bonds of gravity, open upward like wings or prayers. They are never ephemeral, rather intensely ecstatic—the headlong imperative joy of the child, the sufi, poet-debauchee. —Carol Muske. A lyric account of a woman's life stared down with remarkable clarity, no indulgence at all. The poems impart a stoic thrill. —Richard Howard

Gephart, Ted; David Saetre, and Matt Welter, eds. *Even the Restless Must Have a Voice: Twenty Poems from the Chequamegon Bay.* 31p. pap. $5.00 (188-689-500-7). Bayfield, WI: Big Bug Books, Spring 1996. Poetry from a group of small town artists. —Big Bug Books

Gerding, Greg. Illustrations by Phil Merkle. *Poetry in Hell.* 58p. pap. $8.95 (0-9637704-1-1). Alexandria, VA: Red Dragon Press, Spring 1995. Selected works of Greg Gerding's unique poetry and prose, depicting his personal struggles with contemporary ideals and conflicts between behavior and morality. —Red Dragon Press

Gery, John. *The Enemies of Leisure.* 88p. $19.95 (1-885266-09-X); pap. $10.95 (1-885266-01-4). Brownsville, OR: Story Line Press, Fall 1995. Selected as one of the "Best Books of 1995" by *Publishers Weekly, The Critics Choice*, and the New Orleans *Times-Picayune*. Gery's frequent, subtle use of traditional meters and forms renders an edgy, hard-won elegance to his lines. The struggle between leisure and work is examined through layers of old-fashioned lyricism, political metaphor and real-life contexts. —*Publisher's Weekly*, starred review

Gesner, George, ed. *Anthology of American Poetry.* 752p. $12.99 (0-517-11890-4). Avenel, NJ: Gramercy Books, Fall 1994. This is a comprehensive collection of American poetry from the 17th century to the best of contemporary work. —Gramercy Books

Gibbons, Patrick Russell. *Chaos Uncorked.* 36p. pap. $5.00 (0-9637704-5-4). Alexandria, VA: Red Dragon Press, Spring 1996. Patrick Russell Gibbons is a prominent figure in poetry circles in Northern Virginia and Washington, D.C. His poetry is characterized by the use of vivid imagery expressing an emotional intensity of fear and love for man and nature. —Red Dragon Press

Gibbons, Reginald, and Susan Hahn, eds. *TriQuarterly New Writers.* 198p. pap. $14.95 (0-8101-5058-1). Evanston, IL: Northwestern University Press/ TriQuarterly Books, Spring 1996. This collection is a show-case for a group of new writers whose work has so far appeared only in literary magazines. Con-taining both poets and fiction writers, the anthology shows a great diversity of aesthetic ap-proach, cultural materials and background, and artistic project. —TriQuarterly Books

Gibbs, Barbara. *Poets Like Oysters: Last Poems.* 87p. pap. $35.00. Omaha, NE: Cummington Press, Spring 1996. Concise, direct poems dealing with the metaphysical in the ordinary world. Seven wood engravings by Karen Kunc. Visible spine stitching into Japanese paper covers. —Cummington Press

Gibbs, Michele. *Riffin to a Maroon Tune.* 85p. pap. $8.00 (0-940713-11-X). Detroit, MI: Broadside Press, Fall 1996.

Gibson, Becky Gould. *Holding Ground.* 22p. pap. $5.95. Fox River Grove, IL: White Eagle Coffee Store Press, Spring 1996. It is the time when farming is the backbone of American life and a woman is left to run the farm and raise her children alone. There is no time for grief; there is only a mother teaching her surviving children to harvest and sow new seeds, "to bury the hurt, layer by layer." In these poems, written by her great-grandchild, the woman herself becomes a metaphor for her hard won land. "She's her own/field,/never fallow/ for long." —Leilani Wright

Gibson, Grace Evelyn Loving. *Frayed Edges: Poems 1982-1994.* 103p. pap. $10.00 (1-879934-37-X). Laurinburg, NC: St. Andrews College Press, Spring 1995. Here is a wonderful poet—poised, alert, warm, completely engaged. A treat! —Fred Chappell. Meaning loads Grace's poems low, the tone is low, solemn often, catching at times on grief, but the language sustains and buoys the shipping with such precision that meaning and language live as one. —A.R. Ammons

Gilbert, Jack. *The Great Fires.* 90p. $20.00 (0-679-42576-4); pap. $13.00 (0-679-74767-2). New York, NY: Alfred A. Knopf, Spring 1994. He takes himself away to a place more inward than is safe to go; from that awful silence he returns to us poems of savage compassion. Gilbert is the rarest of beings: a necessary poet, who teaches us not only how to live but to die creatively, and with all meaning. —James Dickey

Gilbert, Marie. *Connexions.* 100p. pap. $10.00 (1-879934-28-0). Laurinburg, NC: St. Andrews College Press, Fall 1994. These are poems about the human need to connect, to break down the barriers of race, class, gender, culture, time, and most of all the barriers between the human and natural worlds. This is a lovely, gentle, honest, finely crafted, and accessible book of poems. —Anthony Abbott. Marie Gilbert's poems,

like all the ones we admire, are "perfect in the human way / which is almost." I've enjoyed the freshness in these lines and their utter willingness to belong to the world. —Fred Chappell

Gilbert, Sandra M. *Ghost Volcano.* 112p. $17.95 (0-393-03783-5). New York, NY: W.W. Norton & Company, Fall 1995. Like a field guide to grief or the litany of an obsession, Sandra Gilbert's *Ghost Volcano* traces one woman's response to the death of a husband. The sorrow in these poems is gripped and gripping. —Alicia Ostriker. These visionary, brilliant poems merit every honor. They are in the realm of great art. —Ruth Stone

Gilbert, Virginia. *That Other Brightness.* 112p. pap. $9.95 (1-887810-40-4). Lincoln, NE: Black Star Press, Fall 1995. [Gilbert's] voice can leap from that of a clear anecdotal narrative to that of a power-charged dream vision. [Her work preserves the] integrity of highly personalized expression in the service of complex understanding and a conscienceful witnessing. —Albert Goldbarth

Gill, Evalyn Pierpoint. *Entrances.* 90p. pap. $15.00 (1-879009-23-4). Whispering Pines, NC: Persephone Press, Fall 1996. These poems are intimate, delicate, pulled taut with tensile strength stemming from precision of language, instinctive skill—and always the fresh perception, vibrant and alive: "in love with every slant of light / and slender movement of the leaves." —Mary Carleton Snotherly. Hers is a winning voice. —Fred Chappell

Gillan, Maria Mazziotti, and Jennifer Gillan, eds. *Unsettling America: An Anthology of Contemporary Multicultural Poetry.* 406p. $27.95 (0-670-85170-1); pap. $13.95 (0-14-023778-X). New York, NY: Penguin Books/Viking Penguin, Fall 1994.

Gillespie, Jane Baldwin. *East Hampton: Echoes and Horizons.* 80p. pap. $9.95 (0-87233-113-X). Dublin, NH: William L. Bauhan, Publisher, Spring 1995. Gillespie's poems, with their graceful rhythms and rhymes and heartfelt affirmations of faith, are a salutary antidote to the vulgarity, cynicism and pessimism in modern life. —Karen Cassard Dreher

Ginsberg, Allen. *Howl and Other Poems.* 57p. $12.95 (0-87286-310-7). San Francisco, CA: City Lights Books, Spring 1996. The prophetic poem that launched a generation when it was first published in 1956 is here presented in a commemorative 40th anniversary edition. —City Lights Books

Ginsberg, Allen. *Illuminated Poems.* Paintings and drawings by Eric Drooker. 144p. $35.00 (1-56858-045-2); pap. (1-56858-070-3). New York, NY: Four Walls Eight Windows, Spring 1996. *Illuminated Poems* is the collaboration between two visionaries of different generations: Allen Ginsberg, the quintessential Beat and America's best-known poet, and Eric Drooker, an artist of the metropolis whose provocative images reflect life at the turn of the millennium. —Four Walls Eight Windows

Ginsberg, Allen. *Selected Poems: 1947-1995.* 384p. $27.50 (0-06-016457-3). New York, NY: HarperCollins Publishers, Fall 1996. Allen Ginsberg, one of America's foremost living poets, has spent the last half century redefining the art of poetry. For this volume Ginsberg has chosen representative work from his voluminous opus, offering a wide survey of writing that affirms his indisputable contribution to the century's literature. —HarperCollins

Ginsberg, Allen, and Kenneth Koch. *Making It Up: Poetry Composed at St. Mark's Church on May 9, 1979.* 35p. New York, NY: Catchword Papers, Spring 1995. This book records what happened when Allen Ginsberg and Kenneth Koch collaborated at the St. Mark's Poetry Project in a discussion moderated by Ron Padgett. Rarely had two famous poets made themselves so vulnerable in public, [letting] their generous inventiveness burst forth in brilliant, entertaining, and friendly poetic combat. —Ron Padgett

Gioseffi, Daniela. *Word Wounds and Water Flowers.* 86p. pap. $8.00 (1-884413-03-8). West Lafayette, IN: Bordighera, Spring 1995. Visionary and powerful. Tremendous vitality. A gifted and graceful writer. —Galway Kinnell. [Gioseffi's] work overflows with poetic vision. Nothing is ever pretentious or done for effect. She has achieved what the surrealists

hoped. —Nona Balakian, *The New York Times.* Startlingly fresh. Animated. Voluptuous. Gioseffi's writing is Mythopoeic. —Mary Pradt, *Library Journal*

Giovanni, Nikki. *The Selected Poems of Nikki Giovanni.* 287p. $20.00 (0688-140475). New York, NY: William Morrow & Company, Fall 1995. Return, remember, relive the beauty, energy, and poignancy of Nikki Giovanni. This wonderful collection of her poetry from the past three decades [will remind you] to feel again what it has always meant to be Black, to be a woman, to be vulnerable, to be empowered, to be human. —Marian Wright Edelman. Nikki Giovanni is one of our national treasures. For decades she has offered her wit and wisdom, her bruising honesty and, above all, her unbounded love through these poems as a healing for herself, her community, and her country. —Gloria Naylor

Giscombe, C.S. *Here.* 64p. pap. $9.95 (1-56478-058-9). Normal, IL: Dalkey Archive Press, Fall 1994. *Here* confirms G.S. Giscombe's place as a major figure in contemporary African

American letters. His deft use of the black vernacular is as impressive as his obvious command of the American poetic tradition. Together, these two voices combine into a distinctive poetic diction, timeless as Giscombe's great themes of love and departure. *Here* is a major book. —Henry Louis Gates, Jr.

Giuliani, Alfredo, ed. This edition edited by Luigi Ballermi and Paul Vangelisti. *I Novissimi: Poetry for the Sixties.* 410p. pap. $14.95 (1-55713-137-6). Los Angeles, CA: Sun & Moon Press, Fall 1995. This first English language publication of *I Novissimi*, the explosive anthology of neo-avant-garde poets, provides a recontextualization of the critical debate regarding the impact and significance of this important anthology. Bilingual edition. —Sun & Moon Press

Gizzi, Michael. *Interferon.* 24p. pap. $5.00 (0-935724-73-7). Great Barrington, MA: The Figures, Fall 1995. Razor sharp but also rich and generously compelling, Gizzi's poetry lambastes as it celebrates, bringing us finally to a place of poignant irresolution. *Interferon*

is one of the most exciting collections to land in some time. —John Ashbery

Glass, Jesse. *The Life & Death of Peter Stubbe.* 64p. pap. $12.00 (0-913559-27-X). Delhi, NY: Birch Brook Press, Fall 1995. Letterpress edition. Devils and monsters, human and imaginary, dominate as Glass interlaces bizarre archaic and medieval figures, events and diction with contemporary ones. —Robert Peters

Glassgold, Peter, trans. *Boethius: The Poems From On the Consolation of Philosophy.* 236p. pap. $11.95 (1-55713-109-0). Los Angeles, CA: Sun and Moon Press, Spring 1995. Glassgold has translated a work out of one antique language into another—or others, many "Englishes," revealing the various derivations, twistings, and turnings of language. These translations [seek to] evoke a pure text, or a pure language that exists somewhere in between the original and its translations. —Sun and Moon Press

Glatt, Lisa. *Monsters and Other Lovers.* 96p. pap. $11.95 (1-888219-00-9). Long Beach,

CA: Pearl Editions, Spring 1996. I love these bold, intense, funny and deadly serious poems. This is a brilliant debut. —Thomas Lux. Lisa Glatt's poems cover sex-related rites of passage, from the first pubic hairs to the (anticipated) loss of breasts to cancer. Her cutting humor and blunt candor left us gasping and cheering with the same breath. —*Next . . . Magazine*

Glazner, Greg. *Singularity.* 92p. $19.00 (0-393-03992-7). New York, NY: W.W. Norton & Company, Fall 1996. *Singularity*, Glazner's latest collection of narrative meditative poems, is a powerful summons to plumb the richness of a conscious life: "aren't the weekend's moon and the stars pressed flat,/ like little metal flowers, into the black slate? . . . / the deepest cravings silenced/ by the entertainment center and the sparkling wine." —W.W. Norton & Company. Singularity is a moral book. Glazner's voice is tenderly lyrical, thoughtful, provocative, as he considers what it might mean to be whole. —Forrest Gander

Glück, Louise. *Meadowlands.* 61p. $22.00 (0-88001-452-0).

Hopewell, NJ: Ecco Press, Spring 1996. Among hard-edged, limpid parables about "violence of human feeling," Glück (whose previous book, *The Wild Iris*, won a Pulitzer) utilizes Homer's long-suffering family as revisionist metaphor to articulate postmodern relationships among husband, wife, and child. She probes the "dark freedoms" of family life and "complex terms" of love with clear eye and steady hand. [These are] chastened, internally tense, spiritual poems. —Frank Allen, *Library Journal*

Glück, Louise. *The First Four Books of Poems.* 216p. $22.00 (0-88001-421-0). Hopewell, NJ: Ecco Press, Fall 1995. This collection shows Louise Glück in conscious evolution. Readers will hear the ferocious tension of her first book, the lyricism of her second, will note the use of icons in her third book, and the archtypal mythic scale of her fourth. —Ecco Press

Goldbarth, Albert. *A Lineage of Ragpickers, Songpluckers, Elegiasts & Jewelers: Selected Poems of Jewish Family Life, 1973-1995.* 166p. $22.95 (1-56809-021-8); pap. $14.95 (1-56809-022-6). St. Louis, MO: Time

Being Books, Spring 1996. Goldbarth succeeds not only in entertaining and moving his readers but in perfectly evoking the meld of faith and legacy that is modern Judaism. —*Booklist*

Goldbarth, Albert. *Marriage, and Other Science Fiction.* 119p. $19.95 (0-8142-0650-6); pap. $13.95 (0-8142-0651-4). Columbus, OH: Ohio State University Press, Spring 1995. Goldbarth has written yet another quirky, compassionate book, drawing together his many enthusiasms—for the sciences, the arts and literature—into a new and expansive universe. —*Publishers Weekly*

Goldberg, Barbara. *Marvelous Pursuits.* 85p. pap. $10.00 (09638364-4-7). Valdosta, GA: Snake Nation Press, Fall 1995. Winner of the Violet Reed Haas Prize for Poetry. Barbara Goldberg's powerful, passionate poems explore the intimate mysteries of love and attachment, the body's "curious, various hungers," with brave frankness and energy. They have an appealing, unflinching gaze. Their vigor and intelligence ignites revelation. —Naomi Shihab Nye. A moving and witty collection by a poet who [has] a string of honors behind her already. —*Tallahassee Democrat*

Goldring, Elizabeth. *Without Warning.* 64p. pap. $10.00 (1-884235-13-1). Kansas City, MO: Helicon Nine Editions and BkMk Press (co-publishers), Spring 1995. Goldring writes with the wild vision of an unconventional visual artist for whom language itself is corporeal. —Helicon Nine Editions. Her vision illuminates intimate moments and draws the reader in to share her unique reality. —Paula Dawson

Goldschmidt, Allan David. *Wood Winds.* 64p. pap. $10.00. Long Island City, NY: Allan David Goldschmidt, Fall 1996. These poems were written over a period of 16 years and reflect a process of self-identification. —Allan David Goldschmidt

Goldstein, Laurence. *Cold Reading.* 64p. pap. $9.95 (0-914278-66-5). Providence, RI: Copper Beech Press, Fall 1995. This poet is a student of culture in the midst of his culture, an examining man in the midst of his examined life. He looks backward, looks forward, looks everywhere around him, using material from body surfing to thrift shops, to give us a fiercely personal reading of life in mid-journey. —Molly Peacock

Gomes, Antonio. *Visions From Grymes Hill.* 96p. pap. $19.95 (0-938999-06-0). Stamford, CT: Turn of River Press, Fall 1994. Antonio Gomes invites us to partake in the pathos and passion of being fully human. A cardiologist by profession, he follows the vocation of a luminous poet of the heart with his fingers on the pulse of creation. —Turn of River Press

Gomez, Jewelle. *Oral Tradition: Selected Poems, Old and New.* 80p. $20.95 (1-56341-064-8); pap. $9.95 (1-56341-063-X). Ithaca, NY: Firebrand Books, Fall 1995. Lamba Literary Award Finalist (Lesbian Poetry). Taking their inspiration from the author's African American and Native American storytelling heritage, these are poems of finding home, making love, learning history. —Firebrand Books

Gonzalez, Ray. *The Heat of Arrivals.* 104p. $20.00 (1-880238-38-1); pap. $12.50 (1-880238-39-X). Rochester, NY: BOA Editions, Fall 1996. In this his

fifth collection of poetry Ray Gonzalez takes the reader to the heart of the Chicano/American Southwest experience. His is the voice of the desert flowers, hardscrabble border cities, the scorpion, the snake, adobes, petroglyphs, arroyos and mesas. —BOA Editions. The poety of Ray Gonzalez is intelligent, subtle, complex, the poetry of an honest craftsman. From the desert to the barrio, his images resonate. —Martín Espada

Goodison, Lorna. *To Us, All Flowers Are Roses.* 88p. pap. $11.95 (0-252-06459-3). Champaign, IL: University of Illinois Press, Fall 1995. One of the most distinguished contemporary poets of the Caribbean, Goodison draws on both African and European inheritances in these finely crafted poems, which deal with the struggle of Caribbean women. —University of Illinois Press. A marvelous poet, one to savor and chant aloud. —*Booklist*

Goodman, Miriam. *Commercial Traveler.* 60p. pap. $13.00 (1-882329-06-6). Truro, MA: Garden Street Press, Spring 1996. Poet and photographer Miriam Goodman shows us in these fine poems, and in her jacket photo of a disused greenhouse, how the dusty facts of economic life can be made to live. Magic . . . which makes these poems irreplaceable. —Sarah Kafatou, *Harvard Review*

Gordon, Ruth, ed. *Pierced by a Ray of Sun: Poems About the Times We Feel Alone.* 108p. $16.00 (0-06-023613-2). New York, NY: HarperCollins Publishers, Fall 1995. Gordon's selection reveals the universality of the feelings of loneliness and alienation, but stresses, in Jim Northrup's words, that people have "Toughed it out/ Survived." —HarperCollins

Gorham, Sarah. *The Tension Zone.* 64p. pap. $11.95 (1-884800-06-8). Marshfield, MA: Four Way Books, Spring 1996. Winner of the 1995 Four Way Books Award. [Gorham] administers her art toward that rare end—[the coming together] of two things, structural necessity and intellectual surprise, a convergence that nature has always made convincing. —Heather McHugh

Gottlieb, Michael. *The River Road.* 70p. pap. $10.00 (0-937013-60-0). Elmwood, CT: Poets & Poets Press, Spring

1996. Gottlieb's honest, funny and challenging poems are sites of resistance to the limits of everyday life and to what can be known, or stated outside of a poem. These gorgeous writings are more sophisticated than the wildest dreams. —Carla Harryman

Gould, Janice. *Earthquake Weather.* 96p. $24.95 (0-8165-1610-3); pap. $10.95 (0-8165-1630-8). Tucson, AZ: University of Arizona Press, Fall 1996. The signs of earthquake weather are familiar to Janice Gould, a poet, a lesbian, and a mixed-blood California Indian of Koyangk'auwi Maidu descent. Her sense of isolation is intense, her search for identity is relentless, and her words can take one's breath away. —University of Arizona Press. A beautiful, poignant collection. Bravo! —Greg Sarris

Gousseland, Pascale. *Farandole of Titled and Untitled.* 24p. pap. $3.75. Kew Gardens, NY: The Poet Tree, Fall 1994.

Gousseland, Pascale. *Love Is Laughing at Us.* 35p. pap. $4.75. Kew Gardens, NY: The Poet Tree, Fall 1994. Winner of the 1995 Gradiva Award. A wonderful psychotherapeutic approach to poetic verse. Ms. Gousseland explores the subject of love, its quests and conquests. —The Poet Tree

Gousseland, Pascale. *Selected Leftovers.* 22p. pap. $3.75. Kew Gardens, NY: The Poet Tree, Fall 1995.

Gousseland, Pascale. *The Chapter Is Closed: Poems in French and English.* 28p. pap. $6.00. Kew Gardens, NY: New Spirit Press, Spring 1996. Winner of a 1996 Gradiva Award. The *Chapter Is Closed* is the final book in a series of five dealing with the long-term recovery from a near fatal automobile accident. —New Spirit Press

Graffeo, Ignatius. *She Came With the Magazine.* 20p. pap. $3.75. Kew Gardens, NY: New Spirit Press, Fall 1995. Palatable verse with a slant toward mythology and the "B" movie. —New Spirit Press

Graham, Jorie. *Materialism.* 146p. $22.00 (0-88001-342-7); pap. $13.00 (0-88001-394-X). Hopewell, NJ: Ecco Press, Spring 1995. No other current American poet has exposed the mechanics of narrative, of form, of strategic inquiry more fully, and no other poet is able to deploy so fruitfully and invitingly the diverse systems of philosophy, science and history. *Materialism* shows her working at the height of her powers. —David Baker, *The Kenyon Review.* Graham's fierce sense of the philosophic universal may help remind us that there is a dimension of the lyric that goes beyond the merely personal, the merely social. It is a dimension we find in Emily Brontë and Emily Dickinson—austere, renunciatory, far-seeing, but also detailed, intimate, saturated with phenomena. —Helen Vendler, *The New Republic*

Graham, Loren. *Mose.* 64p. $22.50 (0-8195-2215-5); pap. $10.95 (0-8195-1220-6). Middletown, CT: Wesleyan/University Press of New England, Fall 1994. A terrific book— readable, original, lucid, moving. —Thomas Lux. This poem is astonishing: [Graham] tells the story of Mose, a convicted murderer in a Texas prison, with all the insight and suspense of a Dostoevsky novel. —*Publishers Weekly*

Graham, Taylor. *Casualties: Search-and-Rescue Poems.* 50p. pap. $5.00 (1062-5011). Lawrence,

KS: Coal City, Spring 1995. Poems about people who are not spiritually astray, but quite literally *lost*, and about the people who search for and rescue them, all too frequently becoming casualties themselves. —Ken Hill

Grass, Gunter. Translated by Michael Hamburger. *Novemberland: Selected Poems 1956-1993*. 176p. $25.00 (0-15-100177-4); pap. $15.00 (0-15-600331-7). San Diego, CA: Harcourt Brace/Harvest Books, Spring 1996. These fifty-four poems, spanning four decades, depict a landscape at once recognizably mundane and grotesquely surreal. Grass's spirited humor and linguistic creativity transcend the cant of political poetry. —Harcourt Brace

Green, Samuel. *Vertebrae*. 61p. $18.00 (0-910055-18-1); pap. $11.00 (0-910055-17-3). Cheney, WA: Eastern Washington University Press, Fall 1994. Think of the affection that transcends love. This is what I find in Sam Green's poems, such a warm, egoless generosity for the harsh world—wind and sea, cedar and rock, death and pain—which he nevertheless depicts with perfect accuracy. These are the strongest gentle poems I have ever read. —Hayden Carruth

Greenberg, Blu. *Black Bread: Poems, After the Holocaust*. 120p. (0-88125-490-8). Hoboken, NJ: KTAV Publishing House, Fall 1994. Greenberg's poems reveal an inner world shaped by the Holocaust experience as if she were there, as if she lived through the horror in a real physical sense. She is an aggregate of Holocaust pain [but] each poem hints that ultimate victory does not belong to evil; but to love, family, kindness, commitment and faith. —Livia Britton Jackson, *The Jewish Press Magazine*

Greene, Jeffrey. *Glimpses of the Invisible World in New Haven*. 28p. pap. $5.00 (0-9647127-3-3). Lawrenceville, GA: Coreopsis Books, Spring 1995. This lovely collection offers constant witness to that barely expressible exchange between the seen and unseen. —Pamela Stewart. From the quotidian details of a particular place—once a vital and now declining city—rises a universal narrative of modern America, fraught with tentative connections and mercurial love. —Susan Prospere

Greene, Jonathan. *The Man Came to Haul Stone*. 16p. $65.00; pap. $25.00. New York, NY: Dim Gray Bar Press, Spring 1995. Winner of the First Annual Poetry Prize from the Center for Book Arts. Letterpress edition.

Greger, Debora. *Desert Fathers, Uranium Daughters*. 84p. pap. $14.95 (0-14-058774-8). New York, NY: Penguin Books, Fall 1996. She is in every sense a special poet. —J.D. McClatchy, *Poetry*. [Her's is] a distinctly modern American vision. —*Publishers Weekly*. [She writes with] deadpan wit, intelligence and marvelous insight. —*The Nation*

Gregerson, Linda. *The Woman Who Died in Her Sleep*. 80p. $19.95 (0-395-82290-4). Boston, MA: Houghton Mifflin Company, Fall 1996. Tender and harrowing, jagged, severely precise and floodlit with compassion, Linda Gregerson's poems break and mend poetic language as they break and mend the heart. —Rosanna Warren. The poems in Linda Gregerson's new book are engrossing as much for their music as for the stories they tell, as much for their clarity, wit, and

intelligence as for the hard truths they deliver. Throughout *The Woman Who Died in Her Sleep* ordinary experience assumes, with almost preternatural ease, the force of allegory, and plain speech magically turns into resonant speech. Such transformations are possible only in the very best poetry. —Mark Strand

Gregor, Arthur. *The River Serpent and Other Poems*. 98p. pap. $10.95 (1-878818-36-8). Riverdale-on-Hudson, NY: Sheep Meadow Press, Spring 1995. Surely one of the most deeply spiritual poets of our time, Gregor revives the power in us to respond to beauties in people that transcend their worldy personalities. This impersonal—or transpersonal—beauty is, for Gregor, the supreme reality. —Laurence Lieberman, *The Yale Review*. [Gregor's is] an enterprise that is frankly Rilkean in its 'struggle toward absolute verities' and its emphasis on praise as the poet's proper activity. —*The New York Times Book Review*

Grenier, Arpine Konyalian. *Whores From Samarkand*. 96p. pap. $9.00 (1-877978-46-9). Sarasota, FL: Florida Literary Foundation Press, Fall 1994. Grenier's new work reshapes her emotional inheritance into a legend that celebrates contingency, neither augmenting it nor being paralyzed by it. —Florida Literary Foundation Press

Grennan, Eamon. *So It Goes.* 96p. pap. $14.00 (1-55597-232-2). St. Paul, MN: Graywolf Press, Fall 1995. Eamon Grennan's writing brings us over and over again to the discovery of what is naturally so and had passed unrecognized. —W.S. Merwin. Grennan's poems show us what we may have glimpsed but never really seen, heard but not listened to. —*Publishers Weekly*

Griffin, Penny. *A Dash Through Leaves: Haiku.* 60p. $25.00; pap. $15.00. Whispering Pines, NC: Persephone Press, Fall 1995.

Grim, Jessica. *Locale.* 86p. pap. $10.00 (0-937013-56-0). Elmwood, CT: Potes & Poets Press, Spring 1995. Jessica Grim has tapped into the secret of a fourth dimension. Playful, serious, intense and wise all at once, *Locale* contains some of the most riveting poems of our time. —Ron Silliman

Grosjean, Ok-Koo Kang. *A Hummingbird's Dance.* 59p. pap. $10.00 (0-938077-74-0). Berkeley, CA: Parallax Press, Fall 1994. Quite elegant . . . like a flower arrangement. —Gary Snyder. The unattainable world of no-distinctions is delineated momentarily in Ok-Koo Kang Grosjean's poems. —Leslie Scalapino

Gross, Pamela. *Birds of the Night Sky/Stars of the Field.* 104p. pap. $11.95 (0-8203-1776-4). Athens, GA: University of Georgia Press, Fall 1995. Pamela Gross's first full-length collection is marked by intelligence, verbal dexterity, and grace, the poems drawing on an intense emotional core. —*Choice*

Grossman, Allen. *The Philosopher's Window and Other Poems.* 112p. pap. $12.95 (0-8112-1300-5). New York, NY: New Directions, Fall 1995. I would like to crown Grossman one of the great new Low Moderns. . . . Dear God, spare him the academic embellishment that Stevens and Eliot suffered. His real enamorata (like theirs) is the green world. —Mary Karr, *Harvard Review*

Gruenewald, Tony. *Headlines From the Daily Grind.* 85p. pap. $4.95 (1-880764-04-0). Red Bank, NJ: Northwind Publishing, Fall 1995.

Grumman, Bob, ed. *Light.* 14p. pap. $3.00 (1-57141-002-3). Port Charlotte, FL: Runaway Spoon Press, Fall 1994. Visual poems about light by five poets, each from a different country: Bob Cobbing (England), Pierre Garnier (France), Bill Keith (US), Arrigo Lora-Totino (Italy), and Hiroshi Tanabu (Japan). —Runaway Spoon Press

Grumman, Bob, and Crag Hill, eds. *Vispo auf Deutsch: An Anthology of Verbo-visual Art in German.* 58p. pap. $10.00 (1-57141-018-X). Port Charlotte, FL: Runaway Spoon Press, Fall 1995. Artworks combining visual and textual matter by 19 artists from Austria and Germany. —Runaway Spoon Press

Guenther, Charles. *Moving the Seasons: Poems and Reformations.* 80p. pap. $12.00 (0-933532-98-9). Kansas City, MO: BkMk Press of the University of Missouri-Kansas City, Fall 1994. He stands for the elegance of the honest line, the achievement of precise articula-

tion, the need for the unique perspective, the wonder of deep connections between words and people. —Dan Jaffe

Guest, Barbara. *Fair Realism.* 114p. pap. $10.95 (1-55713-245-3). Los Angeles, CA: Sun & Moon Press, Fall 1995.

Guest, Barbara. *Quill, Solitary Apparition.* 77p. pap. $12.95 (0-942996-26-7). Sausalito, CA: Post-Apollo Press, Fall 1996. Of late, her work increases in acceleration. *Quill, Solitary Apparition* is of perfect weight. The whole is on a blade. I feel the poetry moves beyond me and fills in where I will go. —Mei-mei Berssenbrugge

Guest, Barbara. *Selected Poems.* 200p. $22.95 (1-55713-200-3). Los Angeles, CA: Sun & Moon Press.

Guest, Barbara. Drawings by Anne Dunn. *Stripped Tales.* 48p. pap. $14.00 (0-932716-36-9). Berkeley, CA: Kelsey Street Press, Fall 1995.

Guevara, Maurice Kilwein. *Poems of the River Spirit.* 65p. $24.95 (0-8229-3934-7); pap. $10.95 (0-8229-5591-1).

Pittsburgh, PA: University of Pittsburgh Press, Spring 1996. *Poems of the River Spirit* is an anthem, at once tender and gleeful, cognizant of suffering and without regret. Half documentary, half luminous post-industrial imagism, this book evokes a world utterly specific and individual and, at the same time, the world we all live in: a world both beautiful and ruined. —Lynn Emanuel

Gullans, Charles. *Selected Earlier Poems.* 32p. pap. Edgewood, KY: Robert L. Barth (R.L.B.), Spring 1995.

Gullans, Charles. *The Trees.* 28p. pap. Edgewood, KY: Robert L. Barth (R.L.B.), Spring 1995.

Gundy, Jeff. *Flatlands.* 77p. pap. $10.00 (1-880834-14-6). Cleveland, OH: Cleveland State University Poetry Center, Spring 1995. Gundy's poems travel deep into their midwestern landscapes and rise to take you somewhere past where you began . . . a spiritual journey of the real. —Lucia Cordell Getsi. Reading *Flatlands*, you feel the author's honesty palpably, his lack of side; these

are genuine, searching poems, with no airs about them, full of wry wonder and warmth. —Jean Valentine

H.-Aigla, Jorge. *The Aztec Shell.* 85p. pap. $9.00 (0-927534-49-5). Tempe, AZ: Bilingual Press, Fall 1995. He has a clean, objective, passionate style. —*The Albuquerque Tribune.*

Ha Jin. *Facing Shadows.* 72p. $20.00 (1-882413-25-3); pap. $12.00 (1-882413-24-5). Brooklyn, NY: Hanging Loose Press, Spring 1996. These poems are unflinchingly lucid, luminous, brave, and the shadows faced in this book are faced with a powerful light. —Thomas Lux. Memory, simplicity, honoring of deeds past and present, humility and gratitude before global and private horrors—Ha Jin's poems reveal a mind and heart fresh to significance and foreign to the anomic. —Olga Broumas

Haberman, Daniel. *The Lug of Days to Come: New and Selected Poems and Translation*s. 129p.

$20.00 (1-880284-13-8). Santa Barbara, CA: John Daniel and Company, Spring 1996. This is a poetry of spareness and rectitude. And yet there are frequent touches of pre-Raphaelite grace [and] wistfulness. All this makes for an unusual combination of strength and charm, and produces a poetry that seems at once familiar and exotic. —Anthony Hecht. There is a rare simplicity that is both classical and romantic, where the atmosphere is calm and peaceful and the inhabitants speak tenerly and couteously to each other, and there's always music in the air. —Carl Rakosi

Hacker, Marilyn. *Love, Death and the Changing of the Seasons.* 212p. pap. $11.00 (0-393-31225-9). New York, NY: W.W. Norton & Company, Spring 1995. First published in 1986, this critically acclaimed sonnet sequence is the passionately intense story of a love affair between two women, from the electricity of their first acquaintance to the experience of their parting. —W.W. Norton & Company. Elegant and versatile in the strictest forms, [Hacker] is inventive and exuberant in content. She's colloquial, lyrical, uncouth, old-fashioned, and fun. No one sings quite like this. A cappella, she's a whole choir. —*New York Times Book Review.* An account of lust, ecstasy, yearning, jealousy and betrayal. These sonnets are graphic, colloquial, and immediate. . . . A stunning achievement. —*Publishers Weekly*

Hacker, Marilyn. *Selected Poems 1965–1990.* 288p. $22.00 (0-393-03675-8); pap. $13.00 (0-393-31349-2). New York, NY: W.W. Norton & Company, Fall 1994. A collection of work from five books by a poet who, praised for her technical virtuosity, forthright feminism, political acuity and unabashed eroticism, is one of America's most acclaimed and controversial poets. —W.W. Norton & Company. This is a poet of dazzling opposites. Her formal vivacity exists with a strong-willed vernacular; her lyric wryness with a determined narrative. These poems tell her story. —Eavan Boland

Hacker, Marilyn. *Winter Numbers.* 95p. $17.95 (0-393-03674-X); pap. $10.00 (0-393-31373-5). New York, NY: W.W. Norton & Company, Fall 1994. *Winter*

Numbers is Hacker at the top of her form, bending rhyme and meter to her uses, dazzling us with her formalist prowess and breaking our hearts with her impassioned narrative. —Maxine Kumin. These poems are among the most incisive pieces of writing we have. —Hayden Carruth. Hacker has an uncanny ability to express relationships between women. —*Publishers Weekly*

Hadas, Rachel. *The Empty Bed.* 93p. $22.50 (0-8195-2221-X); pap. $10.95 (0-8195-1225-7). Middletown, CT: Wesleyan/University Press of New England, Spring 1995. With crafted solemnity (many poems use formal rhyme), Hadas combines Romanlike stoicism with a dislike of emotional equivocation. Death, she argues, is not the end of the "short time we're let to live," and grief inaugurates an enlargement of human spirit. Despite the "pristine dominion of the dead," the elegies here are about awakenings: "Winter's secret melts. I am restored./ Hard spring light pours down without a word/into the pure, the newly naked eye." For most poetry collections. —Frank Allen, *Library Journal*

Hägglund, S. Gustav. *Jaguar Newsprint.* 14p. pap. $5.00 (1-57-41-021-X). Port Charlotte, FL: Runaway Spoon Press, Spring 1996. A nearly non-referential visual poetry sequence. —Runaway Spoon Press

Hague, Richard. *A Beastiary.* 41p. pap. $7.75. Johnstown, OH: Pudding House Publications, Fall 1996. Richard Hague writes about the many beasts of modern life, including the beasts of ego, beer, the law, and one's own deep roots. —Pudding House Publications

Hahn, Kimiko. *The Unbearable Heart.* 80p. $24.00 (1-885030-01-0); pap. $11.95 (1-885030-00-2). New York, NY: Kaya Production. Reading *The Unbearable Heart* you have the sense of someone tearing the past apart and rebuilding with naked raw hands. The work is furious, flawed and absolutely necessary. —Adrienne Rich. Alternately daring and intensely elegiac, Hahn has the ability to ambush the reader with her unexpected images, direct voice, and willingness to tackle subjects of great emotional or political weight.

—*A. Magazine.* Hahn's gaze is confident and immediate. —*Poetry Calendar*

Hahn, Robert. *All Clear.* 71p. $15.95 (1-57003-132-0); pap. $9.95 (1-57003-133-9). Columbia, SC: University of South Carolina Press, Spring 1996. A stunning book, the work of a philosophic mind which is fascinated by the idea of truth and by the question of where to corner it. . . . Among the marvels of this book is Hahn's ability to express the nearly inexpressible. —Richard Wilbur

Haines, John. *The Owl in the Mask of the Dreamer: Collected Poems.* 278p. pap. $14.95 (1-55597-246-2). Saint Paul, MN: Graywolf Press, Fall 1996. Winner of the William Stafford Memorial Poetry Award. Available for the first time in paperback, this updated and expanded edition of *The Owl in the Mask of the Dreamer* showcases Haines's remarkable insights into the art of nature and the nature of art. —Graywolf Press. Splendidly odd, somberly beautiful. . . . John Haines's spare, oracular lyrics feel as if they have come from a great distance. It be-

hooves us to listen to a poet who deepens the silence around us and touches upon an ancient environmental wisdom. —*The New York Times Book Review*

Haines, John. *Where the Twilight Never Ends.* 28p. pap. $12.00 (0-93-1659-21-3). Boise, ID: Limberlost Press, Fall 1994. Letterpress edition.

Hair, Jennie. *A Sisterhood of Songs.* 62p. pap. $11.00 (1-886435-00-6). Sag Harbor, NY: Canio's Editions, Fall 1995. This selection of Jennie Hair's poetry carefully probes the human condition as women find it. —Lois V. Walker. How I like these poems, their robust register: no droning groove here, just bold sound leaps that resonate. I appreciate such sure footing, the poems knowing when—and where—to shop, always "taut, honed, precious boned." The speaker, the woman of flesh, blood and bone behind these poems, is a poet. —Vince Clemente

Halchin, Mike. *Formaldehyde Brains Under a Rat-Colored Sky.* 20p. pap. $2.00. Los Angeles, CA: Undulating Bedsheets Productions, Spring 1996.

Hall, Daniel. *Strange Relation.* 69p. pap. $13.95 (0-14-058771-3). New York, NY: Penguin Books, Fall 1996. One of the best books of this year or any year. Open it, open to its riches. —J.D. McClatchy. Daniel Hall's poems progress "out of harm's way, into joy's," though harm and joy are inextricably linked. Hall's a student of the complicated bonds of family, of sexuality, of longing across boundaries of language and culture. These turbulences electrify the elegant surfaces of his work. —Mark Doty

Hall, Donald. *Apples and Peaches.* 15p. pap. Edgewood, KY: Robert L. Barth, Spring 1995.

Hall, Donald. *The Old Life: New Poems.* 144p. $19.95 (0-395-78841-2). Boston, MA: Houghton Mifflin Company, Spring 1996. These autobiographical poems are free of self-pity, engagingly frank without being in any sense 'confessional' and often wildly comic. All are first-rate. —*Minneapolis Star-Tribune.* Hall's new collection contains just four poems, all autobiographical. The 97-page title poem is the meat here, an involving, entertaining, poignant life testament. The relatively shorter "Without" is Hall's lament for his wife Jane Kenyon; in it, grief mingles her illness and death and his own life's decline. —Ray Olson, *Booklist*

Hall, Irving C. *Keeping the Lady at Bay.* 72p. pap. $10.00 (1-886157-03-3). Kansas City, MO: BkMk Press of the University of Missouri, Fall 1996. A collection of terse, vivid poems told in a quiet but resonant voice with the distilled, unafraid truthfulness of a man who is sifting the lasting memories of a long life. —BkMk Press

Hallerman, Victoria. *The Woman in the Magic Show.* 14p. pap. $5.00. Staten Island, NY: Firm Ground Press, Spring 1995.

Hallerman, Victoria, ed. *Standing in Midair.* 24p. pap. $6.00. New York, NY: Firm Ground Press, Spring 1996. The poets whose work appears here include Janet Broff, Priscilla Ellsworth, Sabra Loomis, Victoria Hallerman, Wendy Wilder Larsen, Myra Shapiro, and Susan Sindall. They have been meeting together as a group for almost fifteen years. —Firm Ground Press

Halme, Kathleen. *Every Substance Clothed*. 96p. pap. $11.95 (0-8203-1762-4). Athens, GA: University of Georgia Press, Fall 1995. Winner of the 1995 Balcones Poetry Prize. In these contemporary experiences of the sacred, the spiritual is material and unsentimental, profound and penetrable, often wryly humorous. —University of Georgia Press. Halme's first book of poems is nothing less than splendid. —Anthony Hecht

Halpern, Daniel. *Selected Poems*. 220p. $23.00 (0-679-42986-7); pap. $15.00 (0-679-76565-4). New York, NY: Alfred A. Knopf, Fall 1994. These poems speak to me in the best, most private way, as poetry should. —Nadine Gordimer. Halpern's themes mature and intertwine during the twenty-some years of work excerpted here. [This collection] allows us to track the progress of a writer's struggling dialogue between connection and detachment, a process that marks the evolution of the heart. —Mark Doty, *Los Angeles Times Book Review*

Halpern, Daniel, ed. *Holy Fire: Nine Visionary Poets and the Quest for Enlightenment*. 288p.

$25.00 (0-06-018240-7); pap. $13.00 (0-06-098203-9). New York, NY: HarperCollins Publishers, Fall 1994. The nine visionaries selected for *Holy Fire* are the Sufi poet Jelaluddin Rumi, fourteenth-century Kashmiri poet Lalla, sixteenth-century Hindu mystic Mirabai, William Blake, Hart Crane, Rainer Maria Rilke, Arthur Rimbaud, Allen Ginsberg, and W.B. Yeats. Outwardly completely dissimilar, these poets share only a contempt for the mainstream tradition of their own time, and a fierce devotion to their vision of the Divine. —HarperCollins

Hamby, Barbara. *Delirium*. 93p. pap. $10.95 (1-57441-003-2). Denton, TX: University of North Texas Press, Fall 1995. Winner of the Vassar Miller Poetry Prize, the Kate Tufts Discovery Award for Poetry, and The Poetry Society of America's Norma Farber First Book Award. Once started, it's hard to stop reading Hamby, so tightly does she knit each line of her rich, full, strong poetry to the next. —*Booklist*

Hamby, Barbara. *Skin*. 28p. pap. $6.00 (1-878851-07-1). Eugene,

OR: Silverfish Review Press, Fall 1995.

Hamer, Forrest. *Call and Response.* 68p. pap. $9.95 (1-882295-06-04). Farmington, ME: Alice James Books, Fall 1995. Winner of the Beatrice Hawley Award. *Call and Response* is a tightly woven tapestry of impulses and life rituals, a tribute to what keeps us whole and true to human complexity. —Yusef Komunyakaa. Forrest Hamer's poems rise out of the place where religion and dancing—spirit and body—join, and in reading *Call and Response* "We are journeying to the source of all wonder,/We journey by dance. Amen." Amen! We call in celebration, Amen! —Andrew Hudgins

Hamill, Sam. *Destination Zero: Poems 1970–1995.* 235p. $25.00 (1-877727-55-5); pap. $15.00 (1-877727-53-9). Fredonia, NY: White Pine Press, Fall 1995. Sam Hamill has learned, perhaps from the Asian poets he loves and translates, a deceptive plainness, a light touch, a sureness of eye whether what is being observed is a pine tree or the feeling of growing older and being alone. He has learned how to bring his world up close and transparent, and set it in words that are a pleasure to come upon and to remember. —W.S. Merwin

Hamill, Sam, ed. *The Erotic Spirit: An Anthology of Poems of Sensuality, Love, and Longing.* 200p. $18.00 (0-87773-957-9). Boston, MA: Shambhala Publications, Spring 1996. From the swift grip and succor of today's Dorianne Laux to the plums of ancient Tzu Yeh, these are voices echoing off the walls of a cave, becoming one voice, one song of eros. I've seen no better collection. —Lily Pond

Hamill, Sam, ed. *The Gift of Tongues: Twenty-five Years of Poetry from Copper Canyon Press.* 400p. $30.00 (1-55659-116-0); pap. $16.00 (1-55659-117-9). Port Townsend, WA: Copper Canyon Press, Fall 1996. Copper Canyon Press is an evangelist for poetry. The rich diversity of poets [in this anthology] celebrates 25 years of sagacious and daring publishing. —Maxine Kumin. To read Copper Canyon's list of authors is to know where American poetry comes from and where it is headed. It would be hard to imagine doing without it. —Jorie Graham

Hamill, Sam, trans. *The Sound of Water: Haiku by Basho, Buson, Issa and Other Poets.* 125p. Boston, MA: Shambhala Publications, Spring 1995. Currently out of print. Collected here are over two hundred of the best haiku of Japanese literature, written by the great masters of the genre from the seventeenth to early twentieth century, and translated by-one of America's premier poet-translators. —Shambala Publications

Hamilton, David, ed. *Hard Choices: An Iowa Review Reader.* 490p. pap. $19.95 (0-87745-536-8). Iowa City, IA: University of Iowa Press, Spring 1996. Including selections of note from the first 25 years of a major American literary magazine, *Hard Choices* charts in its own way the development of American literature, from Tillie Olsen and William Stafford in the first volume to James Galvin and Pattiann Rogers in the 24th. —University of Iowa Press

Hammond, Raymond P. *Glacial Reasoning.* 34p. pap. $6.00. Brooklyn, NY: Raymond P. Hammond, Fall 1994.

Han, Stephanie. *L.A. (Lovers Anonymous).* 88p. pap. $8.95 (0-9646433-0-8). Venice, CA:

LALA Press, Fall 1995. *L.A. (Lovers Anonymous)* by Stephanie Han is a collection of erotic/romantic poetry and prose, the first to be published by a Korean American woman. Its theme is people's addictions to love and the city of L.A. The work is very contemporary, hip, California and sexy. —LALA Press

Hansbury, Gia. *Walking 14th Street Home, Poems 1990–1992.* 24p. pap. $5.00. West Chester, PA: Riverstone Press, Fall 1992. Gia Hansbury combines a finely-honed sense of poetic craft with an eye for the gritty undeniable details of the everyday. —Daniel S. Solis

Hanson, Jeanne K., ed. *The Poetry of Angels: More Than 70 Celestial Poems to Inspire and Delight.* 96p. pap. $8.00 (0-517-88623-5). New York, NY: Crown Publishers, Fall 1995.

Harding, Deborah. *The Blazing Shapes of This World.* 34p. pap. $5.00. San Diego, CA: Laterthanever Press.

Hardison, William E. *Bill's Ideals.* pap. $8.95 (1-882185-51-X). Virginia Beach, VA: Cornerstone Publishing, Fall

1996. Humorous, down-to-earth poems for the young at heart. —Cornerstone Publishing

Hardy, Thomas. Edited by Peter Washington. *Poems.* 254p. $10.95 (0-679-44368-1). New York, NY: Alfred A. Knopf/Everyman's Library Pocket Poets, Fall 1995.

Hardy, Thomas. Edited by Joseph Brodsky. *The Essential Hardy.* 120p. pap. $10.00 (0-88001-405-9). Hopewell, NJ: Ecco Press, Spring 1995.

Harer, Katharine. *Hubba Hubba.* 51p. pap. $4.00. Niagara Falls, NY: Slipstream Publications. Winner of the 1995 Slipstream Chapbook Contest. Harer's strong, clear voice makes for honest, unpretentious writing that is mature and insightful. —Slipstream Publications

Harjo, Joy. *The Woman Who Fell From the Sky.* 69p. $21.00 (0-393-03715-0); pap. $10.00 (0-393-31362-X). New York, NY: W.W. Norton & Company, Fall 1994. One of this country's foremost Native American voices, Joy Harjo combines elements of storytelling, prayer, and song in this,

her fourth volume of poetry. —W.W. Norton & Company. I fell in love with these poems, with their clarity and light, their wisdom born somewhere between sky and earth. —Sandra Cisneros. I turn and return to Harjo's poetry for her heartbreaking, complex witness and for her world-remaking language: precise, unsentimental, miraculous. —Adrienne Rich

Harper, H.E. *I Sleep Alone Too Much.* 30p. pap. $8.99 (1-887543-00-7). Norwalk, CT: Mindful Press, Spring 1995. *I Sleep Alone Too Much* is a wonderful collection of this author's glorious poetry. It is unusual . . . in its beauty, sincerity and compassion. —Richard Fuller, *Metaphysical Reviews*

Harper, Linda Lee. *A Failure of Loveliness.* 35p. pap. $7.95 (1-879205-55-6). Troy, ME: Nightshade Press, Fall 1994. Winner of the 1994 William & Kingman Page Competition.

Harper, Michael S. *Honorable Amendments.* 160p. $18.95 (0-252-02143-6); pap. $12.95 (0-252-06514-X). Champaign, IL: University of Illinois Press, Fall 1995. Harper's poetry [draws] its vitality from the incredible energy of his language and the honesty of his perceptions. [He is] one of the finest poets of our time, [as well as] one of the most human and humane. —George Cuomo, *San Francisco Examiner & Chronicle*

Harrison, Jeffrey. *Signs of Arrival.* 70p. pap. $10.00 (0-194278-71-1). Providence, RI: Copper Beech Press, Fall 1996. An engaging sense of wonder graces Harrison's second book of poems. For him, "there is always something calling you back," not merely to childhood but to an Emersonian merging of human spirit with the "purest form" of nature. —Frank Allen, *Library Journal*

Harrison, Jim. *After Ikkyu and Other Poems.* 128p. $20.00 (1-57062-299-X); pap. $11.00 (1-57062-218-3). Boston, MA: Shambhala Publications, Fall 1996. Also available as a spoken word audio cassette. This is the first collection of Harrison's poems that are directly inspired by his many years of Zen practice. —Shambhala Publications. Harrison doesn't write like anyone else, relying entirely on the toughness of his

vision and intensity of feeling to form the poem. He will shock and delight readers who think they already know what a poem should be. —*Publishers Weekly.* Harrison writes so winningly that one is simply content to be in the presence of a writer this vital, this large-spirited. —*New York Times Book Review*

Harrison, Leigh. *Tour de Farce.* 28p. pap. $5.00. Kew Gardens, NY: New Spirit Press, Fall 1996. The debut poetry collection of this marvelously funny performance poet, representing the best of her NYC poetry venue material. —New Spirit Press

Harryman, Carla. *There Never Was a Rose Without a Thorn.* 153p. pap. $10.95 (0-87286-301-8). San Francisco, CA: City Lights Books, Fall 1995. [In these poems] rampant story and rhetoric (our culture's self-descriptions) are raised up, then promptly guillotined for crimes against honesty. Through this creation and destruction, Harryman wages one of contemporary writing's most radical critiques. —Robert Gluck

Harter, Penny. *Grandmother's Milk.* 48p. pap. $7.00 (1-

880286-23-8). Canton, CT: Singular Speech Press, Spring 1995. It is a supreme delight to savor such delectable poems. Harter is a master wordsmith. —Soichi Furuta

Harter, Penny. *Turtle Blessing.* 64p. pap. $11.00 (1-888809-01-9). Albuquerque, NM: La Alameda Press, Fall 1996. In a time of destruction we need a turtle blessing, we need again to hear the voices of all those other lives around us. Penny Harter sings us back to the center of things, to the heart, where everything speaks. —Gary Lawless. These poems—beautiful, perceptive, startling—return us to our senses, and point the way home. —John Brandi

Hartman, Charles O. *Glass Enclosure.* 76p. $22.50 (0-8195-2218-X); pap. $10.95 (0-8195-1222-2). Middletown, CT: Wesleyan/University Press of New England, Spring 1995. Hartman's *Glass Enclosure* dares us to peer into a lyrical funhouse-maze at the beautiful and bizarre which enlighten and amaze. We are a great deal wiser when we emerge from this galaxy of music and tonal imagery. —Yusef Komunyakaa. Charles Hartman's poems

are never predictable, always absorbing. I have been a fan for twenty years. —James Merrill

Hartman, Charles O., and Hugh Kenner. *Sentences.* 84p. pap. $9.95 (1-55713-118-X). Los Angeles, CA: Sun & Moon Press, Fall 1995. The child of the playfully perverse marriage of a 19th century grammar school book and contemporary computer technology, *Sentences* is a surprising lyrical romp. —Sun & Moon Press

Hartman, Steven. *Coffeebreak Poems.* 28p. pap. $2.00 (0-916155-27-7). Parkdale, OR: Trout Creek Press, Fall 1994.

Hartman, Steven, ed. *Ding Dong Dada.* 8p. pap. $1.00. Brooklyn, NY: Pinched Nerves Press, Spring 1995.

Hartman, Yukihide Maeshima. *A Coloring Book.* 81p. $22.00 (1-882413-27-X); pap. $12.00 (1-882413-26-1). Brooklyn, NY: Hanging Loose Press, Spring 1996. Yuki Hartman orders his images around with the temerity of a lion tamer. He's as gifted a poet as they come. —Charles North

Hartnett, Michael. *Selected and New Poems.* 112p. pap. $9.95 (0-916390-62-4). Winston-Salem, NC: Wake Forest University Press, Fall 1994. One of the truest, most tested and beloved voices in Irish poetry in our time. —Seamus Heaney. This is a superb compilation that does Harnett justice. There are masterpieces here, allegories of art and salvation, that run effortlessly beyond the page. —James Liddy, *The Bellingham Review*

Haskins, Lola. *Hunger.* 88p. pap. $10.00 (1-885266-35-9). Brownsville, OR: Story Line Press, Fall 1996. Co-winner of the Edwin Ford Piper Poetry Award. She knows we are rooted to the earth but long for stars. . . . And she's wise enough to know that love searches us out. Dazzling. —*Northwest Arkansas Times* [These poems] richly present the experience of women, as the complexity of their material, emotional, and imaginative lives presses against the constraints of their assigned roles . . . wonderfully evocative. —*The Hudson Review*

Hass, Robert. *Sun Under Wood.* 77p. $22.00 (0-88001-468-7).

Hopewell, NJ: Ecco Press, Fall 1996. United States Poet Laureate Robert Hass writes poems that embrace all that is alive and full of joy. Yet his most indelible lyrics reside in his increasingly acute sense of mortality in a world "so full of pain it must sometimes make a kind of singing." —Ecco Press. [Hass has all the requisites of a major poet]: intelligence, depth, musicality, sweep, intimacy, humor, observation, learning, and above all, compassion. —*The Boston Globe*

Hass, Robert, and Stephen Mitchell, eds. *Into the Garden: A Wedding Anthology.* 192p. $20.00 (0-06-016919-2). New York: Harper Collins, January 1993. This anthology includes pieces about love and marriage from the prayers and meditations of various cultures— Native American, old Chinese, Buddhist, Hindu, Christian; pieces by Biblical psalmists, Sufi mystics, and Zen sages; traditional European love poetry; and work by modern poets and essayists. —Harper Collins

Hassler, David. *Sabishi: Poems From Japan.* 28p. pap. $3.00 (0-87338-513-6). Kent, OH:

Kent State University Press, Fall 1994. These are American poems, in English, but they almost seem like versions of the Japanese. The music is lovely and the form is graceful. They are a delight to read. —Gerald Stern

Hathaway, Michael. *Ratboy, Etc.* 60p. pap. 12.00 (0-9637483-4-3). St. Augustine, FL: Kings Estate Press, Fall 1994. Illustrated by Wayne Hogan. *Small Press Review* Pick of the Month, January 1995. Hathaway's is a full, risk-taking engagement with life. Though gay, he celebrates the lives and loves of us all. —Robert Peters

Hausman, Mary Diane. *A Born Again Wife's First Lesbian Kiss and Other Poems.* 73p. pap. $9.95 (0-9646371-3-8). South Hackensack, NJ: Relief Press, Fall 1995. Mary Diane Hausman captures—no, sets free—the power and complexity of womanhood. Her poems take the reader on a journey to places as mystical as Nirvana, as passionate as the silky nape of a lover's neck, and as sensible as a strong red beet pulled from the earth. She is a stumbling warrior, making her way through a life for which she offers no apologies. —Linda

Simons. By turns romantic, erotic and wise, but always honest and accessible. Hausman's work strikes the flint of true poetry. —*Pearl Magazine*

Haxton, Brooks. *The Sun at Night.* 82p. $20.00 (0-679-44179-4). New York, NY: Alfred A. Knopf, Spring 1995. Writing with a new intensity of emotion and imagination, Brooks Haxton has made *The Sun at Night* by far his most ambitious as well as his tenderest, most personal work. —Alfred A. Knopf

Hayden, Robert. Edited by Frederick Glaysher. *Collected Poems.* 205p. $23.00 (0-87140-651-9). New York, NY: Liveright Publishing, Spring 1996. Hayden was a remembrancer, a poet of faith and superb execution, and one of the best teachers by example one can find in the poetry of the twentieth century, or in any age. His words enhance and engage us as awakened selves, a nation in process, an abiding transcendent world voice. —Michael S. Harper

Hayes, Marian. *Melanated Mood.* 28p. pap. $5.00. Chicago, IL: Word/Life Press, Spring 1996.

Head, Beverly V. *Walking North.* 62p. pap. $9.00 (0-87013-402-7). East Lansing, MI: Michigan State University Press / Lotus Poetry Series, Fall 1995. Winner of the 1995 Naomi Long Madgett Poetry Award.

Heaney, Seamus. *The Spirit Level.* 82p. $18.00 (0-374-26779-0). New York, NY: Farrar, Straus and Giroux, Spring 1996. Throughout the collection, which inevitably takes account of the situation in his native Northern Ireland. Heaney's poetry keeps rising to its occasions in a language that never ceases to be vivid, confident, and completely truthful. —Farrar, Straus and Giroux

Hearne, Vicki. *The Parts of Light.* 80p. $30.00 (0-8018-4939-X); $12.95 (0-8018-4940-3). Baltimore, MD: John Hopkins University Press, Fall 1994. Hearne's poems demand participation, refuse enjoyment. She recognizes that an animal's union of body and spirit, and radical unself-consciousness, represent a quiet, humble superiority over humankind. —*Publishers Weekly.* There is a sense of real excitement in reading Hearne's best poems—

the excitement of seeing the familiar world from an entirely fresh perspective. This is honest, admirable poetry. —Dana Gioia, *Hudson Review*

Hebert, Mary, ed. *Not Black & White: Inside Words From the Bronx WritersCorps.* 248p. pap. $17.95 (0-911051-83-X). Austin, TX: Plain View Press, Spring 1996. An eloquent reflection of the success of WritersCorps projects. —Jane Alexander. Poetry from the ground up! Grass roots poets brilliantly inventing metaphors that, even when painful, spread the word-joy of being alive. Mother Earth is covered with concrete, tar and beer can roses—yet the verbs, adjectives, in fact, the grammar in these poems has dug its living roots into the breathing soul of the Bronx. —Miguel Algarin

Hecht, Anthony. *Flight Among the Tombs.* 88p. $23.00 (0-679-45095-5). New York, NY: Alfred A. Knopf, Fall 1996. Wood engravings by Leonard Baskin. Anthony Hecht's development into a great poet has progressed across half-a-century. *Flight Among the Tombs* is his poignant and ironic masterpiece. With this book, he clearly becomes a fourth in the sequence of John Crowe Ransom, W.H. Auden, and James Merrill—great verse-artists who are also humanist sages and wise sensibilities. —Harold Bloom

Hedin, Robert, ed. *The Great Machines: Poems and Songs of the American Railroad.* 251p. pap. $17.50 (0-87745-550-3). Iowa City, IA: University of Iowa Press, Spring 1996. All the railroad songs and poems I know are here, plus about three times as many more. A feast for railroad lovers. —Noel Perrin

Heffley, Carole J., ed. *Womankind.* 192p. pap. $23.95 (1-883331-14-5). Easton, PA: Anderie Poetry Press, Fall 1995. *Womankind* is an annual collection of the best— most thought-provoking and accessible—contemporary poetry written by women. —Anderie Poetry Press

Heffley, Carole J., ed. *Words of Wonder.* 96p. pap. $19.95 (1-883331-15-3). Easton, PA: Anderie Poetry Press, Spring 1996. Contemporary inspirational verse. —Anderie Poetry Press

Heine, Heinrich, ed. *Songs of Love and Grief: A Bilingual Anthology in the Verse Forms of the Original.* 227p. pap. $13.95 (0-8101-1324-4). Evanston, IL: Northwestern University Press/ TriQuarterly Books, Fall 1995.

Heinowitz, R. Cole. *Daily Chimera.* 124p. pap. $12.00 (0-884615-06-6). San Diego, CA: Incommunicado Press, Fall 1995. Heinowitz is a young poet of great power and promise. Her work is polymorphous, polyvocal, and exploratory. What emerges here is a bold, bright woman able to take on the given, to take it to somewhere new. —Rae Armantrout

Hellus, Al. *A Vision of Corrected History With Breakfast.* pap. $5.00 (0-932412-08-4). Saginaw, MI: Mayapple Press, Spring 1995. These wry and intelligent poems combine political awareness, surrealist sensibility and greatness of heart. —Mayapple Press

Hempel, Amy, and Jim Shepard, eds. *Unleashed: Poems by Writers' Dogs.* 176p. $19.00 (0-517-70140-5). New York, NY: Crown Publishers, Spring 1995. In styles as diverse as Arthur Miller's, Cynthia Heimel's, and

Stephen Dunn's, the dogs hold forth. With extraordinary humor and tenderness, this collection not only shows us what it's like to run with the poodles, it makes us consider how much of what we call the dog's life is actually our own. —Crown Publishers

Henderson, Bill, ed., with the Pushcart Prize Editors. *The Pushcart Prize XXI: 1996/97 Best of the Small Presses.* 550p. $29.50 (0-916366-96-0). Wainscott, NY: Pushcart Press, Fall 1996. Poetry editors this year were William Matthews and Patricia Strachan. Previous volumes include: *The Pushcart Prize XX: 1995/96.* 600p. $29.50 (0-916366-99-5). *The Pushcart Prize XIX: 1994/95.* 580p. pap. $15.00 (0-916366-98-7). The single best measure of the state of affairs in American literature today. —*The New York Times Book Review.* Striking in its literary breadth and accomplishment. —*Publishers Weekly* (starred review)

Henley, Patricia. *Back Roads.* 64p. pap. $11.95 (0-88748-217-1). Pittsburgh, PA: Carnegie Mellon University, Spring 1996.

Henning, Barbara. *Love Makes Thinking Dark.* 85p. pap. $7.00 (0-935992-03-0). Brooklyn, NY: United Artists Books, Fall 1995. Not since the Metaphysical Poets have there been love poems like these— assembled from a tantalizing collection of analytic lyricism, philosophical speculation and wickedly witty word play. In politics, as well as poetics, Henning cuts across categories with surprising and pleasurable results. These poems glow darkly in the mind. —Elaine Equi

Herbert, George. Edited by Ann Pasternak Slater. *The Complete English Works.* 509p. $20.00 (0-679-44359-2). New York, NY: Alfred A. Knopf/Everyman's Library, Fall 1995.

Herbert, Zbigniew. Translated by John and Bogdana Carpenter. *Mr. Cogito.* 62p. $22.95 (0-88001-330-3); pap. $12.00 (0-88001-381-8). Hopewell, NJ: Ecco Press, Spring 1995. In the late 1960s, the post-modernist poet Zbigniew Herbert developed the character of Mr. Cogito, who appears in many of his poems. Mr. Cogito is slightly foolish, slightly flummoxed and always sincere as he confronts the problems of our age. There is no other living poet whose work I enjoy as much or whom I admire more. —Stephen Dobyns, *The New York Times Book Review*

Herrera, Juan Felipe. *Love After the Riots.* 64pp. pap. $10.95 (1-880684-28-4). Willimantic, CT: Curbstone Press, Spring 1996. Explores a cinematic delirium that opens as the L.A. riots of 1992 close into the night. —Curbstone Press. Highly recommended: an intense literary work rooted in the Chicano culture. —*The Bookwatch*

Hewett, Greg. *To Collect the Flesh.* 65p. pap. $12.95 (0-89823-167-1). Minneapolis, MN: New Rivers Press, Fall 1996. Greg Hewett's deft, sure poems have an amazing range. They are subtle evocations of an intense life of loving connections with his father—these are among the best poems on father-son relations—and acute, gentle love poems for men he's known here and abroad. These poems are unrushed, modulating over many stanzas, vibrant, and always movingly personal. —Robert Peters

Heyen, William. *Crazy Horse in Stillness.* 271p. $25.00 (1-880238-28-4); pap. $15.00 (1-880238-29-2). Rochester, NY: BOA Editions, Spring 1996. *Crazy Horse In Stillness* explores the collision of North America's two civilizations through the lives and mythic personas of General George Armstrong Custer and the Sioux warrior-mystic Crazy Horse, both of whom believed themselves messianic, embodying both the visionary and the historical. —BOA Editions. William Heyen writes with the wild, radiant audacity of the visionary; yet his eye and ear are sharp, unsparing. His *Crazy Horse In Stillness* is a fantastic meditation that only Heyen might have dared—lyric, tender, appalling, heart-rending, unique. —Joyce Carol Oates

Hicok, Bob. *The Legend of Light.* 90p. $17.95 (0-299-14910-2); pap. $10.95 (0-299-14914-5). Madison, WI: University of Wisconsin Press, Fall 1995. Winner of the 1995 Felix Pollack Prize in Poetry. Whether Hicok is considering the reflection of human faces in the Vietnam War Memorial or the elements of a "Modern Prototype" factory, he prompts an icy realisation that we may have never seen the world as it truly is. From the shadowed corners into which we dare not look clearly, Hicok makes us witness and hero of *The Legend of Light.* —University of Wisconsin Press. Hicok's poems have a kind of severity, a moral accuracy, that both chills and refreshes the spirit. —Carolyn Kizer

Higginbotham, Keith. *Carrying the Air on a Stick.* 31p. pap. $3.00 (1-57141-17-1). Port Charlotte, FL: Runaway Spoon Press, Spring 1995. These poems are gnomic, usually surrealistic, and often funny. —Runaway Spoon Press

Higgins, Dick. Artwork by Paul Woodbine. *Octette.* 44p. $225.00 (0-916258-26-2). Warwick, RI: Woodbine Press, Fall 1994.

Highfill, Mitch. *Liquid Affairs.* 64p. pap. $7.00 (0-935992-02-2). Brooklyn, NY: United Artists Books, Fall 1995. I'm delighted to see Mitch Highfill's poems in a book, so I've made a poem from some of his words:
Music   Here
fInds   dIsappearing
BiTe-sized neGlected
speCific   ligHt
elepHants bullFighter
                beautIful

crystaLized
particuLar
—Jackson Mac Low

Hill, Crag. *Yes James, Yes Joyce & Other Poems.* 32p. pap. $5.00 (0-9647342-0-6). Petaluma, CA: Loose Gravel Press, Spring 1995. *Yes James, Yes Joyce & Other Poems* shows Crag Hill's exploration of the edges of language. —Loose Gravel Press. The sense of haunted lyric spaces is characteristic of Hill. —A.L. Nielsen

Hill, Judyth. *A Presence of Angels.* 66p. pap. $12.00 (0-9644196-1-0). Santa Fe, NM: Sherman Asher Publishing, Fall 1995. These poems approach angels with a uniquely wry romanticism that touches on the surreal. A wild, revisionist romp that is also reverent. —John Nizalowski, *Telluride Times Journal*

Hill, Judyth. *Men Need Space.* 72p. pap. $12.00 (0-9644196-3-7). Santa Fe, NM: Sherman Asher Publishing, Spring 1996. Focusing on men, women and relationships, this collection brings together Hill's most popular performed work on marriage, divorce, love and passion. —*Santa Fe Reporter.*

Hill's work is a marriage of word craft and life-passion capable of seducing even an atheist into new acts of faith. —*Telluride Daily Planet*. Judyth Hill is energy with skin. —*St. Helena Examiner*

Hillila, Bernhard. *Cutting Edge.* 70p. pap. $10.00 (0-9627300-2-5). Valparaiso, IN: Chimney Hill Press, Spring 1996. [Bernie Hillila's poems, in both traditional forms and free verse,] are earthy, and ethereal, erudite and enjoyable, all at the same time. —John Dickson

Hillman, Brenda. *Autumn Sojourn.* 36p. pap. $75.00 (0-963423085-7-8). Mill Valley, CA: Em Press, Fall 1994. Limited letterpress edition. End papers embedded with Japanese maple leaves sewn into handmade St. Armand covers. —Em Press

Hirsch, Edward. *Earthly Measures.* 93p. $20.00 (0-679-43070-9); pap. $13.00 (0-679-76566-2). New York, NY: Alfred A. Knopf. Fall 1994. Notable Book of the Year, 1994, *The New York Times Book Review.* With *Earthly Measures*, Edward Hirsch breaks through the ring of fire and captures his Muse.

—Harold Bloom. These are poems of immense wonder and rigor. To say that they are religious poems is only to recognize their grandeur and generosity, and their heartbreaking longing. —Patricia Hampl, *The New York Times Book Review*

Hix, H. Edgar. *The St. Cloud Café & Motor Inn.* 24p. pap. $4.00. Kew Gardens, NY: New Spirit Press, Fall 1996. Winner of the 1996 New Spirit Press Quarterly Chapbook Contest.

Hix, H.L. *Perfect Hell.* 80p. pap. $9.95 (0-87905-780-7). Layton, UT: Gibbs Smith, Publisher/Peregrine Smith Books, Fall 1996. Winner of the 1995 Peregrine Smith Poetry Competition. There is simply no one else looking at the world with the same astonishment and delight, the same intelligence combined with humor and despair, as this man in this book. —Bin Ramke. Meet the virtuoso H.L. Hix, whose sonnets skate triple axels on the thinnest of ice: the *Perfect Hell* of human entanglements. Hix's poems are written with a passion of defining passion itself. —Molly Peacock

Hoch, James. *Holler.* 43p. pap. $8.00. Lancaster, PA: Zero Degree Press, Fall 1996. Hoch's poems are like extended haiku. He doesn't waste words or observations. A very moving collection. —Hal Sirowitz

Hoffman, Daniel. *Middens of the Tribe.* 77p. $17.95 (0-8071-2000-6); pap. $9.95 (0-8071-2001-4). Baton Rouge, LA: Louisiana State University Press, Spring 1995. Each of the 43 sections of this book-length poem is an interior monologue spoken by one of several interesting characters: an aged, infirm Wall Street tycoon; his doctor, wife, lover, and children; the artist whose work adorns his walls, etc. —*Library Journal*

Hofmann, Michael, and James Lasdun, eds. *After Ovid: New Metamorphoses.* 298p. $25.00 (0-374-10197-3); pap. $14.00 (0-374-52478-5). New York, NY: Farrar, Straus and Giroux/Noonday, Fall 1994. *After Ovid*'s editor-poets challenged some of the best poets currently writing in English to play fast and loose with Ovid's text and themes. The result is racy, memorable, and vividly contemporary. —*The Economist.* [This anthology stands] in its own right as a testament to

the richness of contemporary poetic practice and to the protean powers of our poets. —Rachel Campbell Johnston, *The Times* (London)

Hogan, Wayne. *Five Quarter Moons Rose Over Egypt: Poems and Drawings.* 48p. pap. $12.00 (0-9637483-2-7). St. Augustine, FL: Kings Estate Press, Fall 1994.

Hogan, Wayne. *The Sound of Agamemnon.* 20p. pap. $5.00. Cookeville, TN: Wayne Hogan, Fall 1995.

Hogan, Wayne, and Edmund Conti. *Eb & Flo.* 46p. pap. $5.00. Cookeville, TN: Wayne Hogan, Spring 1996.

Holden, Jonathan. *The Sublime.* 72p. pap. $10.95 (1-57441-020-2). Denton, TX: University of North Texas Press, Fall 1996. Winner of the Vassar Miller Prize in Poetry. The twenty-nine poems in this, Holden's seventh poetry collection, are mainly epistemological, balancing adult desire against adult knowledge, dramatizing with painful accuracy the inevitable dissonance. —University of North Texas Press. Jonathan Holden is one of our most intelligent poets, brilliant and generous of spirit. —Ted Kooser

Holland, Bernard. *Suspicious Wounds.* 103p. $15.00 (0-9646700-0-3). New York, NY: L I A Publishing Co., Fall 1995. *Suspicious Wounds* is a volume of poems about emotion and spiritual quest. —L I A Publishing Co.

Hollander, John. *Selected Poetry.* 340p. pap. $15.00 (0-679-76198-5). New York, NY: Alfred A. Knopf, Spring 1995. This varied and far-ranging volume includes work from eleven collections, almost all out of print. —Alfred A. Knopf

Hollander, John. *Tesserae: And Other Poems.* 92p. pap. $12.00 (0-67976200-0). New York, NY: Alfred A. Knopf, Fall 1995. Perfection is a rare accomplishment, particularly in American poetry, and the perfection of much of Hollander's work makes it essential reading for anyone who genuinely cares for the craft of poetry. Hollander's poetry has shown a visionary power just often enough to secure him a place as one of the major figures of our moment.

—Vernon Shetley, *The New Republic*

Hollander, John, ed. *Committed to Memory: 100 Best Poems to Memorize.* 160p. $22.95 (1-885983-15-8). Chappaqua, NY: Turtle Point Press/Books & Co. and the Academy of American Poets, Fall 1996. Selected with an eye to bringing back the lost art of memorization, this publication includes selections from the Psalms through the works of the mid-twentieth century. —Turtle Point Press. John Hollander's anthology gives me fresh heart that the experience of knowing great poetry will not die out among us. —Harold Bloom

Hollander, John, ed. *Garden Poems.* 256p. $12.50 (0-679-44726-1). New York, NY: Alfred A. Knopf, /Everyman's Library Pocket Poets, Spring 1996.

Holley, Margaret. *The Gallery of Owls.* 12p. pap. $5.00. West Chester, PA: Riverstone Press, Spring 1995. A limited letterpress edition of a single poem, printed and hand-sewn by the author. —Riverstone Press

Hollo, Anselm. *Corvus.* 142p. pap. $11.95 (1-56689-039-X).

Minneapolis, MN: Coffee House Press, Fall 1995. Anselm Hollo has always had the world's lightest touch when it comes to balancing a poem on the invisible wire between sentimental openness and ironic judgement. —Tom Clark, *San Francisco Chronicle.* Ironic, in-jokey, post-beat hipster and quietly beautiful lyricist, avant-gardist Hollo graciously draws readers to his work . . . never trite or off-balance, these are poems that sustain. —*Publishers Weekly* (Starred review)

Holman, Bob. *Bob Holman's The Collect Call of the Wild.* 158p. $22.50 (0-8050-3674-1); pap. $12.00 (0-8050-3672-5). New York, NY: Henry Holt and Company, Fall 1995. Holman's mission is to liberate poetry from the clutches of the academics and the highbrows. He oversees poetry slams and writes everything from silly little ditties to earthy love lyrics, and, best of all, rapping, ranting, and howlingly funny commentary on our habits of compromise and consumption, futility and denial. Smart, sharp, and fast, Holman runs cliches, advertising babble, and other tired remarks through the centrifuge of his liberal,

fun-loving, outrageous, sexy, secretly very literary, and compassionate mind, then churns out poetry that makes us laugh, groan, and (that most dangerous of activities) think. —*Booklist.* Holman's advice to the "dazzed/the bored/The goofed-off" is "Poetry is exploding a different Future! Becoming part of the world again, entering your livingrooms via television [and] the Internet." Recommended for most poetry collections. —Frank Allen, *Library Journal*

Holstad, Scott C. *Distant Visions, Again and Again.* 20p. pap. $3.75. Kew Gardens, NY: The Poet Tree, Fall 1994. An introspective, autobiographical glimpse of a working class hero/loner. —The Poet Tree

Holstad, Scott C. *Places.* 48p. pap. $6.95 (1-56315-043-3). Pittsburgh, PA: Sterling House, Spring 1996.

Holt, Rochelle Lynn. *From Swamp to Mountaintop: The YoYo Series.* 54p. pap. $9.00 (0-9637483-3-5). St. Augustine, FL: Kings Estate Press, Fall 1994. Holt is courageous enough to recognize beauty wherever she finds it and is

not afraid to probe deeply into the sources of happiness, tragedy, love and boredom.
—Maryanne Raphael, *The Pilot*

Holub, Miroslav. *Intensive Care: New and Selected Poems.* 205p. $25.95 (0-932440-75-4); pap. $15.95 (0-932440-76-2). Oberlin, OH: Oberlin College Press, Fall 1996. This collection spans work from 1958 to the present, presenting many new poems for the first time. Its range, its wit, its power to both disturb and enlighten, confirm Holub's status as a major writer, a Czech poet and immunologist whose voice is sometimes and somehow the voice of our age, the second half of the twentieth century, and whose sense of our rights and wrongs is a corrective to our more foolish fads and infatuations. —Oberlin College Press

Honton, Margaret, ed. *The Poet's Job: To Go Too Far.* 237p. pap. $17.95 (0-933981-11-2). Johnstown, OH: Pudding House Publications, Fall 1994. An anthology of poems presented together with poets' narrative accounts of having written the poem on the facing page, intended to help therapists and their clients come to a better appreciation of the power and use of metaphor, and to help readers participate in the breaking of taboos, legitimizing of dreams, and the bringing of words to life. —Pudding House Publications

Hooper, Patricia. *The Flowering Trees.* 28p. pap. $6.00 Brockport, NY: State Street Press Chapbooks, Spring 1995.

Hoover, Susan. *The Magnet and the Target.* 24p. pap. $4.00. New York, NY: The New School Chapbook Series, Fall 1995. I am very attracted to the bold voices and lively subjects of these poems. —Michael Burkard

Hope, Akua Lezli. *Embouchure: Poems on Jazz and Other Musics.* 41p. Audiotape $14.00 (0-9647876-1-X); pap. $7.95 (0-9647876-0-1). Corning, NY: ArtFarm Press, Fall 1995. There is a sacred power to these words. There is a sustained lyricism, a sureness of craft and an uncanny concentration of ambitious dazzling images. —Robert Fleming. It is the musicality of Lezli's poems that most appeals to me. Each poem is a song unto itself—especially when verbally performed by the poet. Accompanying the book is an audiocassette tape featuring Lezli's vocal interpretation of her own work. —Nancy MacCaig, *The Leader*

Hope, Warren. *Reflections of a Returnee*. 16p. pap. Edgewood, NY: Robert L. Barth (R.L.B.), Spring 1995.

Hopkins, Gerard Manley. Edited by Peter Washington. *Poems and Prose*. 256p. $10.95 (0-679-44469-6). New York, NY: Alfred A. Knopf/Everyman's Library Pocket Poets, Fall 1995.

Horace. Translated by William Matthews. *Satires II, ii*. 8p. pap. $25.00. New York, NY: Dim Gray Bar Press, Fall 1996. Limited letterpress edition, papyrus covers.

Horiuchi, Toshimi. *Oasis in the Heart: Haiku With Exposition*. 152p. pap. $10.95 (0-8348-0330-5). New York, NY: Weatherhill, Spring 1995. This collection brings together the finest haiku of Toshimi Horiuchi. In the introduction, he uses examples from his own work to show how composers of haiku in English can follow the Japanese form while maintaining originality and spontaneity. —Weatherhill

Horvath, Brooke. *Consolation at Ground Zero*. 97p. $24.00 (0-910055-21-1); pap. $14.00 (0-910055-22-X) Cheney, WA: Eastern Washington University Press, Fall 1995. This is a book of portraits, memories posed in the acid preservative of photographs. In their steady, quiet accumulation of details, these poems work their careful way down to a conclusion that can only be called hard-won and wise: "There is nothing so small it does not matter,/nor so marred it cannot charm./There is nothing so common it cannot save you./" —Elton Glaser

Host, R.M. *Reality Sandwiches*. 28p. pap. $4.00 (0-916155-26-9). Parkdale, OR: Trout Creek Press, Spring 1995.

Howard, Julie Kate. *Elegy in Pieces*. 24p. pap. $7.95 (1-879205-58-0). Troy, ME: Nightshade Press, Spring 1995. Winner of the 1994 William & Kingman Page Competition.

Howard, Richard. *Like Most Revelations*. 112p. $20.00 (0-679-

43163-2). New York, NY: Pantheon Books, Fall 1994. This brilliant collection of poems by one of America's most distinguished men of letters shows Richard Howard in a new phase: stronger, more resonant, more distinctive than ever. Harold Bloom has called Richard Howard "the Robert Browning of our century," and certainly the monologues here have a power similar to Browning's. But they are also as immediate as today's newspaper. —Pantheon Books

Howard, Richard, and David Lehman, eds. *The Best American Poetry 1995*. 302p. $27.50 (0-684-80150-7); pap. $13.00 (0-684-80151-5). New York, NY: Scribner/Simon & Schuster, Fall 1995.

Howe, Irene King. *The Song She Guards*. 96p. pap. $8.00 (1-879418-18-5). Brunswick, ME: Biddle Publishing Company, Fall 1995. Irene Howe's poetry approaches life honestly, and I can honestly say I enjoyed every poem in this collection. It is a rich collection. Here one does not have to dig through heaps of gray rock poems to find the occasional gold

nugget—here is a gold rush. —Rod Farmer

Howe, Susan. *Frame Structures: Early Poems 1974–1979*. 160p. pap. $12.95 (0-8112-1322-6). New York, NY: New Directions, Spring 1996. Her work is a voyage of reconnaissance in language, a sounding out of ancient hiding places, and it is a voyage full of risk. "Words are the only clues we have," she has said. "What if they fail us?" —Geoffery O'Brien, *Poetry Pilot*

Howes, Barbara. *Collected Poems 1945–1990*. 80p. $20.00 (1-55728-335-4); pap. $12.00 (1-55728-336-2). Fayetteville, AR: University of Arkansas Press, Spring 1995. What a fine thing it is to have the best of Barbara Howes' dazzling poems and translations in one volume! For decades discriminating readers have valued her impeccable prosody and quirky originality, and now a new generation of readers can discover for themselves the richly personal achievement of one of America's important lyric poets. *Collected Poems 1945–1990* is cause for celebration. —Robert Phillips

Hu, Jane Hwa. *To Love.* 96p. pap. $9.95 (1-880016-18-4). Painter, VA: Road Publishers, Spring 1995.

Hudgins, Andrew. *The Glass Hammer: A Southern Childhood.* 97p. $18.95 (0-395-70011-6); pap. $9.95 (0-395-70010-8). New York, NY: Houghton Mifflin, Fall 1994. Hudgins recounts a childhood spent in a Southern military family during the 1960s, a time when staunch piety and angry disbelief converged, and racism wore a familiar face. —Houghton Mifflin. Hudgins] takes the tradition of the Southern narrative poem and gives it a new edge, paring down picturesque elements and allowing only the vital details. This combination of craft and grit yields a poetry of aggressive charm. —*Publishers Weekly*

Hughes, Langston. Edited by Arnold Rampersad and David Roessel. *The Collected Poems of Langston Hughes.* 717p. pap. $18.00 (0-679-76408-9). Vintage Books, Fall 1995. Here, for the first time, are all the poems that Langston Hughes published during his lifetime, arranged in the general order in which he wrote them and annotated. —Vintage Books [Hughes's] poetry has a pulse, a beauty and familiar kindness. His best work sticks with you—forever. —*Cleveland Plain Dealer.* The ultimate book for both dabbler and serious scholar. [Hughes] is sumptuous and sharp, playful and sparse, grounded in an earthy music. This book is a glorious revelation. —*Boston Globe*

Hull, Lynda. *The Only World.* 80p. $22.00 (0-06-055363-4); pap. $12.00 (0-06-095112-5). New York, NY: HarperCollins/Harper Perennial, Fall 1995. *The Only World* is the third and most ambitious collection by Lynda Hull. Completed shortly before her death in 1994, *The Only World* displays the dazzling lyric richness, the narrative sweep, and the unflinching examination of harrowing subject matter that were the hallmarks of her work. —HarperCollins. Of all the poets of my generation, Lynda Hull remains the most heartbreaking, merciful, and consoling. Because Hull has troubled the waters, her poetry makes us truer to ourselves and those around us. —Yusef Komunyakaa

Humes, Harry. *The Bottomland.* 62p. $18.00 (1-55728-377-X); pap. $10.00 (1-55728-380-X). Fayetteville, AR: University of Arkansas, Fall 1995. In language that is like a cool splash of springwater, Humes recreates a life lived close to, and sometimes in bitter contention with, nature. The Appalachia of these poems is pure, unsentimentalized, beautiful, demanding, and giving. And so are the poems. —Kelly Cherry

Hummer, T. R. *Walt Whitman in Hell.* 80p. $18.95 (0-8071-2060-X); pap. $10.95 (0-8071-2061-8). Baton Rouge, LA: Louisiana State University Press, Spring 1996. T. R. Hummer is one of the finest poets now writing anywhere, and this is his best book so far. —Fred Chapell. Hummer chronicles an America in which Whitman's promises and hopes (for equality, democracy, individual achievement, appreciated diversity, spirituality made manifest in human flesh) are in eclipse. Hummer sees a nation which has lost its soul, and he yearns for revival and for a sign of compassion and redemption. —*Southern Seen*

Humphrey, James. *Bud.* 66p. pap. $14.00 (0-936641-19-3).

Yonkers, NY: Poets Alive! Press, reissued Spring 1966. The power of James Humphrey's writing always bears exceptional witness. He tells it as best as it can be. —Robert Creeley.

Hunt, Erica, and artist Alison Saar. *Arcade.* 56p. pap. $15.00 (0-932716-39-3). Berkeley, CA: Kelsey St. Press, Spring 1996. *Arcade* brings together Hunt's imaginative explorations of the personal and political realms and artist Alison Saar's Santeria, Voodoo and Catholic inspired assemblages of urban artifacts. The result is a unique dialogue between two African-American women. —Kelsey, St. Press. Custom has it that a woman gets up first to solve the dilemma of the burning moment. Erica Hunt invents a language to do just that. —Ann Lauterbach

Hunt, Laird. *Snow Country: Fragments for Radio.* 60p. (1-887289-07-0). Boulder, CO: Rodent Press, Fall 1995.

Hunt, Mildred, ed. *Pershing Poetry Anthology.* 28p. pap. $2.50. Detroit, MI: Broadside Press, Spring 1995.

Hunter, Al; Adrian Louis, Denise Sweet, and Jim Northrup.

Days of Obsidian Days of Grace: Selected Poetry and Prose by Four Native American Writers. 143p. pap. $13.95 (0-9641986-0-6). Duluth, MN: Poetry Harbor, Fall 1994. There is no surer proof of the flourishing of Native American writing than the appearance of this anthology, featuring the work of four indisputably gifted writers. Highly recommended. —*Library Journal.* This does what a good anthology should; whets the appetite for more. —Pat Monagham, *Booklist*

Hureaux, Michael (Mikey Iniko). *fool moon rising.* 32p. pap. $6.00 (1-878888-24-2). Winston, OR: nine muses books, Fall 1996. A distillation of the Seattle work of this powerful performance poet, now in New York. —nine muses books

Hurlow, Marcia L. *Dangers of Travel.* 24p. pap. $5.00. West Chester, PA: Riverstone Press, Fall 1994. Winner of the 1994 Riverstone Poetry Chapbook Contest. This book is marked by a talented simplicity of statement, admirable devotion to tactile detail, and a gently unhinged reality. These are beautifully crafted pieces that ultimately evince a wise wry humor, a cautious spiritual optimism, even a long-rooted, strong-willed love. —Lance Olsen, *The Chiron Review*

Huth, G. *Wreadings.* 64p. pap. $3.00 (1-57141-007-4). Port Charlotte, FL: Runaway Spoon Press, Spring 1995. A collection of infra-verbal pwoermds such as "throught." —Runaway Spoon Press

Hyett, Barbara Helfgott. *The Tracks We Leave: Poems on Endangered Wildlife of North America.* 120p. $24.95 (0-252-02235-1); pap. $13.95 (0-252-06575-1). Champaign, IL: University of Illinois Press, Fall 1996. Each of these poems focuses on a North American animal judged "endangered" by the U.S. Department of Wildlife and Fisheries. Each is accompanied by an illustration by Robert W. Treanor of the animal in the wild. —University of Illinois Press. Hyett marries fact to lyric . . . Hers is an original conception, one I confess I view with envy.—Maxine Kumin. Wonderful poetry, haunting and evocative—a reminder to us all that wilderness in its aesthetic splendor is vanishing. —Thomas Eisner

I

Ignatow, David. *I Have a Name.* 75p. $25.00 (0-8195-2232-5); pap. $11.95 (0-8195-2240-6). Middletown, CT: Wesleyan/ University Press of New England, Fall 1996.

Inman, P. *Criss Cross.* 69p. pap. $7.95 (0-937804-57-6). New York, NY: Roof Books, Fall 1994. A tour of the process of navigating the realms of experimentation, witness, and critique, an invitation to participatory poetic locution. —Diane Ward. By fully semanticizing the so-called non-semantic features of language, Inman creates a dialectic of the recuperable & the unreclaimable, where what cannot be claimed is nonetheless *most* manifest. —Charles Bernstein

Irwin, Mark. *Quick, Now, Always.* 88p. $20.00 (1-880238-30-6); pap. $12.50 (1-880238-31-4). Rochester, NY: BOA Editions, Spring 1996. Mark Irwin imaginatively compresses language, startles and satisfies the reader with fluid lineation and inventive numerical breaks and locates an inquiring, intellectually informed voice infused with the sleek power of wise, unpretentious poetry. —Joel Lipman, *Small Press*

Iskrenko, Nina. Translated by John High, Patrick Henry, and Katya Olmstad. *The Right to Err.* 108p. $15.00 (0-89410-806-9); pap. $14.00 (0-89410-807-7). Pueblo, CO: Passeggiata Press, Fall 1995. Bilingual edition.

Ivy, Evie. *King of Fear.* 21p. pap. $5.00. Brooklyn, NY: Meta 4, Spring 1996.

J

Jacobsen, Josephine. *In the Crevice of Time: New and Collected Poems.* 224p. $29.95 (0-8018-5116-5). Baltimore, MD: Johns Hopkins University Press, Spring 1995. National Book Award Finalist, 1995. Jacobsen's poetry demonstrates not only scrupulous verbal craft but a kind of auditory seriousness, a preference for depth and precision over mere charm or beauty. —*New York Times.*

Healthful and pure, protein and green salad for the mind. —*Parnassus: Poetry in Review*

James, Anthony. *Language of the Heart.* 112p. $35.00 (1-885203-05-5). Boston, MA: Journey Editions, Fall 1994. A deeply compassionate and beautiful book, *Language of the Heart* shows us the spirit that informs an artist's work. For James, art is a primal voice that chronically stutters when it means to speak, crawls when it aches to fly, and finally soars into eloquence and resurrects itself into beauty. —Journey Editions

Janeczko, Paul B., ed. *Wherever Home Begins: 100 Contemporary Poems.* 128p. pap. $15.95 (0-531-09481-2). New York, NY: Orchard Books, Fall 1995. Once again, Janeczko brings us powerful poems of small-town America: casual, immediate, precise images. —*Booklist.* Janeczko's trained eye delivers nothing less than unqualified realism. Both the painful and joyous memories of home offer this volume its power. —*School Library Journal.* First-rate, mature poetry for serious readers. —*Kirkus*

Jarman, Mark, and David Mason, eds. *Rebel Angels: 25 Poets of the New Formalism.* 262p. $25.00 (1-885266-33-2); pap. $12.00 (1-885266-30-8). Brownsville, OR: Story Line Press, Fall 1996. *Rebel Angels* is the first anthology to present the most exciting and unexpected new movement in American poetry—the revival of rhyme, meter, and narrative among young poets. —Story Line Press. [*Rebel Angels*] is a collection of poems that clearly gain focus and accessibility from the rigor of the formulas and rules they unabashedly embrace. These are good poems that render a wide variety of contemporary American experiences. —*Library Journal*

Jarnot, Lisa. *Some Other Kind of Mission.* 112p. pap. $11.00 (1-886224-12-9). Providence, RI: Burning Deck, Spring 1996. A mock-epic of the everyday composed of poems, prose, and visual pieces. —Burning Deck. Amazing. . . . The diction riffs between biblical and Dylanesque registers, simultaneously formal and colloquial. —Lee Ann Brown, *Poetry Project Newletter*

Jarvis, David. *The Born Again Tourist*. 36p. pap. $4.95 (1-881692-10-8). St. Albans, WV: Trillium Press, Fall 1995. David Jarvis (1954-1994) thought of the poet as a "tourist"—one who sees the ordinary world from a new and different viewpoint. These poems, brought together from scraps of paper in shoeboxes, are his legacy to the world he both loved and feared. —Trillium Press

Jason, Philip K. *The Separation*. 88p. pap. $12.00 (1-885215-18-5). Woodbridge, CT: Viet Nam Generation/Burning Cities Press, Fall 1995. I don't know of another poet writing so well of displacement in the professional/corporate world. —Robert Peters, *Abraxas*. Jason's strength is that he does not consider that the ordinary must remain ordinary, but imagines rather that the ordinary very likely conceals the beauty and truth of our lives. —Dave Smith, *The New England Review*

Jauss, David. *Improvising Rivers*. 80p. $15.00 (1-880834-41-3); pap. $10.00 (1-880834-40-5). Cleveland, OH: Cleveland State University Poetry Center, Fall 1995. Jauss writes poems as intense as prayers. His focus on memento mori, however, leads him not to some afterlife but more deeply into this one, including imaginative engagement with the lives of others—Flaubert, Kafka, jazz musicians, a Vietnam vet. —Philip Dacey. Jauss sees the exercise of style as a form of pilgrimage to the human heart. —David Wojahn

Jenkins, Louis. *Nice Fish: New and Selected Prose Poems*. 72p. pap. $10.00 (0-930100-61-1). Duluth, MN: Holy Cow! Press, Fall 1995. Louis Jenkins captures—nails down really!—whole moments in time and space, completely decorated with all the essential textural things needed to make them vibrate and shudder with life. —Clarence Major

Jenks, Dorothy. *Patterns of the Quilted Plains*. 50p. pap. $12.00 (0-9637483-8-6). St. Augustine, FL: Kings Estate Press, Fall 1995. A first collection of poems about the High Plains of Kansas, with illustrations by Wayne Hogan. —Kings Estate Press

Jiro, Nakamo. *Outcry From the Inferno*. pap. $10.00 (0-910043-

33-7). Honolulu, HA: Bamboo Ridge Press, Fall 1995.

Johnson, Dan. *Come Looking.* 64p. pap. $10.00 (0-931846-46-3). Washington, DC: Washington Writers' Publishing House, Fall 1995. Dan Johnson's is a poetry of heightened listening— to signals that are barely audible, to gestures that sometimes mimic silence. —Merrill Leffler. More hauntingly than any other poems I know, Dan Johnson's combine quietness and urgency. This is a splendid collection, with strength for a lifetime's rereading. —Henry Taylor

Johnson, Dave. *Marble Shoot.* 80p. $40.00 (0-964-9765-0-1); pap. $10.00 (0-964-9765-0-X). Winston-Salem, NC: The Hummingbird Press, Fall 1995. Dave Johnson writes with a kind of alarmed candor, as if accuracy and truth-telling were not only an ethical imperative, but also an esthetic pleasure and the truth of a job well done. This is a very fine first book. —William Matthews

Johnson, Denis. *The Throne of the Third Heaven of the Nations Mil-*

lennium General Assembly. 225p. $22.00 (0-06-017180-4). New York, NY: HarperCollins Publishers, Fall 1995. The author has chosen from his first four books of poetry work that represents the last 20 years of his writing. —HarperCollins. Denis Johnson responds with narrative vigor and sustained comic-apocalyptic vision to the depravity of the world around and within him. [His poetry] is full of the audacious rhetoric of despair, the grim humor of life at the edge. —Carolyne Wright, *Missouri Review*

Johnson, Lemuel. *Carnival of the Old Coast: Sierra Leone Trilogy, Vol. 3.* 124p. $24.95 (0-86543-480-8); pap. $9.95 (0-86543-481-6). Trenton, NJ: Africa World Press, Spring 1996. This third volume of Johnson's trilogy recovers the years from the 1500's to the 1950's, tracing the creolization of Sierra Leone. —Africa World Press

Johnson, Lemuel. *Hand on the Navel: Sierra Leone Trilogy, Vol. 2.* 100p. $24.95 (0-86543-484-0); pap. $9.95 (0-86543-485-9). Trenton, NJ: Africa World Press, Spring 1996. The second volume of Johnson's trilogy focuses in on the half-forgotten story of The Royal West Africa Frontier Force, which fought with the Allies in both World Wars. —Africa World Press

Johnson, Lemuel. *Highlife for Caliban: Sierra Leone Trilogy, Vol. 1.* 136p. $24.95 (0-86543-482-6); pap. $9.95 (0-86543-483-2). Trenton, NJ: Africa World Press, Spring 1996. The first volume of Johnson's trilogy sets us up to enter the worlds of Caliban, Tarzan, St. Augustine and Ophelia. —Africa World Press

Johnson, Margery A. *Sea Moods.* 84p. pap. $10.00 (1-56474-107-9). Santa Barbara, CA: Fithian Press, Fall 1994. This is a book of poems and photographs depicting the sea in all its moods, from Hawaiian sunsets to storm-tossed whitecaps. —Fithian Press. I like this work for [its] rhythmic sense and conscious movement. —Shigeo Urabe

Johnson, Marilyn. *A Necessary Fire.* 64p. $14.95 (0-9627501-1-5); pap. $9.95 (1-888219-01-7). Long Beach, CA: Pearl Editions, Spring 1996. It has been noted by the great anthropologist Ed Abbey that women

are a completely separate species from men. And quite frankly we men are somewhat surprised, and thankful, that they allow us to mate with them. These poems make me feel that way. —Mark Weber. Johnson is a terrific lyricist, elegiac in tone, smooth in her cadences, celebrating relationships with an honest, and often harrowing, sensitivity. —Robert Peters, *Small Press Review*

Johnson, Nancy. *Zoo and Cathedral.* 80p. pap. $14.00 (1-877727-58-X). Fredonia, NY: White Pine Press, Spring 1996. Nancy Johnson is extraordinary at depicting the despair and daily brutality of our lives. In her love poems, often written along the razor's edge, we find the abandon of great passion and faith. It is an astonishing combination. —David St. John. Neither real nor surreal, the style hovers between those two horizons, always self-aware, always informed. —Lynn Emanuel

Johnston, Agnes Nasmith. *Bridges to Beginnings.* 96p. pap. $10.95 (1-880016-22-2). Painter, VA: Road Publishers, Spring 1996. *Bridges to Begin-*

nings is perceptive and compassionate, especially the poems set in China, which explore the oneness of nature and the search for serenity and clarity in a flawed universe. —Betty Parry. This is a poetry of pleasure and peace. —Grace Cavalieri

Jones, Alan. *Long After Hannibal Had Passed with Elephants: Poems and Epigrams.* 64p. pap. $10.00 (0-9646466-0-9). New York, NY: Edgewise Press, Fall 1995. These are caustic love lyrics in the tradition of Catullus. —Edgewise Press

Jones, Patricia Spears. *The Weather That Kills.* 75p. pap. $11.95 (1-56689-029-2). Minneapolis, MN: Coffee House Press, Spring 1995. The sights and smells, rhythms and caresses of many lives waft up from Memphis and Manhattan. —Thulani Davis. She writes with a marvelous combination of street-smart eloquence and earthy passion. —Jessica Hagedorn. Music and brains are allowed to co-exist with instinct . . . it is a tough, honest, even humorous universe. —Cornelius Eady

Jones, Robert. *The Cave.* 48p. pap. $6.95 (1-881692-11-6).

St. Albans, WV: Trillium Press, Fall 1995. Jones writes about people and places on the landscape of the great Allegheny lift, from the valleys to the mountains. —Trillium Press

Jones, Rodney. *Things That Happen Once: New Poems.* 96p. $19.95 (0-395-77143-9). Boston, MA: Houghton Mifflin Company, Spring 1996. Nobody can match him for the range of unflinching sensibility, or the miraculous capacity to wrench blessing out of dailiness and degradation and active harm. —Linda Gregerson. Jones's poems are blood-stirring, white-hot things—pugnacious and brooding, dramatic and discursive, copious and rangy and possessed of a Whitmanesque appetite. —David Barber, *Washington Post Book World.* Writing like this is, well, like magic. [Jones] is one of the best, most generous, and most brilliantly readable currently making poems in America. —David Baker, *Poetry*

Jones, Sonya. *Small Claims, Large Encounters.* 64p. $17.95 (0-9646230-0-5). New York, NY: Brito & Lair, Spring 1995. By turns irreverent and heartfelt, these poems explore the very personal and mysterious bonds of the Guru-disciple relationship. Jones's work combines the cool joy of Rumi with the simplicity of Thomas Merton and the wry humor of John Berryman. —Brito & Lair

Judd, Kirk. *Tao-Billy.* 52p. pap. $10.00 (1-881-692-12-4). St. Albans, WV: Trillium Press, Fall 1996. His words are music and emotion, his poetry has a mountain resonance, a rumbling emotion, like the mountains with machinery inside, grinding up their carbon for our fires, for our lights, and to take the scare out of our nights. Kirk Judd. A damn good word man. A damn good poet. —Bill Drennen

Jurek, Thom. *Memory Bags.* 32p. pap. $6.00 (1-56439-045-4). Roseville, MI: Ridgeway Press, Fall 1995. This ten part poem, complete with napkin drawings by French artist Jacques Karamanoukian, renders homage to punk rocker Patti Smith and the impact of her art on the poet himself. —Ridgeway Press

Justice, Donald. *New and Selected Poems.* 180p. $25.00 (0-679-44173-5). New York, NY: Alfred A. Knopf, Fall 1995. National Book Award Finalist. Donald Justice believes that poems should be beautiful and clear. His always are. He is one of this century's superb poets, one of the writers of genius that our country has produced. —Mark Strand

K

Kamo-no-Chomei. Translated by Yasuhiko Moriguchi and David Jenkins. *Hojoki: Visions of a Torn World.* 96p. pap. $9.95 (1-880656-22-1). Berkeley, CA: Stone Bridge Press, Spring 1996. Poet, reporter, social philosopher, monk, Kamo-no-Chomei is one of the great noble and solitary figures in all of Japanese literature, his incomparable *Hojoki* as relevant today as it was eight hundred years ago. Thanks to Yasuhiko Moriguchi and David Jenkins for this luminous translation and for their brilliant introduction to this ancient masterpiece. —Sam Hamill

Kane, Paul, ed. *Poetry of the American Renaissance: A Diverse Anthology From the Romantic Pe-*

riod. 383p. pap. $14.95 (0-8076-1398-3). New York, NY: George Braziller, Fall 1995. Among anthologies, there is nothing comparable to this. It gathers a remarkable selection of our best poetry in the most crucial period of our national literature. —Harold Bloom

Karrer, Pearl. *Weathering.* 40p. pap. $8.00 (0-9624178-0-7). Tarrytown, NY: Slapering Hol Press, 1993.

Kasischke, Laura. *Housekeeping in a Dream.* 80p. $20.95 (0-88748-194-9); pap. $11.95 (0-88748-195-7). Pittsburgh, PA: Carnegie-Mellon University Press, Spring 1995. These are strong, vivid poems that deal with the basic confusion between violence and sexuality that is central to our culture. They are witty, sometimes laying about with a broad sword and sometimes piercing with a needle. The imagery is forceful and the tone intense and the subject an extraordinary vision of the lives of ordinary women. —Marge Piercy

Kaufman, Andrew. *Cinnamon Bay Sonnets.* 23p. pap. $25.00. New York, NY: Center for Book Arts, Fall 1996. Winner of the Center for Book Arts Poetry Chapbook Competition. We were impressed by [Kaufman's] use of a language of extreme compression and a highly cadenced vernacular that moves fluidly between moments of personal crisis and spiritual transcendence. —Sharon Dolin and William Matthews

Kaufman, Bob. Edited by Gerald Nicosia. *Cranial Guitar.* 165p. pap. $12.95 (1-56689-038-1). Minneapolis, MN: Coffee House Press, Spring 1996. Recognized early on as a major figure in the Beat Generation of writers and poets, Kaufman is also known as one of America's true surrealist poets, a premier jazz poet, and a major poet of the black consciousness movement. —David Henderson. Straight from some astral plane comes the ghost of this great Beat poet. This is not so much a collection as it is a steam-pipe explosion. —*Publishers Weekly*

Kaufman, Shirley. *Roots in the Air: New and Selected Poems.* 204p. pap. $14.00 (1-55659-111-X). Port Townsend, WA: Copper Canyon Press, Fall 1996. The powerful exactitude of these lucid, lyrical poems makes this a book to cherish. —Maxine Kumin. Progressive, passionate and unfailingly feminist, Kaufman is a breathtakingly fine poet. —*The Nation*

Kavanaugh, James. *A Lifetime Isn't Long Enough To Love You*. 96p. pap. $9.95 (1-878995-24-3). York, PA: Steven J. Nash Publishing, Fall 1995. James Kavanaugh explores romantic love, love within the family, love of friendship, nature, and even pets. —Steven J. Nash Publishing. James Kavanaugh is the poet of the American people . . . He should be read by all of America. He will be! —*Dear Abby*. A rare mind and a powerful heart! This man has something to say to everyone. —Alan Watts

Keegan, Linda. *Heeding the Wind*. 36p. pap. $5.50 (1-877801-29-1). Galloway, NJ: Still Waters Press, Spring 1995.

Keenan, Deborah. *Happiness*. 101p. pap. $11.95 (1-56689-033-0). Minneapolis, MN: Coffee House Press, Spring 1995. Keenan re-visions the miracle of ordinary life until the past becomes a dialogue she holds with mother language and us. —Carol Conroy. Reading Keenan is like visiting a friend's kitchen: there are laughter, fighting, coffee guzzling, child interruptions, [and the] telephone rings. —*St. Paul Pioneer Press*

Keenan, Terence. *Practicing Eternity*. 56p. pap. $6.95 (0-7880-11000-4). Lima, OH: Basfal Books, Fall 1996.

Keener, LuAnn. *Color Documentary*. 82p. $21.95 (0-934971-40-4); pap. $11.95 (0-934971-39-0). Corvallis, OR: Calyx Books, Fall 1994. Keener explores not only the blood tie among humans, but between the human and animal worlds. This is a moving first collection. —Maxine Kumin. These poems are spiritual, precise, sensual in their pure pleasure. —Michael Waters.

Kein, Sybil. *An American South*. 85p. pap. $10.00 (0-87013-412-4). East Lansing, MI: Michigan State University Press/ Lotus Poetry Series, Spring 1996. *An American South* blends poetic excellence with the unique history of Louisiana, its racial code, legends, and languages. —Michigan State University Press

Keineg, Paol. Translated by Keith Waldrop. *Boudica.* 64p. pap. $6.00 (0-930901-94-0). Providence, RI: Burning Deck, Fall 1994. Poems that raise a monument to the Breton Queen Boudica, defeator of the Roman legions, and to the Bretons, who have resisted forced assimilation through the centuries. —Burning Deck

Keith, Bill. *Pictographs.* 48p. pap. $9.00 (1-880516-20-9). Barrytown, NY: Left Hand Books, Spring 1996. *Pictographs* mixes different types of picture-writing with fragments of prose-writings in a formal arrangement linked to West African visual traditions. Keith's constructions employ designs intended to be scanned metrically, a visual counterpart to the off-beat phrasing of melodic accents in African and Afro-American music. —Left Hand Books

Kelly, Brigit Pegeen. *Song.* 90p. $20.00 (1-880238-12-8); pap. $12.50 (1-880238-13-6). Rochester, NY: BOA Editions, Spring 1995. 1994 Lamont Poetry Selection of the Academy of American Poets. Lyrical, surreal, Brigit Pegeen Kelly writes a poetry that flies toward the fantastic and the magical. —BOA Editions

Kelly, Jack. *The Next Room.* 12p. $25.00 (0-87699-005-7). New York, NY: Crambruck Press, Fall 1995. Eleven 16-line sonnets chronicling the life of a person dying of AIDS, using the rooms of life as focal points to encapsulate memories. —Crambruck Press

Kelly, Robert. *Red Actions: Selected Poems 1960-1993.* 398p. $25.00 (0-87685-978-3); pap. $17.50 (0-87685-977-5); sig. $35.00 (0-87685-979-1). Santa Rosa, CA: Black Sparrow Press, Fall 1995. Robert Kelly's poetry reflects a postmodernism the terms of which are essentially projective. Searching, tensile, diffusive, open, Kelly's poems refuse definition, discovering revelation in associational fields and constellations of image and voice. —Black Sparrow Press

Kemmett, William. *The Bradford Poems.* 24p. pap. $5.00. Bedford, NH: Igneus Press, Spring 1996.

Kennedy, Richard S. *Dreams in the Mirror.* New York, NY: W. W. Norton & Company, Fall 1994.

Kennedy, X.J. *Jimmy Harlow.* 12p. pap. $6.00. Anchorage, AK: Salmon Run Press, Spring 1995. X.J. Kennedy, who has been writing poetry for longer than I have been alive, is without question one of our best and most intelligent poets. In this well-crafted poem, Kennedy has examined his own history, and has found a part of himself that he had forgotten. This is a sensitive and serious poem— one that asks forgiveness. —John E. Smelcer

Kennelly, Louise. *Tracking God in Italy.* 40p. pap. $6.00 (1-880286-21-1). Canton, CT: Singular Speech Press, Fall 1995. Kennelly's poetry has a way of getting under people's skins. It surprises and leads to a sense of inner complexities, and insights. —John Hersey

Kenney, Richard. *The Invention of the Zero.* 160p. pap. $12.00 (0-67974997-7). New York, NY: Alfred A. Knopf, Fall 1995. Richard Kenney's work demonstrates that the way forward may depend as much on a profound look into the past as on one's grasp of the present. *The Invention of the Zero* is an astonishing book, one that with each reading yields more pleasure. —Christopher Merrill, *The Los Angeles Times Book Review*

Kenny, Maurice. *On Second Thought.* 288p. $24.95 (0-8061-2766-X). Norman, OK: University of Oklahoma Press, Fall 1995. As one of the earliest and strongest voices in contemporary American Indian literature, Maurice Kenny has proved himself to be very much a "high steel" Iroquois—a Mohawk famed for scaling the heights of New York City and forging an identity know nationwide. This latest collection includes old and new poetry, fiction, criticism, and political commentary, plus an unusual literary memoir of New York in the 1950s, 1960s and 1970s. —University of Oklahoma Press. There goes Maurice again, tap-dancing and grinning along Turtle's Back. Maurice Kenny's poetry has been an inspiration to a generation of indigenous American writers. I value greatly the times when I can rock on my porch with Maurice's poetry, daring to read it aloud to the squirrels and hummingbirds. —Wendy Rose

Kent, Joseph. *Streams.* 84p. pap. $12.95 (0-9623751-3-6). San Francisco, CA: Sunlight Publishers, Spring 1996. The poems swirl in and out of things, always bearing a spiritual presence. . . . [Kent's] poems are hinges around which we swing to close and open the doors of perception. . . . We come to life in these poems of greater being. —*The Book Reader*

Kenvin, Natalie. *Bruise Theory.* 70p. $20.00 (1-880238-20-9); pap. $12.50 (1-880238-21-7). Rochester, NY: BOA Editions, Spring 1995. The bruises examined in this book are actual, and they are also the marks of extremity, present as the evidence of what occurred. These poems are not *about* abuse, confinement, isolation, urban anonymity or sex. They offer us, in evidentiary language, poetic lucidity and strength, a glimpse of the mind at labor in the unknown. —Carolyn Forché

Kenyon, Jane. *Otherwise: New and Selected Poems.* 232p. $23.95 (1-55597-240-3). St. Paul, MN: Graywolf Press, Spring 1996. Publication of this book marks the first anniversary of Kenyon's death from leukemia in April 1995. She completed her selection of these poems in the days just before her death. —Graywolf Press. Kenyon's poetry is honest and earnest, rich in imagery yet free of clutter. This collection is generous, cohesive and moving. —*Publishers Weekly,* starred review

Keriotis, Keri. *A Mélange of Treasures from the Lavender Chameleon.* 176p. pap. $12.95 (0-9644816-0-X). Brooklyn, NY: Heos Press, Fall 1995. *A Mélange of Treasures* is just that. —Rita Mae Brown. [It is] an interesting piece of work. Its concepts vary (which is a treat) from piece to piece—funny in parts, political and sociological in others. —Flora Sussely, *The Lesbian News*

Kerouac, Jack. *Book of Blues.* 274p. pap. $12.95 (0-14-058700-4). New York, NY: Penguin Books, Fall 1995. Eight extended poems employing instrumental blues forms. —Penguin Books. Kerouac's work represents the most extensive experiments in language and literary form undertaken by any American writer of his generation. —*New York Times Book Review*. To read previously unpublished works of Jack Kerouac is to re-experience exhilaration of the pioneer spirit. —Frank Allen, *Poet Lore*

Khosla, Maya. *Heart of the Tearing.* 28p. pap. $4.00 (0-87376-082-4). New York, NY: Red Dust, Fall 1996. Maya Khosla writes of people and animals and their interconnectedness, exploring the fractures that occur when natural processes are disrupted. —Red Dust

Kidd, Peter. *Bear Stew.* 32p. pap. $5.00. Bedford, NH: Igneus Press, Spring 1996.

Kijima, Hajime. *Responses Magnetic.* 120p. $29.90 (0-942668-48-0); pap. $14.95 (0-942668-48-0). Honolulu, HI: University of Hawai'i Press, Fall 1996. Kijima Hajime is one of the most original of contemporary Japanese poets. Many of his works have been written for music by European as well as Japanese composers. This book is illustrated with his collages and ink drawings. —University of Hawai'i Press

Kiley, Eve. *Reflections.* 36p. pap. $5.00 (1-57502-296-6). Brooklyn, NY: Eve Kiley, Fall 1996.

King, June, and Larry Smith, eds. *Coffeehouse Poetry Anthology.* 240p. pap. $10.95 (0-933087-40-3). Huron, OH: Bottom Dog Press, Spring 1996. A collection of 62 poets from around the US with poems, statements, profiles and photos. This is the coffee house revolution of the '90s! —Bottom Dog Press

King, Martin. *A Distant Face.* 96p. pap. $8.95 (1-56474-106-0). Santa Barbara, CA: Fithian Press, Fall 1994. When your heart seems far away, let *A Distant Face* bring it back home again. —Dustin Castleberry

Kinnell, Galway. *Imperfect Thirst.* 96p. $19.95 (0-395-71089-8); pap. $12.95 (0-395-75528-X). Boston, MA: Houghton Mifflin Company, Fall 1994. Themes Kinnell has pursued for decades—death, love, language, aging, music—emerge here with his typically succinct and wise parceling of perfect words. —*San Francisco Chronicle*

Kinsey, Leland. *Not One Man's Work.* 89p. $25.00 (1-55821-430-5); pap. $16.95 (1-55821-431-3). New York, NY: Lyons & Burford Publishers, Spring 1996. Kinsey's third collection pursues familiar themes: the love of the outdoors, the melancholy of childhood memories, the fleet passing of human time compared to nature's slow progression. Kinsey utilizes an extremely plainspoken style, [a directness which] contributes to the collection's accumulated power. —*Publishers Weekly*

Kinzie, Mary. *Ghost Ship.* 86p. $21.00 (0-679-44645-1). New York, NY: Alfred A. Knopf, Spring 1996. Mary Kinzie's new book of poems is characterized by its moral intensity and rigor. Her seriousness is perpetually adventurous. Her adventurousness shows itself in the constantly surprising angles from which she sees things and in the extraordinarily wide variety of successful formal experimentation in her poems. —David Ferry

Kipling, Rudyard. *Poems of Rudyard Kipling.* 128p. $8.99 (0-517-12276-6). Avenel, NJ: Gramercy Books, Spring 1995.

Kirby, David. *Big-Leg Music.* 100p. pap. $12.95 (0-914061-48-8). Alexandria, VA: Orchises Press, Fall 1995. From Henry James to the Moonglows, Botticelli to Jerry Garcia, this coruscating book of narrative poems is by turns tender, whimsical, profound. —Orchises Press

Kircher, Pamela. *Whole Sky.* 64p. pap. $11.95 (1-884800-10-6). Marshfield, MA: Four Way Books, Spring 1996. It is Pamela Kircher's genius that she makes of familiar material something unexpected and strange. This is hard-won work, luminous and necessary and alive. —Michael Ryan

Kirschner, Joseph. *A Ribbon of Silver Thread: Haiku.* 36p. pap. $5.95. Johnstown, OH: Pudding House Publications/Little Stone Books, Fall 1995.

Kirwan, Anna. *The Alchemist's Retort.* 69p. pap. $12.00 (0-941895-06-8). Amherst, MA: Amherst Writers and Artists Press, Fall 1995. Anna Kirwan's poetry is a perfect blend of clear-eyed observation and sudden high dives into the numinous. She makes you look again, feel again, and touch—as she does—the mystery of all that is ours. —Jane Yolen

Kistler, William. *Poems of the Known World.* 92p. $14.95 (1-55970-301-6). New York,

NY: Arcade Publishing, Spring 1996. *Poems of the Known World* come to us from the paradoxes and harsh juxtapositions of late 20th-century life—the unkempt homeless sleeping beside a smoothness of marble cut from mountains they will never see and used as the facings of buildings they will almost never enter; male and female reaching toward union while memories of the brutality of war pass between them. —Arcade Publishing

Kitzis, Lee, ed. *The Anti-Mensch.* 30p. pap. $2.50. Chicago, IL: Puddin'head Press, Spring 1996. A collection of poetry from Chicago area poets, from the ages of 14 to 84. It includes the work of Charles Bernstein, Samuel Blechman, Lee Kitzis, and others. Some are veteran poets, others are appearing here for the first time in print. —Puddin'head Press

Kizer, Carolyn. *Harping On: Poems 1985-1995.* 80p. $22.00 (1-55659-114-4); pap. $12.00 (1-55659-115-2). Port Townsend, WA: Copper Canyon Press, Fall 1996. Sharp, smart and tender, Kizer's poetry restores, redresses and delights. —William Matthews. The

poems are at once lucid and musical, full of the wry wisdom of a worldly tale-bearer. —*Library Journal*

Kizer, Carolyn, ed. *100 Great Poems by Women: A Golden Ecco Anthology.* 192p. $22.00 (0-88001-422-9). Hopewell, NJ: Ecco Press, Fall 1995. Five centuries of women's verse speak here with breath and freshness and consistent strength. —Richard Wilbur

Kleinzahler, August. *Red Sauce, Whiskey and Snow.* 64p. $21.00 (0-374-28924-7). New York, NY: Farrar, Straus and Giroux, Spring 1995. Kleinzahler makes lyric sense of urban grit and neon. His wide-awake poems have an intimacy of attention new to American writing. —Guy Davenport

Knauth, Stephen. *Twenty Shadows.* 77p. pap. $11.95 (1-884800-01-7). Marshfield, MA: Four Way Books, Spring 1995. These poems have the arc of tragedy, and the glint and silence of objects just washed up from the ocean. Clear-eyed and logical, the work reveals a core of existence beyond aesthetics, a love that is in the last analysis inhuman. *Twenty Shadows* is a beautiful, desperate book. —D. Nurkse

Knight, Brenda, ed. *Women of the Beat Generation: The Writers, Artists, and Muses at the Heart of a Revolution.* 240p. $22.95 (1-57324-061-3). Berkeley, CA: Conari Press, Fall 1996. An anthology of the life and work of the magnificently creative women related to the Beat Movement with over 40 rare photographs and never-before published writings. —Conari Press

Knight, Ginny. *Song of a Father-less Child.* 70p. pap. $10.00 (0-9635690-6-6). Brooklyn Center, MN: TA Publications, Fall 1995. Intensely personal but very powerful poems merge imperceptibly into less personal material. The flow is one of the great strengths of the book. —Morgan Kier

Knight, Leon. *If, Because of Me: Memories and Love Poems for Ginny.* 60p. pap. $10.00 (0-9635690-8-2). Brooklyn Center, MN: TA Publications, Spring 1996. Poems that celebrate 40 years of love. —TA Publications

Knobloch, Marta. Translated by Dino Tebaldi. *The Room of Months / La Stanza dei Mesi.* 80p. pap. $12.00 (88-7232-201-4). Hedgesville, WV: The Bunny and the Crocodile Press/Forest Woods Media, Spring 1995. Published with Book Editore, Bologna, Italy. From the Etruscans on down to Kristallnacht ("On this night of shattered glass/ I honor you, Primo Levy"), Marta Knobloch explores and guides vibrantly. —James H. Brady, *The Sun*

Knott, Bill. *Collected Short Poems 1965-1995.* 38p. Boston, MA: Bill Knott, Spring 1996. I think Bill Knott is *the* best poet in America right now. —Thomas Lux, *Emerson Review.* Other chapbook titles available from Bill Knott include: *Homages* (1996); *Plaza De Loco* (1996); *Ten Parables and Ten Paintings* (1996); *Collected Political Poems, 1965-1994* (1994); and *Sixty Poems of Love and Homage* (1994).

Knott, Bill. *The Quicken Tree.* 83p. $20.00 (1-800238-24-1); pap. $12.50 (1-800238-25-X). Rochester, NY: BOA Editions, Fall 1995. Bill Knott has been first among originals. Comic or caustic, verbally athletic, of a force forever thought immoderate and imprudent by Authority—every Knott poem is a surprise because the man himself has been a constant student of means . . . Knott can sing like an open-throated nightingale or twist the neck of syntax until it turns true blue. —Marvin Bell

Knowles, Alison. *Bread and Water.* 48p. pap. (1-880516-07-1). Barrytown, NY: Left Hand Books, Spring 1995. Looking at the cracks in homemade bread, Alison Knowles noticed their resemblance to rivers. Using atlases, she matched each pattern to a river. By tracing the patterns onto a transparent paper and imposing it over a page of text pertaining to the rivers, Knowles was able to "find" a poem by lifting the words which the meandering lines passed through. —Left Hand Books. The poetry that is the best of Fluxus. —*The Village Voice*

Knox, Ann B. *Staying Is Nowhere.* 64p. pap. $12.00 (0-930526-19-8). College Park, MD: Scop Publications and Writer's Center Editions, Spring 1996. Ann Knox's generous meditations have an unforced eloquence and

authority. In these rich landscapes, there is loss without self-pity, experience without melodrama—and a great deal of beauty. —Rachel Hadas

Koch, Kenneth. *On the Great Atlantic Rainway: Selected Poems 1950-1988.* 336p. $25.00 (0-679-43418-6); pap. $17.00 (0-679-76582-4). New York, NY: Alfred A. Knopf, Fall 1995. [Kenneth Koch is] one of our greatest poets. —John Ashbery. A masterly innovator who has used his extravagant powers of wit and invention to enlarge the sphere of the poetic. He has stretched our ideas of what it is possible to do in poetry. —David Lehman, *American Poetry Review*

Koch, Kenneth. *One Train.* 88p. $20.00 (0-679-43417-8); pap. $13.00 (0-679-76583-2). New York, NY: Alfred A. Knopf, Fall 1995. Winner of the Bollingen Prize in Poetry for 1995 with Koch's selected volume, *On the Great Atlantic Rainway* (simultaneously published). Koch's idea "to do something with language / That has never been done before" is made good throughout. —Frank Kermode

Kochanowski, Jan. Translated by Stanislaw Baranczak and Seamus Heaney. *Laments.* 59p. $17.50 (0-374-18290-6). New York, NY: Farrar, Straus and Giroux, Fall 1995. Kochanowski, a great Polish Renaissance poet, was a contemporary of the French poet Ronsard and Edmund Spenser, yet the Renaissance literature of Poland is virtually unknown in the West due to a lack of translations. The *Laments* of Kochanowski should be ranked with the world classics. [This excellent translation] preserves its meters and rhymes. It is a rare accomplishment. —Czeslaw Milosz

Kogon, Nicolaus P., ed. *The Age of Koestler.* 1088p. pap. $29.95 (0-9626690-0-8). Kalamazoo, MI: Practices of the Wind Press, Fall 1994. Dedicated to Arthur Koestler, this anthology contains extracts from Koestler's work, [as well as a] huge selection of poems and translations by hundreds of writers representing 15 foreign languages. —*St. Louis Post Dispatch.* A fine collection of modern poets. A solid addition for almost any kind or size of library. —Bill Katz, *Library Journal*

Kohler, Sandra. *The Country of Women.* 112p. $21.95 (0-934971-46-3); pap. $11.95 (0-934971-45-5). Corvallis, OR: Calyx Books, Fall 1995. Sandra Kohler writes about human sexuality with far more integrity than most of her contemporaries. She speaks eloquently. All of us can learn from this wonderful book. —Tom Ferté. In the troubadour's aubade or dawn song, the lover sings as the morning light draws him reluctantly from his lady's bed. In the poems of Sandra Kohler the aubade tradition is given fresh and surprising shape in poems of rich harmonies where a dark undertow, a sweet languor, pulls back toward dream, while an equal force rises toward full awakening into the daylight space of the mundane. —Eleanor Wilner

Kolm, Ron; Bart Platenga, and others, eds. *Unbearables.* 288p. pap. $12.00 (1-57027-053-8). Brooklyn, NY: Autonomedia, Fall 1995.

Kono, Juliet S. *Tsunami Years.* 173p. pap. $10.00 (0-910043-35-3). Honolulu, HI: Bamboo Ridge Press, Fall 1995. Themes of childhood heartbreaks and affinities, familial obligation, love and devotion, death and dying are explored with language that shimmers with multiple luminescent layers of meaning, each poem a pearl of truth wrested out of the heart of living. —Cathy Song

Koriyama, Naoshi, and Edward Lueders, trans. *Like Underground Water: The Poetry of Mid-Twentieth Century Japan.* 250p. $30.00 (1-55659-102-0); pap. $15.00 (1-55659-103-9). Port Townsend, WA: Copper Canyon Press, Fall 1995. This book is significant for its comprehensive look at this century through Japanese eyes and for the quality and accessibility of the translations. —*Booklist*

Kostelanetz, Richard. *Minimal Fictions.* 103p. pap. $9.95 (1-878580-06-X). Santa Maria, CA: Asylum Arts, Spring 1995. Kostelanetz [practices] a truly radical minimalism. Since 1970 [he] has produced highly original fictions in the forms of lines, numbers, one-, two-, and three-word sequences, and other severely attenuated elements. —Larry McCaffery. The theme is stark eroticism, and some of [these

pieces] are monstrously hilarious. —Sam Prestianni, *The Retriever*

Krauter, Mary Jackson. *Clippings.* 27p. pap. $6.95. Johnstown, OH: Pudding House Publications, Spring 1995. A new voice from the Nebraska plains, Krauter writes about Camp Clarke, Wonder Bread, and Creedence Clearwater; spare narratives in the style of Bosveld's "Virtual Journalism." —Pudding House Publications

Krukowski, Damon. *5000 Musical Terms.* 32p. pap. $5.00 (1-886224-04-8). Providence, RI: Burning Deck, Fall 1995. "Statements, when repeated, gain a measure of truth," says the author, his tongue in his cheek. In these poems, found texts are used to probe the concepts of tradition and learning, as well as our place in the late phase of a culture. —Burning Deck

Kumin, Maxine. *Connecting the Dots.* 86p. $18.95 (0-393-03962-5). New York, NY: W. W. Norton & Company, Spring 1996. Her poems become increasingly unforgettable, indispensable. —*New York Times Book Review*

Kunihiro, Kei. *Poet and Killer Chronicles.* 120p. pap. $15.00 (1-55618-154-X). Lawrenceville, VA: Brunswick Publishing, Fall 1995. Jack Keroac left seeds for a new generation of Beat verse. Kei is the most hardcore of the new generation of Beat poets. —Brunswick Publishing

Kunitz, Stanley. *Passing Through: The Later Poems, New and Selected.* 128p. $18.95 (0-393-03870-X). New York, NY: W. W. Norton & Company, Fall 1995. Winner of the National Book Award. Marking the year of his ninetieth birthday, Pulitzer Prize winning poet Stanley Kunitz presents his ninth collection, a collection which demonstrates his own prefatory statement: "Art is that chalice into which we pour the wine of transcendence." —W.W. Norton & Company. No other poet in our time has brought forth out of himself, out of his imagination, so many different, intense affirmations of being. —Gregory Orr, *American Poetry Reviews*

Kunstler, William M. *Hints & Allegations: The World in Poetry and Prose According to William M. Kunstler.* 208p. $17.00 (1-56858-017-7). New York, NY: Four Walls Eight Windows, Fall 1994. The poems in this collection rattle the foundations of venerable American institutions, in this case our poetry canon and our entrenched notion that institutionalized racism is a thing of the past. There is nothing rarer than a man who has lived a long life in the public eye fighting for social justice. In many ways, this book is Kunstler's true autobiography. —Four Walls Eight Windows

Kutik, Ilya. Translated by Kit Robinson. *Ode: On Visiting the Belosaraisk Spit on the Sea of Azov.* 63p. pap. $14.00 (1-882509-03-X). New York, NY: Alef Books, Fall 1995. Kutik seems to have absorbed the entire arsenal of technical means offered by Russian poetry over its two-century-long history, and the result is a poetry of verve, nerve, and unique formal daring. —Joseph Brodsky. Kutik's *Ode* is truly magnificent in both Russian and English. What music! What compactness and wit! And imagery: those "Hamlet-like gulls"! —Charles Simic

L

La Mers, Joyce. *Grandma Rationalizes a Reason for Skydiving.* 40p. pap. $5.00 (0-9638843-7-9). Santa Barbara, CA: Mille Grazie Press, Fall 1996. The first book from Joyce La Mers, best known for her light verse. This volume contains some of her most popular work, as well as a few poems that show her gifts as a serious and accomplished narrative poet.

La Prade, Eric. *Things Maps Don't Show.* 50p. pap. $7.95. New York, NY: Aegis Press, Fall 1994.

LaFaso, Vanessa. *Kiss It Where It Hurts.* 28p. pap. $4.00 (0-9637704-4-6). Alexandria, VA: Red Dragon Press, Spring 1996. Poems by the South Jersey performance poet, expressing her belief that life must be balanced between "Love and lust, loathing and loss, lyrical and loony." —Red Dragon Press

Laino, E.J. Miller. *Girl Hurt.* 68p. pap. $9.95 (1-882295-07-2). Farmington, ME: Alice James Books, Fall 1995. *Girl Hurt* is more than a confrontation with daily pain and fear; these poems celebrate survival, the durability of family, the liberation of unheard voices, especially female and working-class voices. The poems of E.J. Miller Laino *transcend*, with all the power and beauty of flight. —Martín Espada

Lalish, Paula. *Midway.* 14p. pap. $5.00. Port Townsend, WA: Sagittarius Press, Spring 1996. Hand set and printed by the author in a limited edition. —Sagittarius Press

Lally, Michael. *Can't Be Wrong.* 125p. pap. $11.95 (1-56689-046-2). Minneapolis, MN: Coffee House Press, Spring 1996. Reading this book I can feel the New York streets under my feet, hear the voices and the traffic, smell the air, all, in romantic retrospect, beautiful. Of course, because Lally's a romantic in the full sense of the word, I also (re)experience the heartache of life on those streets. This is a wonderful book, a beautiful book, a very human book. It's a real joy to read. —Hubert Selby, Jr.

Lally, Michael. *Catch My Breath.* 92p. pap. $13.00 (0-913198-

04-8). Portland, OR: Salt Lick Press, Spring 1995. Lally is the Francois Villon of the 70's. —John Ashbery. Who else, writing like a tough, can be tender with such grace? —Gerald Burns, *Southwest Review*. *Catch My Breath* represents an illumination and expansion of Lally's biographical myth. —Terence Winch, *Washington Review*. [This] book, a mirror image of an entire society, changing and observing its own change, is Lally's best. —John Jacob, *Booklist*

LaMorticello, Barbara. *Rain on Waterless Mountain*. 26p. pap. $5.00. Portland, OR: 26 Books, Fall 1994. Heartfelt poems about the conflict between diminishing natural resources and personal freedom. —26 Books

Lander, Tim. *Les Petits Animaux/ The Little Animals*. 24p. pap. $5.00. Port Townsend, WA: Sagittarius Press, Spring 1996. Designed and printed by Rusty North just for fun and in time for the August star-shower using handset type on Dayglo paper. Art by Tim Lander. —Sagittarius Press

Lander, Tim. *The Myth of Adam and Eve: An Operatic Dialog for*

Three Voices. 16p. pap. $5.00. Port Townsend, WA: Sagittarius Press, Fall 1995. Hand-set, limited edition chapbook.

Lane, John. *Against Information and Other Poems*. 67p. pap. $7.95 (1-883197-06-6). Cullowhee, NC: New Native Press, Spring 1995. For any who might have doubted that the human brain is the most explosively articulate of expert systems or feared that the best minds of our re-generation are being devoured by the Internet, this is the howl of the '90s, a poetic rallying cry for humane technology. —Benjamin Dunlap

Langworthy, Christian Nguyen. *The Geography of War*. 40p. pap. $12.00 (0-939121-04-2). Shreveport, LA: Cooper House Publishing, Fall 1995. Winner of the 1993 American Chapbook Award from Cooper House Publishing and *Poet Magazine*. [Langworthy's *Geography of War*] is delicate and painful, urgent and beautiful. —Lewis Turco

Lansing, Gerrit. *Heavenly Tree/ Soluble Forest*. 214p. $28.95 (1-883689-13-9); pap. $16.95 (1-883689-12-0). Jersey City, NJ: Talisman House, Publishers, Spring 1995. Here is a gnostic luminist apple rights-and-comradeship alchemical American down-home and high-elegant true magic love epic, work song over the compost heap, jewelry out of the ruins, chant of genital intensity, celebration of the profound gush of existence, remorse and loss, orexis and ecstasis of woods and gardens, bars and kitchens, streets and sex and music. —Kenneth Irby. A heavenly tree grows in these poems, a life's inscriptions in shapes that refuse form's containment. —Charles Bernstein

Larson, Michael. *The Light Remaining*. 20p. pap. $4.50. Kew Gardens, NY: New Spirit Press, Fall 1994. Winner of the New Spirit Press Quarterly Chapbook Contest. These poems function as a prism of words refracting poetic imagery onto philosophical and theological concepts. —New Spirit Press

Laskin, Pamela. *Dear Hades*. 22p. pap. $3.75. Kew Gardens, NY: New Spirit Press, Spring 1995. Winner of the New Spirit Press Quarterly Chapbook Contest.

Pithy notes and letters written to or from various mythological characters. —New Spirit Press

Lassell, Michael. *The Hard Way*. 319p. pap. $12.95 (1-56333-231-0). New York, NY: Masquerade Books, Fall 1995. The first collection of renowned gay writer Michael Lassell's poetry, fiction and essays. Widely anthologized and a staple of gay literary and entertainment publications nationwide, Lassell is regarded as one of the most distinctive and accomplished talents of his generation. —Masquerade Books. Michael Lassell's poems are worldly in the best way, defining the arc of a world of gay life in our own decade with his bawdy and bittersweet songs. —Paul Monette

Lassell, Michael, ed. *Eros in Boystown: Contemporary Gay Poems About Sex*. 64p. $12.00 (0-517-70280-0). New York, NY: Crown Publishers, Spring 1996. In addition to lively new voices on the poetry scene, contributors include both living and posthumous masters of contemporary verse: W. H. Auden, Allen Ginsberg, Jean

Cocteau, James Baldwin, and Thom Gunn, to name a few. —Crown Publishers

Lassell, Michael, ed. *The Name of Love: Classic Gay Love Poems.* 87p. $10.00 (0-312-11863-5). New York, NY: St. Martin's Press, Spring 1995.

Laughlin, James. *Remembering William Carlos Williams.* 64p. pap. $7.95 (0-8112-1307-2). New York, NY: New Directions, Fall 1995. This book is a trove of information and human presence—a vital, personal and literary record of a great American poet. —Robert Pinsky

Laughlin, James. *The Country Road.* 160p. $22.95 (0-944072-46-1). Cambridge, MA: Zoland Books, Fall 1995. Lucid, cleanly cut, and graceful, these poems blend the impersonality of myth with the pulse of autobiography as they celebrate love and take the measure of death. —Rosanna Warren. The ancient poets of elegy and epigram guard and define this book, in which a long life is compressed to a Sapphic simplicity. —Thom Gunn

Lawless, Gary. *Somewhere Within the Shell Mound.* 32p. pap.

$2.00. Ashland, KY: BullHead Books, Fall 1995.

Lawless, Gary, ed. *Poems for the Wild Earth.* 96p. pap. $8.95 (0942396-72-3). Nobleboro, ME: Blackberry Books, Fall 1995. Among the poets included here are Beth Brant, Peter Blue Cloud, Sharon Doubiago, and Gary Snyder. These are poems for walking, for quiet, for rallies and public hearings, and for prayer. —Blackberry Books

Lawlor, William. *Let's Go Down to the Beach: Poems and Translations.* 128p. pap. $13.98 (0-9641986-9-X). Duluth, MN: Poetry Harbor. This volume features Lawlor's translations of four Caribbean poets: Belkis Cuza Male, Nicolas Guillen, Pedro Mir, and Carlos Dobal; along with his own work. Poems that are generous, warm, accessible, funny, and sneakily profound. —Larry Watson

Lea, Sydney. *To the Bone: New and Selected Poems.* 240p. $29.95 (0-252-02223-8); pap. $17.95 (0-252-06519-0). Champaign, IL: University of Illinois Press, Fall 1996. Lea's poems live at the level at which lyricism is crowded with the daily lives of those who will not or cannot speak for themselves—the doomed, the disenfranchised, the local dead. At his most vocal, his love ethic is indistinguishable from his elegy. He embraces what he cannot change. —Stanley Plumly

Le Guin, Ursula, and Diana Bellessi. *The Twins, The Dream: Two Voices/Laf Gemelas, El Sueño: Dos Voces.* 230p. $16.95 (1-5585-170-4); pap. $8.95 (1-5585-179-8). Houston, TX: Arte Publico Press, Fall 1996.

Lee, David. *My Town.* 140p. pap. $12.00 (1-55659-074-1). Port Townsend, WA: Copper Canyon Press, Fall 1995. Winner of the 1995 Western States Book Award. Lee's splendid ear for idiomatic, vernacular speech imbues his work with a kind of red-dirt, hog-wallow lyricism, with the direct and uncompromising impact of common talk. —*Bloomsbury Review*

Leftwich, Jim. *Dirt.* 14p. pap. $4.00 (093535056X). Columbus, OH: Luna Bisonte Prods, Spring 1995. Innovative prose poems. —Luna Bisonte Prods

Leftwich, Jim. *Khawatir.* 43p. pap. $3.00 (1-57141-16-3). Port Charlotte, FL: Runaway Spoon Press, Spring 1995. A long, complex idiolinguistic text. —Runaway Spoon Press

Lenski, Jean. *Genesis.* 168p. pap. $9.95 (1-879934-21-3). Laurinburg, NC: St. Andrews College Press, reissued Fall 1994. Lenski looks backward to our traditions and forward to the post-modern world in a distinctive feminist voice. —St. Andrews College Press

Leon, Yvette. *Grandchild Flies/ Un Nieto Vuela.* 20p. pap. $5.00. Port Townsend, WA: Sagittarius Press, Spring 1996. Designed and printed by the author. Handset limited edition. —Sagittarius Press

Leonhardt, Kenneth. *Sex Scells: Light Verses Celebrate the Way of All Flesh.* 72p. pap. $8.95 (1-56474-104-4). Santa Barbara, CA: Fithian Press, Fall 1994. Few people seem to do humorous verse very well anymore, and it's a pleasure to count Leonhardt in that ever-shrinking group that likes to have fun with words. —*The Plastic Tower.* Like saxophonist Charlie 'Bird' Parker, Leonhardt's poems give the impression of hitting every note at once. The effect is at once lyrical and consummately artistic. —John Mella, *Light Quarterly*

Lerner, Linda. *She's Back.* 64p. pap. $9.50 (1-889289-04-3). Manchester, CT: Ye Olde Font Shoppe, Spring 1996. [Linda Lerner] has a strong and distinctive voice, and a fresh view of life in the city. —Hayden Carruth

Lesser, Rika. *All We Need of Hell.* 87p. $15.95 (0-929398-85-8); pap. $10.95 (0-929398-92-0). Denton, TX: University of North Texas Press, Fall 1995. Honest, wise, and harrowing, these are poems absorbing to read and impossible to forget. —James Merrill. This painful, brave odyssey . . . will stand as a powerful, poised testimony that "the worse does pass and can be survived." —*New York Times Book Review.* Detailing her experience with depression—suicide attempts, hospitalizations and the often devastating effects of medication—Lesser demystifies depressive illness in poems . . . direct, reflective and instructive. —*Publishers Weekly*

Lev, Donald. *Twilight.* 34p. pap. $3.00 (1-879969-04-1). Claryville, NY: Outloudbooks, Fall 1995. There's a lightness to Donald Lev's work which belies its serious undertones but accounts for much of its charm. He blends marvelously active images with feelings of dread, abandonment, and intellectual frustration. But his readers won't weep—they're more likely to laugh ruefully. —Shirley Powell, *Oxalis*

Levant, Nancy. *Generations of Sara.* 20p. pap. $5.00 (1-57141-12-0). Port Charlotte, FL: Runaway Spoon Press, Spring 1995.

Levchev, Vladimir. Translated by Henry Taylor. *Leaves from the Dry Tree.* 48p. $8.00 (0-89304-138-6); pap. $5.00 (0-89304-137-8). Merrick, NY: Cross-Cultural Communications, Spring 1996. Bilingual edition, Bulgarian and English.

Levertov, Denise. *Sands of the Well.* 144p. $20.95 (0-8112-1316-1). New York, NY: New Directions, Spring 1996. Book by book, I have read her poems for their subtle music, for their deep compassionate intelligence, for their imagination, for the author's dignity and integrity and grace; and, most of all, for the indomitable and humble spirit that hungers there. I have savored them like salt, like honey. —Sam Hamill, *The American Poetry Review*

Levi, Toni Mergentime. *For a Dancing Bear.* 64p. pap. $9.95 (1-886124-01-9). New York, NY: Three Mile Harbor. Musical, insightful, Toni Levi's collection is filled with poems of grace and offbeat discernment. With joy I salute the maturity and depth of her work. —Colette Inez

Levin, Elliott. *does it swing?* 95p. pap. $9.95 (1-884773-03-6). Los Angeles, CA: Heat Press, Fall 1996. This is a first collection by jazz musician-poet Levin, who cooks a lyrical stew of offbeat rhythms where language becomes a musical score. —Heat Press .

Levin, Gail, ed. *The Poetry of Solitude: A Tribute to Edward Hopper.* 80p. $17.95 (0-7893-0017-6). New York, NY: Rizzoli/Universe Publishing. Edward Hopper's haunting images of twentieth-century America have struck a fundamental chord in many poets, among them John Hollander,

Stephen Dunn, Grace Schulman. This volume combines Hopper's pictures with the poems they have inspired, celebrating the meeting of two art forms. —Rizzoli/Universe Publishing

Levine, Philip. *The Simple Truth.* 80p. $20.00 (0-679-43580-8); pap. $13.00 (0-679-76584-0). New York, NY: Alfred A. Knopf, Fall 1995. Winner of the Pulitzer Prize in Poetry, 1995. I am a longtime admirer of Philip Levine's poetry, but until now thought he would never surpass *The Names of the Lost,* a book I love deeply. But *The Simple Truth* deserves its title—I wonder if *any* American poet since Walt Whitman himself has written elegies this consistently magnificent. The controlled pathos of every poem in this volume is immense. —Harold Bloom

Levy, Julien. *Surrealism.* 192p. pap. $17.95 (0-306-80663-0). New York, NY: Da Capo Press, Fall 1995. At once a history and a primary source, this 1936 limited edition was compiled by a key Surrealist entrepreneur to promote the movement in America. Levy's combination art book, anthology, lexicon, and manifesto is an attic filled with forgotten treasures—including Samuel Beckett's translations from Eluard and Gaston Bachelard's philosophical postscript. —J. Hoberman, *The Village Voice*

Lew, Walter K., ed. *Premonitions: The Kaya Anthology of Asian North American Poetry.* 593p. $44.95 (1-885030-13-4); pap. $22.95 (1-885030-14-2). New York, NY: Kaya Production, Fall 1995. All modes of poetry, from Buddhist odes to video poetry, appear here, but in unpredictable ways that render them uncategorizable. An exquisite artifact of activist experimentalism, theoretically smart and so beautiful it hurts. *Premonitions* promises to be a landmark in American letters for many years to come. —Maria Damon

Lewis, Janet. *The Dear Past and Other Poems 1919-1994.* 48p. pap. $15.00. Edgewood, KY: Robert L. Barth (R.L.B.), Spring 1995.

Lewis, Mary E. *The King of Time and Other Poems.* 48p. $10.95 (0-944957-48-X). New York, NY: Rivercross Publishing, Spring 1995.

Li Po. Translated by David Hinton. *The Selected Poems of Li Po.* 160p. pap. $11.95 (0-8112-1323-4). New York, NY: New Directions, Spring 1996. Civilizations have their great periods of lyric poetry, and one of the greatest was T'ang dynasty China (A.D. 712-760), which produced three or four of the most remarkable poets in world literature. The best-loved of these was Li Po, and a new volume of his work has just appeared, done by one of the best contemporary translators of classical Chinese poetry, David Hinton. —Robert Hass, *Washington Post Book World*

Libby, Anthony. *The Secret Turning of the Earth.* 32p. pap. $3.00 (0-87338-520-9). Kent, OH: Kent State University Press, Spring 1995. This collection announces the arrival of an American poet who moves through space and time exercising a singular vision. Strong, ambitious poems, they pay that fierce and unwavering attention we expect only from the boldest, most perceptive travelers. —David Citino. Libby's learnedness crosses the wide latitudes of passion, mystery, and music, charting history and harm, redemption and erasure. —David Baker

Liddy, James. *Collected Poems.* 359p. $24.95 (1-881871-08-8); pap. $14.95 (1-881871-09-6). Omaha, NE: Creighton University Press, Fall 1995. I have enormous regard for James Liddy's poetry, and on the basis of my knowledge of contemporary poetry in Ireland, I consider him to be one of the most original among living Irish poets, perhaps the most. —John Ashbury

Lieberman, Laurence. *The St. Kitts Monkey Feuds: A Poem in Eight Parts.* 40p. pap. $25.00. Omaha, NE: Cummington Press, Fall 1995. Handmade limited edition.

Liebler, M.L. *Stripping the Adult Century Bare.* 84p. pap. $12.00 (1-885215-09-6). Woodbridge, CT: Viet Nam Generation/ Burning Cities Press, Fall 1995. Liebler writes close clipped verse of a political bent that reflects his anger and angst over the aftermath of the Vietnam War. He extends the legacy of James Wright. —Paul Smart, *Woodstock Times*

Liebowitz, Elsbeth. *A Mixed Fare.* 64p. pap. $6.95 (0-9636373-1-2). Denver, CO: Overboard Press, Fall 1994.

Lifshin, Lyn. *Blue Tattoo: Poems of the Holocaust.* 80p. pap. $9.95 (1-880391-12-0). Desert Hot Springs, CA: Event Horizon Press, Spring 1995. *Blue Tattoo* is a living witness to the deportation, extermination, and cremation of millions of human beings. I recommend this book to anyone who cares about contemporary poetry. —William Packard

Lim-Wilson, Fatima. *Crossing the Snow Bridge.* 107p. $16.95 (0-8142-0680-8); pap. $10.95 (0-8142-0681-6). Columbus, OH: Ohio State University Press, Fall 1995. Winner of the 1995 Ohio State University Press / *The Journal* Award in Poetry. A native of the Philippines, Lim-Wilson explores the immigrant experience in the U.S. How can memories of green mangoes, miniature fish, and the landscape of seven thousand islands contribute to a North American cultural identity? In telling stories of the Philippines and of the United States, these poems build a metaphorical bridge over which we can cross between cultures. —Ohio State University Press

Linville, William. *Boothery 1-2-3.* 40p. pap. $7.95. Johnstown, OH: Pudding House Publications, Fall 1995. Linville writes about his relationships with his computer, his park bench and his notions about education. —Pudding House Publications

Lipman, Joel. *The Real Ideal.* 23p. pap. $6.00 (0935350594). Columbus, OH: Luna Bisonte Prods, Spring 1996. Translitic poems ("fake" translations) with a surrealist flavor. Illustrated with rubberstamp graphics by the author. —Luna Bisonte Prods

Littauer, Andrew. *The Farther Shore.* 28p. pap. $8.00 (1-884725-12-0). Thibodaux, LA: Blue Heron Press, Spring 1996. In quiet, meditative verses that brood on the mysteries of self and world so tenuously connected by language, Littauer finds that only in the journey toward "the farther shore" do we find wisdom. —David Middleton

Little, Jeffrey. *Buckshot & Sammy Davis: A Landscape of Tubas.* 25p. pap. $2.25. Los Angeles, CA: Undulating Bedsheets Productions, Spring 1996. Silly-putty eggs slide off the ceiling while an iguana puppet hogs the remote control, watching test patterns on the TV for days. —Undulating Bedsheets

Liu, Timothy. *Burnt Offerings.* 70p. pap. $12.00 (1-55659-104-7). Port Townsend, WA: Copper Canyon Press, Fall 1995. What distinguishes this poetry is Liu's deft handling of graphic material, his skillful and taut braiding of it with an artful imagery and transcendent lyricism. —*The Boston Review*

Locke, Christopher. *How to Burn.* 26p. pap. $8.00 (0-938566-70-9). Easthampton, MA: Adastra Press, Fall 1995. A first collection from the editor of *Longfish Review*. Hand crafted letterpress edition. —Adastra Press

Locke, Edward. *Advancing Back.* 76p. pap. $7.00 (0-9646587-1-2). Canton, MA: Harlequinade Press, Fall 1995. Impressive. Good, intelligent formal verse. —*Nerve*

Locke, Edward. *Anointing the Tide.* 78p. pap. $7.00 (0-9646587-3-9). Canton, MA: Harlequinade Press, Fall 1996. *Anointing the Tide* offers magical combinations of sound and wry splays of the comic with the somber themes of the twentieth century. —Al Howe, *South Word*

Locke, Edward. *Green Bank.* 85p. pap. $7.00. Canton, MA: Harlequinade Press, Fall 1994. Locke is a poet of serious philosophical concerns, wide learning, and commanding technique. He is talented. He is engaging. He should be widely known and appreciated. —Richard Moore

Locke, Edward. *Parings.* 76p. pap. $7.00 (0-9646587-0-4). Canton, MA: Harlequinade Press, Fall 1995. [This work] proceeds marvelously, in wizardly fashion. —*Dusty Dog Reviews*

Locke, Edward. *Tapers.* 65p. pap. $6.00. Canton, MA: Harlequinade Press, Fall 1994. Edward Locke drives deep, fearlessly takes risks, and approaches reality from surprising angles. His best poems . . . are, I think, absolutely first-rate. *Tapers* is a thoroughly seasoned book, impressive in insights and resonant music. —X. J. Kennedy

Locklin, Gerald. *Not the Pittsburgh Poems.* 22p. pap. $4.00. Albuquerque, NM: Zerx Press, Spring 1996. Bound back-to-back with Mark Weber's *The Pittsburgh Poems.*

Locklin, Gerald. *Two Jazz Sequences.* 45p. pap. $4.00. Albuquerque, NM: Zerx Press, Fall 1995. Bound back-to-back with Mark Weber's *Transitory Like Smoke.*

Loftus, Richard Gilmore. *Houdini.* 23p. pap. $6.00. East Lansing, MI: Gilmore Loftus, Spring 1996.

Logghe, Joan. *Twenty Years in Bed With the Same Man.* 120p. pap. $12.00 (0-9631909-7-0). Albuquerque, NM: La Alameda Press, Fall 1995. These are the first love poems that ever made me want to write love poems. Their splendid power is contagious! —Naomi Shihab Nye. Much of this sprightly collection deals with marriage, which Logghe views with wit, philosophy, and a dash of irreverence. Joan Logghe knows whereof she speaks, and she makes us feel the emotional roads she has traveled. —Peter Thorpe, *Rocky Mountain News*

Logue, Christopher. *The Husbands: An Account of Books 3 and 4 of Homer's Iliad.* 56p. $19.00 (0-374-17391-5). New York, NY: Farrar, Strauss and Giroux, Fall 1995. We have among us a great interpreter of Homer. The writing is beautifully rhythmic, controlled and urgent, sweeping forward as fast as the Greeks, then stopping only to gasp. —Andrew Marr, *The Independent* (London). Like every poet since Homer's day, Logue has used the *Iliad* for plunder but he has come up with something marvelously itself. Logue is in top form. —A. N. Wilson, *The Spectator*. The best translation of Homer since Pope's. —*The New York Review of Books*

Long, Donna; Helen Pruitt Wallace, and Rick Campbell, eds. *Isle of Flowers: Poems by Florida's Individual Artist Fellows.* 224p. $21.95 (0-938078-39-9); pap. $14.00 (0-938078-41-0). Tallahassee, FL: Anhinga Press, Fall 1995. This is a stunning collection. It reminds me of the many sorts of Florida fecundity— lush, pungent, intense, clear.

Again and again it surprised me with the sudden prospect of a wide horizon or a perfectly and poignantly observed detail. Though I have read before many of the poets included here, I suppose until I saw them gathered I was unaware that our natural resources include such a burgeoning. —Janet Burroway

Longfellow, Henry Wadsworth. Edited by Thomas Crofts. *Evangeline and Other Poems.* 64p. pap. $1.00 (0-486-28255-4). Mineola, NY: Dover Publications, Fall 1994.

Longley, Michael. *The Ghost Orchid.* 62p. $15.95 (0-916390-73-X); pap. $9.95 (0-916390-72-1). Winston-Salem, NC: Wake Forest University Press, Spring 1996. *The Ghost Orchid* is, for me, Longley's most purely pleasurable and satisfying book to date. It is a volume in which the preoccupations of a poetic lifetime are richly deepened, intensified and supplemented in poems of lucid, ceremonious courtesy and goodwill: a "flowering" itself, in more than one sense. —Neil Corcoran, *Times Literary Supplement*

Loomis, Sabra. *The Blue Door.* 20p. pap. $5.00. New York,

NY: Firm Ground Press, Fall 1995.

Lopes, Damian. *Transentence.* 28p. pap. $3.00 (1-57141-005-8). Port Charlotte, FL: Runaway Spoon Press, Spring 1995. Acute observations of the everyday in slightly gnomic but accessible verse. —Runaway Spoon Press

Lopez, Tony. *False Memory.* 36p. pap. $6.00 (0-935724-69-9). Great Barrington, MA: The Figures, Fall 1996.

Lorde, Audre. *Coal.* 70p. pap. $10.00 (0-393-31486-3). New York, NY: W.W. Norton & Company, reissued Spring 1996. One of Lorde's earliest collections, *Coal* evokes views of city life that are "acidic and hard-edged, and sardonic 'cables of rage' humming with their own electricity." —Helen Vendler. In poetry that is as compelling for its ethical vision as for its language, Lorde dares to imagine a changed world. —*San Francisco Chronicle*

Lorde, Audre. *Our Dead Behind Us.* 88p. pap. $9.00 (0-393-31238-0). New York, NY: W.W. Norton & Company, reissued Fall 1994. Black, lesbian, mother, cancer survivor, urban woman: none of Lorde's selves has ever silenced the others; the counterpoint among them is often the material of her strongest poems. —Marilyn Hacker

Lorde, Audre. *The Black Unicorn.* 122p. pap. $9.00 (0-393-31237-2). New York, NY: W.W. Norton & Company, reissued Spring 1995. Refusing to be circumscribed by any simple identity, Audre Lorde writes as a Black woman, a mother, a daughter, a Lesbian, a feminist, a visionary; poems of elemental wildness and healing, nightmare and lucidity. —Adrienne Rich

Lorde, Audre. *The Marvelous Arithmetics of Distance.* 72p. pap. $8.95 (0-393-31170-8). New York, NY: W.W. Norton & Company, Fall 1994. This collection, written between 1987 and 1992, is the final volume by Audre Lorde. [Lorde is] a major American poet whose concerns are international, and whose words have left their mark on many lives. —Ardrienne Rich. In these last poems we recognize the same vibrant, brave and generous soul we knew before. A wonder in itself —Alice Walker

Louella, Michael. *What Cannot Be Said.* 19p. pap. $5.00. Lancaster, PA: Zero Degree Press, Fall 1995. An intimate cycle of ten poems. Louella uses poetic form as a way of approaching the limitations of expression. —Zero Degree Press

Louis, Adrian C. *Vortex of Indian Fevers.* 62p. $29.95 (0-8101-5017-4); pap. $11.95 (0-8101-5042-5). Chicago, IL: Northwestern University Press/ TriQuarterly Books, Fall 1995. [Louis accords] no slack in his account of the complex destiny of Native Americans [and] white America's genocidal disenfranchisement of them. Brutally honest, but also beautifully aglow with love of language. —James Tate. Writing with the rage of a conscience that is simultaneously historical and urgent, Louis stands as one of those rare voices we must carry with us into the future. —David St. John. Prophetic, terrifyingly intelligent, unconditionally germane. —Hayden Carruth

Lourie, Dick; Mark Pawlak, Robert Hershon, and Ron Schreiber, eds. *Bullseye: Stories and Poems by Outstanding High School Writers.* 256p. $25.00 (1-882413-13-X); pap. $15.00 (1-882413-12-1). Brooklyn, NY: Hanging Loose Press, Fall 1995. Any teacher who's worked with teen-age writers will be cheered and re-inspired; anyone who reads poetry from force of habit will experience a swift kick in the old assumptions. —X.J. Kennedy. The levels of insight and maturity are often astounding. —*School Library Journal*

Lowell, Robert. *Imitations.* 149p. pap. $11.00 (0-374-50260-9). New York, NY: Farrar, Straus and Giroux/Noonday, reissued Fall 1994. *Imitations* is, so far as I know, the only book of its kind in literature . . . Lowell, who has used material from a variety of other writers, from Homer to Pasternak, has produced a volume of verse . . . which is really [his own] original sequence. —Edmund Wilson, *The New Yorker*

Lowell, Robert. *Notebook.* 265p. pap. $12.00 (0-374-50460-1). New York, NY: Farrar, Straus and Giroux/Noonday, reissued Spring 1995. Throughout [these poems] burns a passionate intelligence, a conscience,

which the reader feels is trust-
worthy. —William Meredith,
*The New York Times Book Re-
view*. [Lowell] appears in *Notebook* as a very subtle man, un-
ashamedly intelligent, well
read and alert, whose poems are
at once delicate and piercing.
—A. Alvarez, *The Observer*
(London)

Lowitz, Leza. *Old Ways To Fold
New Paper*. 98p. pap. $10.00
(0-9653304-1-9). Berkeley, CA:
Wandering Mind Books, Fall
1996. The freshness of these
delicate, dense, sometimes
mysterious, often political
poems comes from the poet's
extraordinary willingness to
look. They are poems of
perception—in all the senses
of the word. Yet at the same
time, Lowitz's poetry is filled
with stories that follow you
like a persistent wound. Her
poems haunt, stay with the
mind; intelligent, edgy, these
poems command attention.
—Jack Foley

**Lowitz, Leza, and Miyuki
Aoyama, trans.** *Other Side
River: Free Verse*. 244p. pap.
$14.00 (1-880656-16-7). Ber-
keley, CA: Stone Bridge Press,
Fall 1995. Companion volume
to *A Long Rainy Season: Haiku*

and Tanka, this collection of
contemporary Japanese wom-
en's poetry introduces some
three dozen of Japan's finest
poets writing in this relatively
new and western form. Many of
the poets here focus inward on
self, home, family, love; others
speak out against war and in-
justice. Many write from a political and social awareness of
being female in Japan's male-
centered society. —Stone
Bridge Press. The lilt, the warp
and woof of the words is Asian;
the sentiments universal.
—Lily Pond

Loy, Mina. Edited by Roger L.
Conover. *The Lost Lunar Baede-
ker*. 236p. $22.00 (0-374-
25872-4). New York, NY:
Farrar, Straus and Giroux,
Spring 1996. [Loy] has written
seven or eight of the most brilliant and unshakably solid sa-
tirical poems of our time, and
at least two non-satirical pieces
that possess for me a beauty
that is unspeakably moving
and profound. —Yvor Win-
ters, *The Dial* (1921). At one
time it was common to couple
the names of Mina Loy and
Marianne Moore. . . . It is
hard to say why [Loy has
recently] been ignored. Perhaps it is due to her extreme

exceptionalism. —Kenneth Rexroth, *Circle* (1944). Miss Loy, heard of last in the 1920's, remains a poet more than thirty years later—which is the test of a poet. —Louis Zukofsky (1957). Her utter absence from all canonical lists is one of modern literary history's most perplexing data. —Hugh Kenner, *The New York Times Book Review* (1982)

Ludwig, Laura Lonshein. *Asian Lake Lies*. 24p. Bayside, NY: Diamond Hitch Press, Spring 1996. Other chapbooks by Laura Lonshein Ludwig from Diamond Hitch Press include *Sunglasses in the Rain* (1996) and *Subway Ride* (1996).

Lunde, David. *Blues for Port City*. pap. $5.00 (0-932412-07-6). Saginaw, MI: Mayapple Press, Spring 1995. In this collection of poems, a world of the future is described vividly in the voice of the fictional poet Nulle. Includes 1995 Rhysling Award winner for Best Long Poem (Science Fiction Poetry Association). —Mayapple Press

Luoma, Bill. *Swoon Rocket*. 28p. pap. $6.00 (0-935724-74-5). Great Barrington, MA: The Figures, Spring 1996.

Lusk, Daniel. *The Cow Wars*. 36p. pap. $7.95 (1-879205-60-2). Troy, ME: Nightshade Press, Spring 1995.

Lux, Thomas. *Split Horizon*. 81p. $18.95 (0-395-70098-1); pap. $9.95 (0-395-70097-3). Boston, MA: Houghton Mifflin Company, Fall 1994. Winner of the 1995 Kingsley Tufts Poetry Award. Lux's level gaze, cool talk and weird rhythms embrace both the gorgeous surfaces and unsuspected inscapes of everyday surreality. —Houghton Mifflin Company. [This is] the poetry of unshed tears, hard-edged and adult. He is a writer who has gambled and won by his refusal to be taken seriously. —Jack Miles

Lux, Thomas. *The Blind Swimmer: Selected Early Poems 1970-1975*. 64p. pap. $10.00 (0-938566-73-3). Easthampton, MA: Adastra Press, Fall 1996. Included in this edition are poems selected from Thomas Lux's first two books along with six previously uncollected poems from the same time period. —Adastra Press. His voice is characterized by that mixture of colloquial and lyrical whose music and spatial relations are those of a born talker. —Helen Chasin, *The Village Voice*. Deadly accuracy and an almost perfect sense of timing. The poems explode into the reader's brain, permanently embedded. —Cynthia Macdonald, *Parnassus: Poetry in Review*

Lyman, Henry, ed. *After Frost: An Anthology of Poetry From New England*. 243p. pap. $14.95 (1-55849-041-8). Amherst, MA: University of Massachusetts Press, Fall 1996.

Lynch, Kathleen. *How To Build an Owl*. 32p. pap. $5.00. Pleasant Hill, CA: Small Poetry Press.

Mac Low, Jackson. *Barnesbook: Four Poems Derived from Sentences by Djuna Barnes*. 66p. pap. $9.95 (1-55713-235-6). Los Angeles, CA: Sun & Moon Press, Fall 1996. Long an admirer of the work of Djuna Barnes, noted poet Mac Low has used five of her books as the source material for this wonderful nonintentional work

that "whispers" Barnes's incredible words "something quick" into the ear. —Sun & Moon Press

Mac Low, Jackson. *From Pearl Harbor Day to FDR's Birthday*. 68p. pap. $10.95 (0-940650-19-3). Los Angeles, CA: Sun & Moon Press, Fall 1995. Upon its original publication in 1982, *From Pearl Harbor Day to FDR's Birthday*, representing work written from the 7th of December 1981 to the 30th of January 1982, was recognized as a significant new direction in the writing of noted poet Jackson Mac Low. Although he had written disjunctive poems since the 1930s, this work evinced a new interest in intentional methodology, as opposed to chance-oriented poems. —Sun & Moon Press

MacFadyen, Janet. *In Defense of Stones*. 32p. pap. $8.50. Sunderland, MA: Heatherstone Press, Fall 1995.

Maciel, Olivia. *Saltier Than Sweet (Mas Salado que Dulce)*. 70p. pap. $7.95 (1-877636-13-4). Chicago, IL: March/Abrazo Press, Spring 1995. Bilingual edition. Olivia Maciel has found the proper tension between the tangible and the ethereal. She uses strong images and lines; they are concise, almost other-worldly. There is pain in her poems but from a survivor's stance and much love. —Luis J. Rodriguez. Like Rosario Ferré, Maciel provides her own English translations, which are really poetic transmutations of the originals. —Susana Cavallo

Mack, Richard, Jr. *Bittersweet.* 62p. $10.95 (0-944957-45-5). New York, NY: Rivercross Publishing, Spring 1996.

Mackay Brown, George. *Selected Poems, 1954-1992.* 176p. pap. $12.95 (0-87745-555-4). Iowa City, IA: University of Iowa Press, Fall 1996. The culminating work of a major 20th century Scottish poet who died in April, 1996. —University of Iowa Press. His vision has something of the skaldic poet's consciousness of inevitable ordeal, something of the haiku master's susceptibility to the delicate and momentary. Since the beginning of his career he has added uniquely and steadfastly to the riches of poetry in English. —Seamus Heaney

Maddox, Marjorie. *Perpendicular as I.* 70p. pap. $9.95 (1-

885926-05-7). Charlotte, NC: Sandstone Publishing, Fall 1995. Marjorie Maddox returns again and again to the ways body becomes landscape and landscape becomes body, internal and external repeatedly merging with one another. In extraordinary poems like "The Truth of Lies, The Lies of Truth," in which she tells of her father's breath and the wind and how they whip "through my eyes,/ my mouth, carve truth and lie/ on the same stone," Maddox's truths and lies are triumphant indeed. —Andrew Hudgins

Mager, Don. *Glosses: Twenty-four Preludes and Etudes.* 62p. pap. $8.00 (1-879934-38-8). Laurinburg, NC: St. Andrews College Press, Spring 1995. An experiment in intertextuality supplemented by a variety of free style improvisations exploring how texts set beside each other may provoke additional significances. —St. Andrews College Press. Mager has it! "If lack of time/ prohibits, read/ only the end;/ if lack of time/ does not permit/ then read all/ but the end only." But, Friends, read, do read, and be richly rewarded. —Ronald H. Bayes

Mahapatra, Anuradha. Translated by Carolyne Wright, Jyotirmoy Datta, and Paramita Banerjee. *Another Spring, Darkness: Selected Poems*. 112p. $23.95 (0-934971-52-8); pap. $12.95 (0-934971-51-X). Corvallis, OR: Calyx Books, Fall 1996. These are excellent translations of an unusual poetry, harsh and ambiguous and beautiful, at once starkly realistic and resonant with myth. —Chitra Banerjee Divakaruni. It's a rare pleasure to read translations of poems that convey them as poetry. These versions from the Bangali evoke that thrill of recognition: that across culture and language we are encountering a great world poet. In their rendering, Anuradha Mahapatra's vision is simultaneously poetic and political, local and horizonless, moved by love and utterly unsentimental. —Adrienne Rich

Mahon, Derek. *The Hudson Letter*. 64p. $14.95 (0-916390-71-3); pap. $8.95 (0-916390-70-5). Winston-Salem, NC: Wake Forest University Press, Spring 1996. The noise and violence and ugliness of New York have offered Mahon, the supreme lover of beauty and form and

irony, a perfect challenge. —Peggy O'Brien, *The Irish Times*

Mahon, Derek. *The Hunt By Night*, Revised Edition. 54p. pap. $6.95 (0-916390-17-9). Winston-Salem, NC: Wake Forest University Press. Mahon is always poised, but his poise is that of a man balanced on the edge of the abyss. What gives Mahon's work its secret weight is absence, the hollow heavy ache of all that is not there: happiness, love, family, the cherished place, whatever. —John Banville, *The New York Review of Books*. Derek Mahon has one of the most distinctive voices in contemporary poetry, Irish or otherwise. He is a witty Romantic, a Belfast Keats with a Popean sting. Mahon can be tragic, but he's never gloomy. —Brendan Kennelly, *The Irish Times*

Maiden, Nell. *Reflections in a Clockshop*. 48p. pap. $8.00 (1-885912-06-4). Abingdon, VA: Sow's Ear Press, Fall 1996. These poems are remarkable for the variety and interest of their subjects, for their unpretentious yet sophisticated forms and diction, and for the assured, complex moments of insight they achieve. —John Lang

Major, Clarence, ed. *The Garden Thrives: Twentieth Century African-American Poetry.* 470p. pap. $17.00 (0-06-095121-4). New York, NY: HarperCollins/ HarperPerennial, Spring 1996. Featuring work from the turn of the century through the Harlem Renaissance and the profoundly political 1960's and 70's to the diversity of contemporary society, [this] is the first truly comprehensive anthology of twentieth century African-American poetry. —Harper-Collins. These many distinctive voices, exploring a legacy of injustice and racism, represent a fundamental achievement of American poetry. This [is] a valuable, comprehensive work. Recommended for all libraries. —Frank Allen, *Library Journal*

Major, Devorah. *Street Smarts.* 64p. pap. $10.95 (1-880684-27-6). Willimantic, CT: Curbstone Press, Spring 1996. Devorah Major writes with one foot in Africa and the other coming through the morning news. *Street Smarts* is a poetry party on paper. Listen to this woman swing! —E. Ethelbert Miller

Malanga, Gerard. *Mythologies of the Heart.* 179p. $25.00 (0-87685-994-5); pap. $13.50 (0-87685-993-7); sig. $35.00 (0-87685-995-3). Santa Rosa, CA: Black Sparrow Press, Spring 1996. Playing on the gaps between photo, fact and dream, this is a book that dissolves old dichotomies of looking and seeing. In Malanga's poems the camera lens opens a window of the soul into the instant of erotic revelation, baring the mysteries of an "infinite mask," "her other self under strobes." —Black Sparrow Press

Mallarmé, Stéphen. *Collected Poems.* 300p. pap. $18.95 (0-520-20711-4). Berkeley, CA: University of California Press, Fall 1994.

Malroux, Claire. Translated by Marilyn Hacker. *Edge.* 81p. pap. $9.95 (0-916390-74-8). Winston-Salem, NC: Wake Forest University Press, Fall 1996. Here's one of the finest poets now writing in France in the magnificent new translation of Marilyn Hacker. Claire Malroux is a name every devoted reader of poetry will want to know. She reminds us that lyric poetry can speak of our lives in the way that nothing else can. —Charles Simic

Mangan, Kathy. *Above the Tree Line.* 64p. pap. $11.95 (0-88748-191-4). Pittsburgh, PA: Carnegie Mellon University Press, Spring 1995. Kathy Mangan is as exciting a new poet as I have seen. —Dave Smith. Kathy Mangan's poetry is mature, moving, and gives its experience with unmistakable authority. These poems reward the reader with their skill; they move and illuminate. —Josephine Jacobsen

Mankiewicz, Angela Consolo. *Cancer Poems.* 19p. pap. $2.00. Los Angeles, CA: Undulating Bedsheets Productions, Fall 1995. Poems dealing with the illness of a loved one. —Undulating Bedsheets

Mannion, James. *Nurture Me, Baby.* 34p. (1-887775-06-4). New York, NY: Cryptic Press, Spring 1995. A little comic relief. —Cryptic Press

Manrique, Jaime. Translated by Edith Grossman and Eugene Richie. *My Night With / Mi Noche con Federico García Lorca.* 90p. pap. $10.00 (1-877593-01-X). Port Washington, NY:

Groundwater Press, Fall 1995. Memories of an ecstatic childhood—walks by the sea, "a happy mambo," eating deceptive tropical fruits—merge with those of recent loves in these luscious, incantatory poems. —John Ashbery

Mansour, Joyce. Translated by Serge Gavronsky. *Screams.* 50p. pap. $10.00 (0-942996-25-9). Sausalito, CA: Post-Apollo Press, Fall 1995. This slim book of poetry is a translation of Mansour's first book, originally published in French in 1953. Anyone familiar with the work of French feminist theorists like Cixous or Kristeva will find much of interest in Mansour's poetry. —*Women In Libraries.* Joyce Mansour writes a poetry of the sacred body in extremis—satiric, lavish, lusting, insatiable. Her distinctive work in the Gavronsky translation should excite serious attention. —Rachel Blau DuPlessis

Manyarrows, Victoria Lena. *Songs From the Native Lands.* 81p. pap. $9.95 (0-9645234-1-8). San Francisco, CA: Nopal Press, Spring 1995.

Mariani, Paul. *The Great Wheel.* 61p. $18.95 (0-393-03921-8).

New York, NY: W.W. Norton & Company, Spring 1996. With *The Great Wheel* Paul Mariani arrives more fully than ever before as our poet of moon-dazzled and faithful but agonized prayer. By way of passionate story and rhythm, he kneels among candles here, 'small wheels/ of fire that tug against their wicks,' and prays the songs that St. John of the Cross and Gerard Manley Hopkins might have sung in the crucible of our time. —William Heyen

Marion, Jeff Daniel. *Lost & Found*. 64p. $19.95 (1-885912-03-X); pap. $9.95 (1-885912-02-1). Abingdon, VA: Sow's Ear Press, Fall 1994. *Lost & Found* confirms Marion's reputation as one of the most accomplished poets writing in—and about—Appalachia. —John Lang, *Appalachian Studies*

Marius, Richard, ed. *The Columbia Book of Civil War Poetry: From Whitman to Walcott*. 543p. (0-231-10002-7). Irvington, NY: Columbia University Press, Fall 1995. This eye-opening collection illuminates the literary meanings and memory of the Civil War as well as key aspects of the place of poetry in American popular culture. *The Columbia Book of Civil War Poetry* is a volume to be dipped into time and again by anyone who cherishes language and history. —Louis P. Masur

Locklin, Gerald. *Not the Pittsburgh Poems*. 22p. pap. $4.00. Albuquerque, NM: Zerx Press, Spring 1996. A double book, bound back-to-back with Mark Weber's *The Pittsburgh Poems*.

Marquart, Debra. *Everything's a Verb*. 80p. pap. $7.95 (0-89823-162-0). Minneapolis, MN: New Rivers Press, Spring 1995. This collection of poetry from North Dakota native Debra Marquart is a stunning compilation. Marquart has a gift for putting to the page fascinating images of common experience. —*The Minnesota Daily*

Marshall, Jack. *Millennium Fever*. 96p. pap. $11.95 (1-56689-054-3). Minneapolis, MN: Coffee House Press, Fall 1996. Throughout *Millennium Fever*, Marshall's reinvigoration of the language and his evocation of the movement of the psyche [is] exhilarating. —Morton Marcus. Marshall's poetry is the kind that unfolds more and more as it is read and re-read. —*Painted Hills Review*

Martin, Richard. *Negation of Beautiful Words*. 32p. pap. $5.00. Bedford, NH: Igneus Press, Spring 1996. Martin's poems are zany, clever, and insightful about American culture. —Peter Kidd

Martínez, Dionisio D. *Bad Alchemy*. 112p. $17.95 (0-393-03733-9). New York, NY: W.W. Norton & Company, Spring 1995. Dionisio Martínex is one of the most exciting new voices in American poetry. His poems are mysterious and intellectually provocative. —Stephen Dunn. Martínez's exuberance is a very winning quality. Decidedly American, it is also an expression of the immigrant's sense of America. These poems reflect poignantly on the poet's status as a Cuban exile destined to a perennial sense of dislocation. Nostalgia combined with ardor results in good chemistry—or *Bad Alchemy*. —David Lehman

Martinson, Linda. *Poetry of Pain*. 45p. pap. $9.95 (0-9648978-2-2). Lynwood, WA: Simply Books, Spring 1996. This is a very important book. Pain is a universal experience and those who must face the challenge of chronic pain on a daily basis can teach us a great deal about what it means to be a human being. —William Collinge, Ph.D.

Martone, John. *Primer*. 58p. pap. $5.00 (1-57141-008-2). Port Charlotte, FL: Runaway Spoon Press, Spring 1995. Haiku and haiku-like poems about day-to-day family life. —Runaway Spoon Press

Martz, Sandra Haldeman, ed. *Grow Old Along with Me—The Best Is Yet to Be*. 216p. $20.00 (0-918949-87-4); pap. $12.00 (0-918949-86-6); Large print: 264p. $17.00 (0-918949-96-3). Watsonville, CA: Papier-Mache Press, Fall 1996. This anthology, reflecting one of the most profound social changes of our times, creates a mirror for us as we grapple with the multi-faceted experiences of growing older. —Ellen Gee, Ph.D. Today's invisible man (and woman) is the old one. In this anthology, each poem speaks eloquently and says, "Here I be." Nothing could be more timely. —Studs Terkel

Martz, Sandra Haldeman, ed. *I Am Becoming the Woman I've Wanted.* 218p. $18.00 (0-918949-50-5); pap. $10.00 (0-918949-49-1). Watsonville, CA: Papier-Mache Press, October 1994. Winner of the 1995 American Book Award. Her newest collection continues to feature prose, poetry, and photography by and about women, but the theme here is life as it is experienced through the female body. Tending toward the emotive and always from the subjective, these pieces articulate what it is like to be Everywoman from every age. —*Library Journal.* At times this anthology achieves a light, greeting card style, yet it also touches upon difficult subjects such as incest, death and rape. Broadly sweeping over the issues the range of writing far outshines its intricacy. It will, however, find a match for many women's experiences, its lack of big name authors contributing to its strength as an Everywoman's book. —*Small Press*

Martz, Sandra Haldeman, ed. *If I Had My Life to Live Over I Would Pick More Daisies.* 240p. pap. $17.00 (0-918949-84-X). Watsonville, CA: Papier-Mache Press, Spring 1996.

Wow! Just plain wow! The cumulative effect of these women's voices challenges us to live life to the fullest. Powerful and poignant. —Glenda Martin, *Minnesota Women's Press.* It is fabulous. . . . We know these women. They are our neighbors, our friends, ourselves. —*Indianapolis News*

Martz, Sandra Haldeman, ed. Images by Deidra Scherer. *Threads of Experience.* 64p. $19.95 (0-918949-92-0). Watsonville, CA: Papier-Mache Press, Fall 1996. In their first collaborative project, internationally acclaimed fiber artist Deidre Scherer and anthologist Sandra Haldeman Martz have created a stunning tribute to the wisdom, strength, and courage of older women and men. —Papier-Mache Press

Martz, Sandra Haldeman, ed. *When I Am an Old Woman I Shall Wear Purple.* Large Print Edition. 181p. pap. $17.00 (0-918949-83-1). Watsonville, CA: Papier-Mache Press, Spring 1996. Winner of the ABBY Honors Award (1991) and two Benjamin Franklin Awards: for design and content, literature (1988); for excellence and innovation in marketing, literature (1992). The literary quality of these stories and poems is consistently high [offering] exciting glimpses into the lives of old women. —*Women's Review of Books.* How do you account for an underground best-seller on the subject of aging women? The answer is easy: *honesty.* This is a small-press runaway success about older women. The book is finely crafted, unusual in its focus, universal in its ability to sensitize us to the human condition. —*Georgia Journal*

Maso, Carole. *Aureole.* 214p. $22.00 (0-88001-482-2). Hopewell, NJ: Ecco Press, Fall 1996. [Maso] brings to life a 'bombardment of images and sounds,' fashioning a pattern of astonishing complexity and beauty. The toughmindedness, originality and wit of her perceptions are intoxicating. —*Publishers Weekly*

Mason, David. *The Country I Remember.* 78p. $21.00 (1-885266-20-0); pap. $12.00 (1-885266-23-5). Brownsville, OR: Story Line Press, Spring 1996. Winner of the Alice Fay Di Castagnola Award from the Poetry Society of America. This family and national saga is

narrative poetry at its best. Told in the voices of a father and daughter, it spans the period 1830 to 1960 and deals with the frontier's lure, westward migration, the Civil War and the modernization and urbanization of America. A model of narrative scope combined with poetic compression. —*Publishers Weekly,* starred review. I wanted it not to end, so quietly powerful are its voices and so intimate its vision. —Joyce Carol Oates. Highly recommended. —*Library Journal*

Mataka, Laini. *Restoring the Queen.* 110p. pap. $8.95 (0-933121-80-6). Baltimore, MD: Black Classic Press, Fall 1994. The poems of Laini Mataka display her sharp wit, sincere political consciousness, and genuine love for Black people. —Black Classic Press

Matherne, Beverly. *La Grande Pointe.* 48p. $15.00 (0-89304-230-7); pap. $7.50 (0-89304-231-5). Merrick, NY: Cross-Cultural Communications, Spring 1995. Bilingual edition, English originals with Cajun French translations by the author. The poet celebrates the culture of her people, the

189

Acadians and Alsatians who in-
termarried and settled along
both sides of the Mississippi
River between New Orleans
and Baton Rouge. —Cross-
Cultural Communications. Beverly Matherne's bilingual poems
are sensual, specific, and
vivid—moving depictions of a
people and of a world. —Jane
Hirshfield

Mathis, Cleopatra. *Guardian.*
105p. $19.95 (1-878818-49-X).
Riverdale-on-Hudson, NY:
Sheep Meadow Press, Fall 1995.

Mattawa, Khaled. *Ismailia Eclipse.*
81p. pap. $12.95 (1-878818-
44-9). Riverdale-on-Hudson,
NY: Sheep Meadow Press, Fall
1995. Khaled Mattawa's *Ismailia Eclipse* filters beautiful
and terrifying images through
multiple lenses. He speaks
from a place fortified with experience and imagination, and
the reader is taken on a journey
that challenges and humanizes.
—Yusef Komunyakaa. It is the
revelation of poetic truth that
is central to this book with
its double vision of the Arab
and American worlds, eclips-
ing and revealing one another.
—Stanley Moss

Matthews, Mary. *As Close as
Possible.* 24p. pap. $7.00

(1-886226-02-4). Chico, CA:
Flume Press, Spring 1996.

Matthews, William. *Time &
Money: New Poems.* 80p. $19.95
(0-395-71134-7); pap. $12.95
(0-395-82526-1). Boston, MA:
Houghton Mifflin Company,
Fall 1995. Winner of the 1995
National Book Critics Circle
Award for Poetry. The applica-
tion of intelligence and classi-
cal training to every stratum of
American life results in poems
that revel in etymology and
delight in colloquialism.
—*The New Yorker*

Maurer-Alvarez, Pansy. *Dolores:
The Alpine Years.* 70p. $20.00
(1-882413-31-8); pap. $12.00
(1-882413-30-X). Brooklyn,
NY: Hanging Loose Press, Fall
1996. The relaxed and elegant
shaping of the poems in this
collection makes a whole world
of friendships, love, travel, food
and opera breathtakingly invit-
ing. —Ed Friedman. This fic-
tional sequence of poems is
humorous, linguistically sensual,
smart and down-home. Our
heroine, an adventurous dental
hygienist, thinks whatever she
pleases, in poems differently
shaped from each other and reg-
istered by a precise musical ear.
A real pleasure. —Alice Notley

Mayerson, Charlotte. *The Death Cycle Machine.* 80p. $16.00 (0-517-70279-7). New York, NY: Crown Publishers, Fall 1995. Only now, so late in the ghastly game, has a mother put into important poetry what it was like to have a grown son die of AIDS. —Kurt Vonnegut

Mayes, Frances. *Ex Voto.* 72p. pap. $12.00 (0-918786-47-9). Barrington, RI: Lost Roads Publishers, Spring 1995. [Mayes is] a poet of her world, a writer inventing the world as she moves through it, unwilling to accept anyone else's version of it. There is an immediacy [here] combined with the sense of an ongoing traditional struggle that pushes the poem out, makes it a poem of necessity. —*The San Francisco Chronicle.* Mayes has an urgent interest in the ways past and present converge. She writes with terse magic. —*The Los Angeles Times*

Mayes, Frances. *The Book of Summer.* 64p. $295.00 (0-940592-27-4). Woodside, CA: The Heyeck Press, Fall 1995. The rich details in these exciting poems take the reader from villages like Montecatini in Italy to Golden Gate Park in California, from the expiations of medieval saints to the pervasive memories of the second World War. Drawings by Corinne Okada. Numbered and signed limited edition; letterpress on handmade paper. —Heyeck Press

Mayo-Smith, Ian. *Poems, Essays and Comments for Everyone (PEACE).* 102p. pap. $9.95 (1-56549-043-6). West Hartford, CT: Kumarian Press, Spring 1995. Mayo-Smith's Christian and Buddhist background and his world-wide experience result in fresh perspectives. His approach ranges from witty and humorous to passionate and contemplative. —Kumarian Press

Mayröcker, Friederike. Translated by Rosmarie Waldrop. *Heiligenanstalt.* 96p. pap. $8.00 (0-930901-95-9). Providence, RI: Burning Deck, Fall 1994. Four prose poems about Chopin and other Romantic composers in Mayröcker's famous "hallucinatory" style. The collection is presided over by Beethoven whose "Heiligenstadt Testament" is evoked in the title. —Burning Deck

Mazer, Ben. *White Cities.* 53p. pap. $10.00 (0-9645516-0-8). Cambridge, MA: Barbara Matteau Editions, Spring 1995. The bulk of the work is mysterious—even opaque—but intriguing. —Richard Wilbur. Ben Mazer in his *White Cities* finds a careening pace of wit, passion and word to display his magic hungers. —Willis Barnstone

Mazur, Gail. *The Common.* 88p. $22.50 (0-226-51439-0); pap. $11.95 (0-226-51439-0). Chicago, IL: University of Chicago Press, Spring 1995. At the heart of Mazur's *The Common* is the refusal to simplify what is paradoxical in our world and a recognition of the tensions in our own divided nature. These unflinching poems create a place where wisdom and foolishness, rage and pity, love and diffidence, naturally co-exist. —University of Chicago Press. Knowing, cheeky, palpably sensuous, and painfully close to home, these poems and what they achieve are anything but common. —Lloyd Schwartz

McBreen, Joan. *A Walled Garden in Moylough.* 52p. pap. $10.95 (1-885266-07-3). Brownsville, OR: Story Line Press, Fall 1995. Joan McBreen is a phenomenon. —*Booklist.* [Reading these poems] one is struck by the lyrical magic of the language, the precision of the diction, the absolute rightness of each and every word. There is a simplicity and straightforwardness to McBreen's poems, but it is the simplicity of a pleasing inviting facade, behind which lie nuances of association, emotion and meaning. —*Washington Review.*

McBride, Mekeel. *Wind of the White Dresses.* 91p. pap. $11.95 (0-88748-185-X). Pittsburgh, PA: Carnegie Mellon University Press, Spring 1995.

McCain, Gillian. *Tilt.* 88p. pap. $10.00 (1-889097-04-7). West Stockbridge, MA: Hard Press and The Figures, co-publishers, Fall 1996. Gillian McCain's poems are like urgent telegrams from next door, or oddly but brilliantly cropped snapshots of the life that is going by. —John Ashbery. In this brilliant collection of prose poems, Gillian McCain takes us on high-velocity spins to the four corners of what we thought was a familiar world. Neither it nor we will ever be quite the same again. So "be careful of the swallows when you open the garage door." —Harry Matthews

McCann, Richard. *Ghost Letters.* 60p. pap. $9.95 (1-882295-04-8). Farmington, ME: Alice James Books, Fall 1994. Winner of the 1994 Beatrice Hawley Award and the 1993 Capricorn Poetry Award. This ferociously tender poet instructs us that to be fully alive is to be entirely haunted. —Mark Doty. Richard McCann blazes, mourns, and sings himself into the only eternity we've got: these words, this page, and the way you looked, beloved, that night, turning away. *Ghost Letters* touches us in a way that feels like forever. —Carole Maso

McClanahan, Rebecca. *The Intersection of X and Y.* 62p. pap. $9.95 (0-914278-70-3). Providence, RI: Copper Beech Press, Spring 1996. Rebecca McClanahan praises the cacaphonous snarl of truth. These open-eyed poems are full of the stunned pleasure of being alert. —William Matthews. *The Intersection of X and Y* is a quiet, powerful book—like good southern bourbon. —Dave Smith

McClatchy, J. D., ed. *The Vintage Book of Contemporary World Poetry.* 656p. pap. $15.00 (0-679-74115-1). New York, NY: Vintage Books, Fall 1996. This may well be the poetry anthology for the global village. As selected by J. D. McClatchy, *The Vintage Book of Contemporary World Poetry* includes masterpieces from four continents and more than two dozen languages in translations by such distinguished poets as Elizabeth Bishop, W. S. Merwin, Ted Hughes, and Seamus Heaney. —Vintage Books

McCleery, David, ed. *A Diversity of Old Malt Quatrains or A Garland of Frothy Sentiments.* 65p. pap. $9.95 (0-9635559-4-4). Lincoln, NE: A Slow Tempo Press, Fall 1995. This collection is a gathering of old poems devoted to ale and beer found among broadside ballads or traditional convivial songs from Elizabethan and Stuart times, with just a few later ones added for good measure. —A Slow Tempo Press

McClure, Michael. *Three Poems: Dolphin Skull, Rare Angel & Dark Brown.* 256p. pap. $14.95 (0-14-047326). New York, NY: Penguin Books, Fall 1995. Without McClure's roar there would have been no sixties. —Dennis Hopper. Celebratory, elusive, freshly deliberate rituals—amazing. —Gary Snyder. Michael McClure's poetry and prose is one of the more remarkable achievements in recent American literature. —*The Times (London)*

McCosker, Karen, and Nicholas Albery, eds. *A Poem a Day.* 496p. pap. $18.00 (1-883642-38-8). South Royalton, VT: Steerforth Press, Fall 1996. 366 poems, old and new, worth learning by heart. —Steerforth Press. This book is a dream, a revivalist campaign, a challenge, a book of days and an anthology, all in one. —*The Guardian*

McCoy, David B. *The Geometry of Blue: Prose and Selected Poems.* 112p. pap. $12.00 (0-945568-17-7). Massillon, OH: Spare Change Poetry Press, Spring 1995. In this, David B. McCoy's newest book, his thoughts range from the woodshed out back to the outskirts of Russia, borne in the pocket of a gypsy, on waves of indignation, and over roads to the past. His warm and provocative poetry, like the "good wood" and the "good love" of his poem, "Wood," will burn long in the minds of his readers. —Peggy Brunyansky

McDaniel, Wilma Elizabeth. *The Last Dust Storm.* 104p. $20.00 (1-882413-17-2); pap. $12.00 (1-882413-16-4). Brooklyn, NY: Hanging Loose Press, Fall 1995. McDaniel's poems bear witness to one of the nation's most dramatic sagas, the Dustbowl exodus of the 1930's, and chronicle the lives of workers in California's Central Valley. —Hanging Loose Press. McDaniel, a farmworker all her long life, writes with full knowledge of its bitterness and hardship, but also with love and humor. —Noel Peattie, *Sipapu*. *The Last Dust Storm* is both scrapbook ("washboard music") and scripture ("tornado music"). The "ghosts" in McDaniel's lean, honest poetry belong to all of us. —Frank Allen, *American Book Review*

McDonald, Walter. *Counting Survivors.* 88p. $24.95 (0-8229-3874-X); pap. $10.95 (0-8229-5555-5). Pittsburgh, PA: University of Pittsburgh Press, Fall 1995. McDonald measures violence and its costs with the grace and sorrow of a man who knows exactly who he is and what he's done—that hard-won wisdom rings true in every line of his wonderful poetry. —Andrew Hudgins. The smells of Vietnam and Texas are interwoven here like the cross-stitches of survival itself, and every poem is as true as an oath. —Samuel Hazo

McDowell, Robert. Introduction by Dana Gioia. *The Diviners.* 72p. pap. $10.00 (1-885266-10-3). Brownsville, OR: Story Line Press, Fall 1995. McDowell relates the most crucial developments in the shared lives of Al and Eleanor and their son, Tom. The whole poem resembles a very good novel-in-story. —*Booklist.* [A poet who has] simply brushed aside Derridean anxieties to write poems with a strong narrative line, [his work] has the scope of a novel and uses effects learned from cinema as well as poetry. —Ian Gregson, *Los Angeles Times/Book Review*

McEwen, R.F. *Heartwood and Other Poems.* 115p. pap. $10.95 (0-9635559-5-2). Lincoln, NE: A Slow Tempo Press, Spring 1996. In the resurgence of American narrative verse, Robert F. McEwen's *Heartwood* is one of the most remarkable poems to come our way. In it we find compelling characters, expert dialog, and the haunting epic sweep of the forest

world of tree trimmers, of men and women working, almost one within the natural world. I was sorry when I reached the end of McEwen's poem. I was jealous that I had not written it. —Robert McDowell. A brave and ambitious poem. —Ted Kooser

McFall, Gardner. *The Pilot's Daughter.* 79p. $18.95 (1-56809-028-5); pap. $12.50 (1-56809-029-3). St. Louis, MO: Time Being Books, Spring 1996. Speaking of her father, lost in the Vietnam war, Gardner McFall writes: 'I have kept/ all the doors open in my life/ so that he could walk in . . .' The vibrant, deeply felt poems in this book open doors for the reader, too. —Linda Pastan. The ardors of domestic experience are what fuel her poems to their (often fierce) heat. I salute the intimate heroism thus revealed. —Richard Howard

McFee, Michael. *Colander.* 80p. pap. $11.95 (0-88748-224-4). Pittsburgh, PA: Carnegie Mellon University, Spring 1996.

McGinnis, Mary. *Listening for Cactus.* 96p. pap. $14.00 (0-9644196-4-5). Santa Fe, NM: Sherman Asher Publishing,

Fall 1996. Poetry celebrating the seen and unseen, the experience of disability and the New Mexico landscape, with its colors and its silences. —Sherman Asher Publishing

McGuckian, Medbh. *Captain Lavender.* 83p. $15.95 (0-916390-67-5); pap. $9.95 (0-916390-66-7). Winston-Salem, NC: Wake Forest University Press, Spring 1995. All metaphor is, of course, strictly speaking illogical. It's the degree to which McGuckian widens the angle between vehicle and tenor that gives her poems their compelling mystery. —Peggy O'Brian, *Colby Quarterly*

McKane, Richard. *Amphora for Metaphors.* 179p. pap. $12.00 (0-922792-56-9). New York, NY: Gnosis Press, 1993.

McKean, James. *Tree of Heaven.* Iowa City, IA: University of Iowa Press, Spring 1995. Winner of the 1994 Iowa Poetry Prize. McKean reminds me of what made sweet James Wright so powerful, a ruthless will to say how terrible life remains for so many and a simultaneous knack for saying how sweet, how honorable,

how splendid can be our best moments of understanding. —Dave Smith

McKee, Glenn. *Raising Doubt.* 44p. pap. $7.00. Monhegan, ME: Green Point Press, Spring 1996.

McKelvey, Douglas Kaine. *Cattail, Fishscale, and Snakeskin.* 45p. pap. $5.00 (0-940895-24-2). Chicago, IL: Cornerstone Press Chicago, Fall 1994.

McKenty, Bob. *Fallout From the Nuclear Family.* 71p. pap. $6.50. Red Bank, NJ: Northwind Publishing. Bob McKenty happens to be one of the most skillful practitioners of light verse now extant in America. A master of speaking with seeming effortlessness within the strict confines of meter and rhyme, he can let a sentence settle gracefully into its final line with a measured impact. —X.J. & Dorothy M. Kennedy. If you've forgotten how enjoyable poetry can be, remind yourself with this collection. —*Light: The Quarterly of Light Verse*

McKinnon, Patrick. *Out Past the Chain Links of Time.* 28p. pap.

$3.95 (0-9641986-5-7). Duluth, MN: Poetry Harbor, Fall 1995.

McLachlan, Meschach. *Seizures of the Sun: First Poems.* 32p. pap. $6.00 (1-883197-11-2). Cullowhee, NC: New Native Press, Fall 1996. Seventeen year old Meschach McLachlan falls into the elite company of such youthful prodigies as Keats, Lamantia, Dylan Thomas and Kenneth Patchen. —Thomas Rain Crowe. Truly one of the best young poets of his generation. —John Lane

McNaughton, Duncan. *Kicking The Feather.* 48p. pap. $10.00. Lawrence, KS: First Intensity Press, Fall 1996. McNaughton submits to languages and places whose violent passions he absorbs and transforms into poems which bear the burnt traces of his loves. —First Intensity Press

McNaughton, Duncan. *Valparaíso.* 132p. (0-9639321-2-8). Berkeley, CA: Listening Chamber, Fall 1995.

McPherson, Sandra. *Edge Effect: Trails and Portrayals.* 104p. $25.00 (0-8195-2225-2); pap. $11.95 (0-8195-2226-

0). Middletown, CT: Wesleyan/University Press of New England, Spring 1996. A fascinating, original, rich and appealing work that furthers McPherson's perspicacious examination of the natural world by paying the same kind of dignifying attention to 'outsider' artists. McPherson's language ranges from the scientific to the meditative, her forms from the notational to the elegant and eloquent. This is a masterful and expansive book. —Alison Deming

McPherson, Sandra. *The Spaces Between Birds.* 76p. $25.00 (0-8195-2227-9); pap. $11.95 (0-8195-2228-7). Middletown, CT: Wesleyan/University Press of New England, Spring 1996. From her first collection forward, Sandra McPherson has been admired for her precise language and unflinching vision. Now she focuses upon one of the toughest subjects a poet can embrace, the relationship with her child. In gathering twenty-eight years' worth of her own poems, as well as poems and sayings by her daughter, McPherson creates a complex fugue of innocence and responsibility. This is art of a high order. —Robert Phillips

McVoy, Terra Elan. *The Table Beneath the Hand.* 40p. pap. $5.00 (1-879934-42-6). Laurinburg, NC: St. Andrews College Press, Spring 1995. In these poems, McVoy deals with the tension between being assertive and sensitive, and the conflicting emotions that result for a young woman growing up in today's world. —St. Andrews College Press

Mead, Jane. *The Lord and the General Din of the World.* 96p. $19.95 (0-9641151-0-7); pap. $12.95 (0-9641151-1-5). Louisville, KY: Sarabande Books, Spring 1996. Selected by Philip Levine as the 1995 Winner of the Kathryn A. Morton Prize in Poetry. [Mead] employs taut, colloquial language and firmly places her personal history (addiction, abuse, suicide and profound isolation) against a searching, almost existential understanding of the world. She gives form to tenuous, seemingly nameless emotions. That precision gives her poetry its power. —*Publishers Weekly.* [This is a] work of strength, heart, and discovery. —*American Book Review.* Mead's poems are dark, inward-turning, demanding, with flashes of wry humor . . .

They labor heroically to understand the relationship of body, mind, and soul. These are poems of rigorous and searing integrity. —*Beloit Poetry Journal*

Meander, Joshua. *Blue Corn Harvest: Collected Poems 1978-1994.* 135p. Chicago, IL: Adams Press, Fall 1995. If you are irked by lack of respect for life, there are words of encouragement here to reaffirm your social consciousness. —Adams Press

Medina, Tony. *No Noose Is Good Noose.* 157p. pap. $15.00 (0-86316-109-X). New York, NY: Writers and Readers Publishing/Harlem River Press, Spring 1996. Medina's poetry is grounded in the dance, laughter, sarcasm, indignation, resistance, and liberation of the people. In the tradition of the radical Black and New World poets of the 60's and 70's, Medina's mission is to force today's poetry from the safe confines of the academy out into the explosive and resistant spaces of the street and the work place. —Writers and Readers Publishing

Meehan, Maude. *Washing the Stones: Selected Poems 1975-1995.* 240p. pap. $13.00. Watsonville, CA: Papier-Mache Press, Spring 1996. These poems celebrate family, children, and long years of sensual love. There are many lovely poems in this collection. —Grace Paley. *Washing The Stones*, Maude Meehan's selected poems, is a moving tribute of a life well-loved, a love well-lived. I am somehow changed by the clarity and authenticity of this generous voice, these fiercely human poems. —Lucille Clifton

Meek, Jay. *Windows.* 63p. pap. $11.95 (0-88748-171-X). Pittsburgh, PA: Carnegie Mellon University Press, Fall 1994. [Meek's poems] are keenly aware of being measured out against silence, aware of how hard it is to say anything with integrity, and that is why they are so precise and carefully difficult, why they can honestly be called 'responsible.' —David Rothman, *Quarterly West*

Meinke, Peter. *Scars.* 76p. $24.95 (0-8229-3935-5); pap. $10.95 (0-8229-5592-X). Pittsburgh, PA: University of Pittsburgh Press, Spring 1996. These poems get hold of us by the coat lapels and when they release us we are delighted,

shaken, and considerably wiser. —Ted Kooser. The poems in this book say truth, and they say it with rue, wit, shapeliness, a wonderful hand on the keyboard of metaphor. —Alicia Ostriker

Mekas, Jonas. Translated by Vyt Bakaitis. *There Is No Ithaca: Idylls of Semeniskiai & Reminiscences.* 181p. pap. $14.95 (0-9628181-1-9). New York, NY: Black Thistle Press, Fall 1996. This is the first English translation of two poem cycles that have become part of the classic repertory of modern Lithuanian literature. Although *Idylls of Semeniskiai* was acclaimed under the Soviet regime as a classic for its depiction of rural life and the richness of its language, *Reminiscences* was banned for its "romanticizing" of the life of Lithuanian exiles. —Black Thistle Press. His sensitivity to the unrepeatable light, color, scents of his native region, in the north of Lithuania, is that of a visionary who lifts the most earthly details of reality to a higher level of intensity. —Czeslaw Milosz

Meléndez, Jesús Papoleto. *Concertos on Market Street.* 79p. (0-9626355-2-9). San Diego, CA:

Kemetic Images, Fall 1994. These are "contemporary beat-poems," urban still-lifes— hanging out on street corners, being homeless in some of the most beautiful cities in the United States, witnessing public outrage and apathy. Written, this poetry seems to jump off the page in a stylized technique of word-upon-space visualization. Presented orally, it is melodic, a rhythmic processional sounding of syllables. —Kemetic Images

Melhem, D. H. *Rest in Love.* 109p. pap. $9.95 (0-913057-22-3). Brookville, NY: Confrontation Magazine Press, reissued Fall 1995. Melhem explores the personal universe of the family circle—the poetry of dailiness. It is the backward journey of a daughter in search of another "lost woman." No one has set forth so well the strong and beautiful bond between mother and daughter. —Olga Cabral

Melnyczuk, Askold, ed. *Take Three: AGNI New Poets Series: I* 129p. pap. $12.95 (1-55597-239-X). St. Paul, MN: Graywolf Press, Spring 1996. The first in a new annual series designed to launch the work of new poets, this volume features Thomas Sayers Ellis, Larissa Szporluk, and Joe Osterhaus. —Graywolf Press

Meltzer, David. *Arrows: Selected Poetry 1957-1992.* 193p. $25.00 (0-87685-939-2); pap. $13.00 (0-87685-938-4). Santa Rosa, CA: Black Sparrow Press, Fall 1994. This new compilation gathers together a generous selection of Meltzer's recent work, including two extended texts, *Bakelite* and *PaRDeS*, with highlights from long out-of-print collections. The book offers an excellent showcase of Meltzer's career, the best of thirty-five years of his poetry. —Black Sparrow Press

Melville, Herman. *Battle-Pieces and Aspects of the War.* 282p. pap. $13.95 (0-306-80655-X). New York, NY: Da Capo Press, Fall 1995. As North and South strove for control of the nation's fundamental character during the Civil War, Melville redefined his own identity as a writer, shifting his emphasis from novels and short stories to poetry. For Melville, this genre best suited the issues surrounding the Civil War, which even today defy confinement to any single perspective. —Da Capo Press

Menes, Orlando Ricardo. *Border-lands With Angels.* pap. $5.00 (0-9637849-5-1). Bristolville, OH: The Bacchae Press, Fall 1994.

Merrill, C. S. *O'Keeffe: Days in a Life.* 140p. pap. $12.00 (0-9631909-8-9). Albuquerque, NM: La Alameda Press, Spring 1996. When I got O'Keeffe mss I sat down after midnite at kitchen table when I should've been in bed & read it thru in an hour because it was interesting, curious, distinctive, focused, condensed, epiphanous, ordinary & understandable. The details are all, sacramentalizing everyday life in a world of genius—a woman, vast space, chewy intelligence, almost selfless observation. —Allen Ginsberg. Merrill's poetic biography of Georgia O'Keeffe chronicles the artist's last days. This is a collection of poems that stand on their own, clean and spare, while fleshing out the icon that is their subject. —Anne Mac Naughton, *The Santa Fe Reporter*

Merrill, James. *A Scattering of Salts.* 112p. $20.00 (0-679-44158-1); pap. $14.00 (0-679-76590-5). New York, NY: Alfred A. Knopf, Fall 1995.

Merrill, for all the poignancy of his work, was a comic poet in the line of Pope and Byron and Auden; and from the very beginning of his long career, the poems he published combined, in sparkling ways, suffering and joy. —Helen Vendler, *The New York Review of Books.* In these last poems, lucid, deft, fond, shrewd, faithful, Merrill once again reveals himself as our most visual poet, combining a superb eye with an unfailing ear . . . American poetry has lost one of its masters, one of the giants of the generation born in the 1920s. —Peter Davison, Boston *Globe*

Merrin, Jeredith. *Shift.* 96p. (est.) $20.00 (0-226-52063-3); pap. $9.95 (0-226-52064-1). Chicago, IL: University of Chicago Press, Fall 1996. Jeredith Merrin has written a book of human encounters, splendid in variety. Haunting or comforting, tangential or at the center of the poet's emotional life, these figures pass breathing under Merrin's distinctively intimate, analytical, respectful and bemused gaze. In that passionate, undistorting attention, Merrin has forged a striking, fresh poetry. —Robert Pinsky.

One of the most poised and thoroughly fulfilled books I've read in years. —Frank Bidart

Merwin, W.S. *The Vixen.* 76p. $21.00 (0-679-44477-7). New York, NY: Alfred A. Knopf, Fall 1995. Merwin's new book of poems is concerned with the people and countryside of the relatively unknown part of southwest France with which he has been associated for many years. Part lyrical, part narrative, these poems are the work of a master. —Alfred A. Knopf

Merwin, W.S. *Travels.* 139p. pap. $12.00 (0-679-75277-3). New York, NY: Alfred A. Knopf, Fall 1994. In *Travels*, one of the most beautiful and moving collections of poetry of his career, W.S. Merwin displays his narrative gifts to provide us with a book of deep historical resonance and luminous poetic grace. With each new book we have been reminded why, for forty years, he has remained a pivotal figure in the literary life of this country. [He] continues to earn his place as one of our most influential and compelling contemporary poets. —David St. John, *Los Angeles Times Book Review*

Messerli, Douglas, ed. *The Gertrude Stein Awards in Innovative American Poetry 1994/95.* pap. $13.95 (1-55713-161-9). Los Angeles, CA: Sun & Moon Press, Fall 1996.

Messineo, David. *A Taste of Italy.* 24p. pap. $12.00. Secaucus, NJ: David Messineo, Spring 1995.

Metras, Gary. *Seagull Beach.* 35p. $30.00 (0-938566-68-7); pap. $10.00 (0-938566-69-5). Easthampton, MA: Adastra Press, Fall 1995. This long poem explores the impact a day at the beach can have on the mind and spirit. Hand-crafted letterpress edition. —Adastra Press

Mezey, Robert. *Natural Selection.* 28p. Edgewood, KY: Robert L. Barth (R.L.B.), Spring 1995.

Michaels, Kevin. *Vice Verses.* 62p. pap. $10.00. Hicksville, NY: Sound Attitude Books, Fall 1995. You are not likely to find a collection of poems as shocking and controversial as *Vice Verses*, a portrayal of our mean streets and our decadent era. Native New Yorker Michaels' poems tackle the topics of alcohol and drug addiction, rape, murder, homelessness, the self image and paranoia of Generation X— putting himself on the front lines of America. —Sound Attitude Books

Middleton, Christopher. *Intimate Chronicles.* 96p. pap. $10.95 (1-878818-47-3). Riverdale-on-Hudson, NY: Sheep Meadow Press, Fall 1995. Middleton is one of the most extraordinary and extraordinarily neglected English poets. —T.J.C. Harris

Middleton, David. *Bonfires on the Levee.* 28p. pap. $8.00 (1-884725-24-X). Thibodaux, LA: Blue Heron Press, Fall 1996. I am intimately reconnected with both my past and my present through the delicacy of the imagery and the reminiscences in these poems. I am privileged to see with new eyes a land I have known for half a century. —Olivia Pass

Midge, Tiffany. *Outlaws, Renegades and Saints: Diary of a Mixed Up Halfbreed.* 104p. pap. $12.95 (0-912678-93-3). Greeville Center, NY: Greenfield Review Press, Fall 1996. Winner of the 1994 North American Writers First Book Award for Poetry. Tiffany Midge has written a wonderful first book, full of beauty and

sadness, horsepower and horseplay, cowboys and Indians, half-acres and half-breeds, outhouses and out-and-out lies, hard truths, and soft places. She's got stories we all need to hear. —Sherman Alexie

Mihalas, Dimitri. *Life Matters.* 63p. pap. $5.00 (1-881-900-03-7). Champaign, IL: Hawk Productions, Fall 1994. Mihalas's title, *Life Matters,* is an intentional double entendre referring at once to the innumerable daily matters that can obscure our lives and a declaration that life *matters.* It is important. These are poems that deal with both meanings. —Hawk Productions

Milder, Ben. *The Good Book Says . . . : Light Verse to Illuminate the Old Testament.* 145p. $20.95 (1-56809-013-7); pap. $14.50 (1-56809-014-5). St. Louis, MO: Time Being Books, Fall 1995. Biblical exegesis may seem an unlikely source of smiles, but Ben Milder's deft verse succeeds both in entertaining and in casting new light on the Old Testament. Guaranteed to cheer you up next time you find yourself in a hotel room with only a Gideon Bible and a broken TV set.

—X.J. Kennedy. A writer of light verse, Milder looks at the world around him with humorous intent. —*St. Louis Post-Dispatch*

Miller, Adam David. *Forever Afternoon.* 80p. pap. $10.00 (0-87013-354-3). East Lansing, MI: Michigan State University Press/Lotus Poetry Series, Fall 1994. Winner of the 1994 Naomi Long Madgett Poetry Award.

Miller, David. *Stromata.* 64p. pap. $8.00 (0-930901-96-7). Providence, RI: Burning Deck, Spring 1995. Poems that sift and resift the lessons of perception, of 'raw' experience, in order to define just what it means to be alive and to think. —Norman Jope

Miller, E. Ethelbert. *First Light: New and Selected Poems.* 194p. pap. $11.95 (0-933121-81-4). Baltimore, MD: Black Classic Press, Fall 1994. From the deep south lore of Black men talking at dusk, to the strained utterances of peasant hope in Central America, to the soft feeling of light passing through a lover's translucent hands at dawn, Miller weaves a brilliant canopy of words.

—Houston A. Baker. E. Ethelbert Miller has chosen for his subjects those unseen 'American moments' of everyday life. His poetry is smooth, without being facile, deep, yet clear, real, yet surreal. —Ishmael Reed

Miller, E. Ethelbert, ed. *In Search of Color Everywhere: A Collection of African-American Poetry.* 255p. $24.95 (1-55670-339-2). New York, NY: Stewart, Tabori & Chang, Fall 1994. One of the best—if not the best—anthologies of Afro-American poetry. E. Ethelbert Miller has done an outstanding job of choosing poems from the beginning to today: poems of love and suffering, of sport and spirit, of striving and arriving. A true work of art. —John Randall

Miller, Jane. *Memory at These Speeds: New & Selected Poems.* 250p. pap. $15.00 (1-55659-118-7). Port Townsend, WA: Copper Canyon Press, Fall 1996. For all her fantasy, she is a marvelously penetrating and synoptic poet, her best moments sublimely diagnostic. —Calvin Bedient, *The Threepenny Review.* Reading Jane Miller's poetry is like channel-surfing on acid: her deliberately interrupted narrative warps and weaves and makes the familiar strange and the strange recognizable as something you might have put away in a shoebox. —Terri Sutton, *L.A. Weekly*

Miller, Philip. *Father's Day.* 38p. pap. $4.00. Glendale, NY: The Ledge Press, Spring 1996.

Millett, John. *Clothe Yourself in Summer.* 76p. pap. $10.00 (1-887573-01-1). Anchorage, AK: Salmon Run Press, Spring 1996. A collection from the editor of *Poetry Australia*, whose work has been characterized by Louis Simpson as "beautifully and movingly written." —Salmon Run Press

Millis, Christopher. *Impossible Mirrors.* 72p. pap. $10.95 (1-880286-18-1). Canton, CT: Singular Speech Press, Fall 1994. In these often ascerbic poems of Christopher Millis, the world comes to us from fresh and startling angles. Richly playful and keenly intelligent, these are poems unlike anyone else's. —X.J. Kennedy

Milosz, Czeslaw, ed. *A Book of Luminous Things: An International Anthology of Poetry.* 248p. $26.00 (0-15-100169-3). New York, NY: Harcourt Brace & Company, Fall 1996. One of the great writers of the twentieth century and one of its great witnesses thought, in the ninth decade of his life, that he ought somehow to make a philosophical reckoning with the world and an aesthetic summing up—a book, perhaps, of sober prose at the end of this violent century; instead he decided to gather together poems, to give the world a book of luminous things. —Robert Hass

Milosz, Czeslaw. Translated by Robert Hass and Czeslaw Milosz. *Facing the River: New Poems.* 120p. $22.00 (0-88001-404-0). Hopewell, NJ: Ecco Press, Spring 1995. A poet of immense moral authority in these poems, the poems of old age, of a long look back at the catastrophic upheavals of the twentieth century, Milosz writes with amazing clarity and a precise vision. —Ecco Press. The work of Milosz reminds us how much power poetry gains from bearing within itself an unforced, natural, and long-ranging memory of past customs; a sense of the strata of ancient and modern history; a wide visual experience; and a knowledge of many languages and literatures. —Helen Vendler

Milstein, Linda Breiner. *Living in the Aftermath.* 36p. pap. $5.50 (1-877801-27-5). Galloway, NJ: Still Waters Press, Spring 1995.

Miltner, Robert. *Against the Simple.* 24p. pap. $3.00 (0-87338-521-7). Kent, OH: Kent State University Press, Spring 1995. What continues to affect me in *Against the Simple* is the silence that haunts the edges of experience and meaning. Miltner's poems, often cast in brief sentences surrounded by an eerie quiet, haunt us with the unseen and the unheard which seem to lurk just around the corners of language and consciousness. —Richard Hague

Milton, John. Edited by Peter Washington. *Poems.* 256p. $12.50 (0-679-45099-8). New York, NY: Alfred A. Knopf/ Everyman's Library Pocket Poets, Spring 1996.

Minfong Ho, trans. *Maples in the Mist: Children's Poems from the*

Tang Dynasty. 32p. $15.00 (0-688-12044-X). New York, NY: William Morrow & Company, Fall 1996. A beautiful anthology of 16 short unrhymed poems written 1000 years ago in China. Timeless themes, fresh and informal translations. —*School Library Journal*

Minskoff, Alan. *Blue Ink Runs Out on a Partly Cloudy Day.* 36p. pap. $12.00 (0-931659-16-7). Boise, ID: Limberlost Press, Fall 1994. Letterpress edition.

Mirosevich, Toni. *The Rooms We Make Our Own.* 112p. $20.95 (1-56341–081-8); pap. $9.95 (1-56341-080-X). Ithaca, NY: Firebrand Books, Fall 1996. Toni Mirosevich builds the complex structure of her lesbian experience section by section. Constructing her life so that its framework is exposed requires more than one voice, more than one form. Here, poetry shares the space with fiction, "interrupting" each other to achieve the texture of real life. —Firebrand Books

Mistral, Gabriela. Translated by Christiane Jacox Kyle. *Poemas de Las Madres: The Mothers'*

Poems. 39p. pap. $25.00 (0-910055-29-7). Cheney, WA: Eastern Washington University Press, Fall 1996. Paintings by Sara Adlerstein González. The prose poems of *Poemas de Las Madres* combine sweet clarity with complexity of emotion and context, and illustrate Mistral's sense of sisterhood with all women. Mistral is Latin America's best known and most beloved woman poet and the first Latin American, male or female, to receive the Nobel Prize for Literature. —Eastern Washington University Press

Moe, H.D. *Only a Cage Should Be in a Cage and Other Poems*. 86p. pap. $7.00. Santa Cruz, CA: We Press, Fall 1995.

Moffatt, Dorothy Hilliard. *Too Many Apples*. 80p. pap. $9.95 (0-87233-116-4). Dublin, NH: William L. Bauhan, Publisher, Spring 1995. [Moffatt's] verse is witty, insightful and touched with wry humor. —Jesse Lee

Moffeit, Tony. *Poetry Is Dangerous: The Poet Is an Outlaw*. 104p. pap. $10.00 (0-912449-44-6). Cedarville, CA: Floating Island Publications, Spring 1995. In Tony Moffeit's poems the rhythms, the music, the wind of ghosts and coyotes are strong. You can taste and smell the darkness of adobe huts, and feel landscapes in the rearview mirror. I love the mix of the colloquial with visions, stars and voodoo. —Lyn Lifshin

Montague, John. *Collected Poems*. 376p. pap. $19.95 (0-916390-68-3). Winston-Salem, NC: Wake Forest University Press, Fall 1995. A world-class poet, [whose work will survive] as long as words have meaning. —Carolyn Kizer. John Montague has been so long an established fact of the poetry of the English speaking world that there is a tendency to take his really quite remarkable achievement for granted. He is a poet of enormous lyrical gifts, but he has as well an acute and dramatic sense of history— Ireland's and the world's—and a gentle moral insistence, all of which makes his *Collected Poems* an absolutely essential volume. —C. K. Williams.

Montejo, Victor. Translated by Victor Perera. *Sculpted Stones / Piedras Labradas*. 128p. pap. $11.95 (1-880684-14-4). Willimantic, CT: Curbstone Press, Fall 1995. These poems give lyric expression to the feelings of exile and to the (sometimes comic) difficulties of living in a foreign culture. —Curbstone Press. [Montejo] brings ancient traditions and contemporary politics together in vivid, unflinching language. Highly recommended for all collections. —*Choice*

Moolten, David N. *Plums and Ashes.* 64p. pap. $9.95 (1-55553-208-X). Boston, MA: Northeastern University Press, Fall 1994. One trusts this writing because, though far from being unmoved by what it sees, it is dispassionate and steady in its gaze, always true to the materials it interprets. —David Ferry

Moore, Barbara. *The Flame Tree.* 64p. pap. $7.95. Lima, OH: Basfal Books, reissued Spring 1996.

Moore, Daniel. *The Ramadan Sonnets.* 125p. pap. $10.95 (0-9652031-0-7). San Francisco, CA: City Lights Books, Fall 1996. Daniel Moore (Abd al-Hayy), a Sufi poet, chronicles his daily experiences with the annual fast of the month-long Ramadan. —City Lights Books. Daniel Moore has combined the strong and spontane-

ous strain of American free verse that flows up through Whitman, Williams, and Ginsberg with the deep well of his Islamic devotion. He's definitely located the water table. —Coleman Barks. A pilgrim's guide to the exploration of intercultural and transpersonal space. —Alan Abd al-Haqq Godias

Moore, Jim. *The Long Experience of Love.* 97p. pap. $12.95 (1-57131-401-6). Minneapolis, MN: Milkweed Editions, Spring 1995. Moore writes of the common losses by which we know our lives—the loss of family, the friends who leave, the desires that don't come to pass. His music is as natural as breathing. —Milkweed Editions. Moore is a public poet in touch with what is universal and true. —*Choice*

Moore, Richard. *Bottom is Back.* 95p. pap. $11.95 (0-914061-43-7). Alexandria, VA: Orchises Press, Fall 1994. Scabrous and outraged formal verse by someone who thinks what he thinks and doesn't alter his opinions for political correctness. Hilarious. —Orchises Press

Moore, Rosalie. *Gutenberg in Strasbourg.* 128p. pap. $12.00 (0-912449-52-7). Cedarville, CA: Floating Island Publications, Fall 1995. An ambitious verse narrative chronicling the life of the 15th century inventor of the printing press. *Guttenberg in Strasbourg* is the fruit of Rosalie Moore's 20-year fascination with the shockwaves that invention sent through medieval culture, a disruption parallel to that of today's computer revolution. In the rush of the gorgeous and grotesque images which are her hallmark, Moore's concern is to capture the intensity of that moment just before we identify a thing, to articulate the look and feel of things just as they are being named. —Floating Island

Mora, Pat. *Agua Santa: Holy Water.* 160p. $17.95 (0-8070-6828-4). Boston, MA: Beacon Press, Fall 1995. In these poems Mora reclaims the history and culture of her Mexican roots, from a tribute to Frieda Kahlo to an interview with an Aztec goddess. Drawing on both oral and lyrical traditions, she explores the intimate and sacred spaces of borderlands and celebrates the spirit of women who nurture and resist on both sides of the U.S.-Mexico border. —Beacon Press

Moran, Daniel Thomas. *Sheltered by Islands: New and Selected Poems 1985-1995.* 95p. pap. $15.00 (0-9629221-2-9). Shelter Island, NY: Daniel Thomas Moran, Spring 1996. Moran's penetrating poems—eulogies, elegies, celebrations of life—come to us as welcome insights, surprises of vision, all couched in a simple but precise language. They take their delight in both sincerity and perplexity—and they remind us, as Chaucer did, that it is perfectly all right for poetry to be hilariously funny. —Philip Appleman

Moran, Ronald. *Getting the Body to Dance Again.* 40p. pap. $6.95. Johnstown, OH: Pudding House Publications, Spring 1995. Winner of Pudding Magazine's 1994 Chapbook competition. Moran's "Virtual Journalism" collection tells of "Bink Travis and the Bloodmobile" and the former car wash turned "Tunnel of Love" drive thru wedding chapel. —Pudding House Publications

Morewood, Brad. *The Adventure of Steve.* 5p. pap. $1.00. Brooklyn, NY: Pinched Nerves Press. Weird, surreal poems inspired by imaginary trips to Third World countries. —Pinched Nerves Press

Morgan, Frederick. *Poems for Paula.* 72p. $14.00 (1-885266-14-6); pap. $8.00 (1-885266-18-9). Brownsville, OR: Story Line Press, Fall 1995. Morgan, a founder of *The Hudson Review*, which he now co-edits with his wife Paula Deitz, honors a 25-year love. In this, his 10th poetry volume, nearly every poem revolves—with grace and gratitude—around the couple or the beloved. At an Easter vigil service in the city, neighbors light candles at midnight: "I, as always, / take my flame from yours." —*Publishers Weekly. Poems for Paula* is Frederick Morgan's best and simplest work. —Hayden Carruth. The poetry of Frederick Morgan speaks of "life freely ventured . . . and durably maintained." It is filled with light and music—a celebration of love and the world. —Louis Simpson

Mori, Kyoko. *Fallout.* 96p. pap. $7.95 (1-882688-04-X). Chicago, IL: Tia Chucha Press, Fall 1994. Such a deft touch, this poet possesses, pushing aside the superficial, never even noticing the unimportant. We are lucky to experience the poetic voice, the *Fallout* of Kyoko. I think I'll turn my umbrella upside down. —Nikki Giovanni

Morley, Judith. *Miss Laughinghouse and the Reluctant Mystic.* 180p. pap. $12.00 (0-9628181-6-X). New York, NY: Black Thistle Press, Fall 1995. I admire how honest, raw, and unselfconscious so many of these poems are. —Merry Aronson

Morrison, R.H. *All I Have Is a Fountain.* 64p. pap. $9.00 (1-880286-24-6). Canton, CT: Singular Speech Press, Spring 1995. Radiant poems with unusual freshness and luminosity. —*Temenos*

Mott, Michael. *Corday.* 84p. pap. $7.95 (0-938872-21-4). Falls Church, VA: Black Buzzard Press/Visions-international, Fall 1995. A provocative study in poetry of women of conscience, especially Charlotte Corday, who stabbed and killed Marat. —Black Buzzard Press. Michael Mott is best known for his award winning biography of Thomas Merton. *Corday* is courageously honest, Mott's most original work. —Kent Johnson, *Grand Street*

Mowrey, Joe, ed. *Sixteen Voices—Poets: Survivors of Incest and Sexual Abuse.* 80p. pap. $12.00 (0-933553-10-2). Santa Fe, NM: Mariposa Printing & Publishing, Fall 1994. This anthology contains work by poets from around the country, selected by an editor who is himself a survivor of childhood sexual abuse. The result is an intimate perspective on the profound affect of recovery from incest on the lives and the craft of working poets. These are voices reclaimed, sharing lessons learned in silence. —Mariposa Printing & Publishing

Moyers, Bill. Edited by James Haba. *The Language of Life: A Festival of Poets.* 480p. $29.95 (0-385-47917-4). New York, NY: Doubleday, Spring 1995. The companion volume to the eight-part PBS series contains expanded interviews with the eighteen poets featured in the series and many others including Rita Dove, Robert Hass, Donald Hall, and the late Jane Kenyon. It is a celebration of the vitality of the spoken word and of the importance of poetry in America. —Doubleday

Mukand, Jon, ed. *Articulations: The Body and Illness in Poetry.* 424p. pap. $19.95 (0-87745-478-7). Iowa City, IA: University of Iowa Press, Fall 1994. Booklist's 1994 Editor's Choice.

Muldoon, Paul. *The Annals of Chile.* 189p. pap. $10.00 (0-374-52456-4). New York, NY: Farrar, Straus and Giroux/Noonday, Spring 1995. Winner of the T.S. Eliot Prize in English. Muldoon's most accomplished book . . . 'Incantata' is a beautiful, wrenching, and unforgettable poem—one, as they used to say, for the ages. —Jonathan Aaron, *Boston Sunday Globe*. Paul Muldoon is one of the most inventive and ambitious poets working today. *The Annals of Chile* is his best book yet. —Lawrence Norfolk, *Times Literary Supplement*

Mullen, Harryette. *Muse & Drudge.* 88p. pap. $12.50 (0-935162-15-1). Philadelphia, PA: Singing Horse Press, Fall 1995. Hip hyperbole, thy queen is Ms. Mullen. Word Rules. Harryette hype hip-hops and bops the taut poetry trapeze. Makes me want to marimba. Makes me want to riff when I raff. To always write write. —Sandra Cisneros. Harryette Mullen's *Muse & Drudge* is a compelling contribution to contemporary African American literature. Mullen's is a stunningly lyrical voice, rich and resonant, engaged and engaging. —Henry Louis Gates, Jr.

Mura, David. *The Colors of Desire.* 105p. $19.95 (0-385-47460-1). New York, NY: Doubleday/ Anchor Books, Spring 1995. Mura's new poems have a jolting, almost unbearable candor: they are elegant and visceral, deeply frank in their daring testimony to one man's struggle with racial and sexual grief. A courageous book. —Cyrus Cassells. Poetry made out of fervor and lust and a purifying intellect. An extraordinary collection by an incomparable artist. —Li-Young Lee

Murphy, Merilene M. *Under Peace Rising.* 39p. pap. $15.00 (0-934172-38-2). San Jose, CA: Woman in the Moon Publications, Fall 1994. These poems cradle, push and challenge our Mother wit and associated spiritual survival skills, which

is to say we need them. —Ntozake Shange

Muske, Carol. *Skylight.* 79p. pap. $11.95 (0-88748-229-5). Pittsburgh, PA: Carnegie Mellon University Press/Classic Contemporary Series, Fall 1996.

Myers, M., ed. *Elvis Presley: An Anthology in Memoriam (Jan. 8, 1935–Aug. 16, 1977).* 59p. pap. $24.95 (1-879183-24-2). Bristol, IN: Bristol Banner Books, Fall 1994.

Myers, M., ed. *Eugene Field: An Anthology in Memoriam (1850-1895)* 178p. pap. $24.95 (1-879183-25-0). Bristol, IN: Bristol Banner Books, Spring 1995.

Myles, Eileen. *Maxfield Parrish: Early & New Poems.* 229p. $25.00 (0-87685-975-9); pap. $13.50 (0-87685-974-0); sig. $35.00 (0-87685-976-7). Santa Rosa, CA: Black Sparrow Press, Fall 1995. Like her prose— lyrical, direct, tough yet tender—Myles' poetry shoots straight to the heart of contemporary life, and amidst its dizzying rush and pulsing energy finds a still, contemplative center. —Black Sparrow Press

N

Nagel, Muska. *Letters to the Interior*. 57p. pap. $8.95 (0-913006-63-7). Orono, ME: Puckerbrush Press, Spring 1996. A narrative element prevails in the work of Muska Nagel. Every line is tangible; even the smallest image has a certain tone. The dialogue, a vital part of her lyric poetry, [is] vivid and clear. —Uwe Pörksen

Nakano, Jiro, and Brien Hallet, eds. *Heiwa: Peace Poetry in English and Japanese*. 176p. pap. $17.00 (0-8248-1813-X). Honolulu, HI: University of Hawai'i Press, Spring 1996. A collection of haiku and tanka on the theme of peace, gathered through an international competition. Bilingual edition. —University of Hawai'i Press

Napoli, Donna Jo; Bradley R. Strahan and Emily Norwood Rando, eds. *Speaking in Tongues: Poems by Linguists*. 80p. pap. $7.95 (0-938872-19-2). Falls Church, VA: Black Buzzard Press/Visions International. Poems that simply play with the sounds of language and with the etymological connections between words, in a way that achieves sometimes a pleasing nonsense and sometimes a deep, non-logical poetic sense. —Black Buzzard Press

Nash, Susan Smith. *A Paleontologist's Notebook*. 80p. pap. $9.00 (1-880516-16-0). Barrytown, NY: Left Hand Books, Fall 1995. During her paleontological work in the southwestern United States and Bolivia Susan Smith Nash recorded findings in a set of field books. *Paleontologist's Notebook* contains interconnected poems and prose writings processed from the information she compiled. —Left Hand Books

Nash, Susan Smith. *Mind Noir & El Siglo De Oro*. 20p. pap. $5.00 (0935350586). Columbus, OH: Luna Bisonte Prods, Fall 1995. Poems that conflate personal reactions to motion pictures with lines from Spanish Golden Age poetry. For example, Fritz Lang's M with a sonnet by Gongora. —Luna Bisonte Prods

Nasrin, Taslima. Translated by Carolyne Wright. *The Game in*

Reverse. 63p. $25.00 (0-8076-1391-6); pap. $14.95 (0-8076-1392-4). New York, NY: George Braziller, Spring 1995. *The Game in Reverse* is the first volume of Bangladeshi feminist doctor-turned-writer Taslima Nasrin to appear in English translation. Nasrin gained widespread recognition when her best-selling novel *Shame* was banned by the Bangladeshi government and she was forced to go into hiding by death threats from Islamic fundamentalist groups. In this collection, Nasrin denounces the indignities women endure in Bangladeshi Muslim society and touches on such subjects as domestic violence, employment discrimination, and sexual abuse. —George Braziller

Nathaniel, Isabel. *The Dominion of Lights.* 61p. pap. $9.95 (0-914-278-69-X). Providence, RI: Copper Beech Press, Spring 1996. With the aura of sacred ritual, *The Dominion of Lights* enacts loving transformations. Nathaniel writes as Degas said he painted—not to show us the things she saw, but the things that will make us see what she saw so deeply. Her service is completed with such a powerfully elevating humil-

ity and grace, it makes the higher spirit within us shimmer. —Jack Myers

Nattell, Tom; Charlie Rossiter, and Dan Wilcox. *3 Guys From Albany.* 16p. pap. $2.00. Albany, NY: A.P.D., Fall 1995. A selection of poems from the popular "3 Guys from Albany" poetry performance group. This second edition bootlegged from the original BOOG Literature version. —A.P.D.

Neale, Susan. *The Heart's Pangaea.* 37p. pap. $4.75 (0-87338-545-4). Kent, OH: Kent State University Press, Spring 1996. Everywhere we have been since beginning/Is mapped in the memory somewhere," writes Susan Neale at the outset of this ambitiously conceived and enormously satisfying collection. Here is a poet who wants to know the past, [exploring] the history of light and darkness, of language, of reality and dreams, and of women and men. —David Citino

Neelon, Ann. *Easter Vigil.* 76p. pap. $10.00 (0-938078-44-5). Tallahassee, FL: Anhinga Press, Spring 1996. Winner of the 1995 Anhinga Prize for Poetry.

It is rare to come upon a poet with such a wide-ranging vision as Ann Neelon. She's a risk-taker with heart, a poet who is in the world as a compassionate observer. These poems deserve your attention. —Joy Harjo. Her long lines, interspersed with very short ones, have a tone unlike anyone else's. A truly auspicious beginning. —Denise Levertov

Neider, Mark. *Hello, Goodbye.* 83p. pap. $10.95. Dobbs Ferry, NY: Witlin Books, Fall 1995.

Neilson, Melanie. *Natural Facts.* 65p. pap. $11.00 (0-937013-57-4). Elmwood, CT: Potes & Poets Press, Spring 1996. A book to read cover to cover. (I did. Without stopping.) The rhythms keep you happily going (often dimeters with departures). And *clarity*! Of images. Of assertions. Of observations. Of childhood looked in from. Of natural facts. —[How many times times has someone lately called a book of poetry a great read?] "*Natural Facts* is a great read." What a fine book! —Jackson Mac Low

Nelson, June. *Double Vision.* 28p. pap. $7.95. Wilkes-Barre, PA: Design Systems Printing, Fall 1995.

Nelson, Stanley. *Immigrant: An Epic Poem, Book III.* 96p. pap. $12.50 (0-913559-31-8). Delhi, NY: Birch Brook Press, Spring 1996. Here we see one of the most complex and original poets of our time grappling with issues that underlie the framework of our culture. —Jared Smith, *Small Press Review*. One of the most important books of the second half of the 20th century. —Hugh Fox, *Asylum Magazine*

Neruda, Pablo. Translated by Maria Jacketti. *Ceremonial Songs/Cantos Ceremoniales.* 144p. pap. $13.95 (0-935480-80-3). Pittsburgh, PA: Latin American Literary Review Press, Fall 1996. Bilingual edition, complete for the first time in English translation. Long, thematically diverse poems in the form of the canto. —Latin American Literary Review Press

Neruda, Pablo. Translated by Alastair Reid. *Fully Empowered.* 144p. pap. $10.95 (0-8112-1281-5). New York, NY: New Directions, Fall 1994. The extraordinary wordsmith is variously ironic, subtle, and profound as he constructs poetic geometries rich with personal and political implications. —*Booklist*. Because he gave us a past and a present, Pablo Nerudo will be with us in the perilous conquest of our future. —Carlos Fuentes, *The N.Y. Times Book Review*

Neruda, Pablo. Translated by Francesca Gonshaw. *Love: Ten Poems by Pablo Neruda From the Movie, The Postman.* 48p. pap. $6.95 (0-78868-8148-8). New York, NY: Hyperion, Fall 1995.

Nesanovich, Stella. *A Brightness That Made My Soul Tremble: Poems on the Life of Hildegard of Bingen.* 32p. pap. $8.00 (1-884725-18-X). Thibodaux, LA: Blue Heron Press, Fall 1996. Here we find Hildegard's courageous struggles against oppression, against misunderstanding, against the forces that threaten her community and her inner peace. This book ends with the exhortation: "Let the green earth embrace me." It is poetry that is both embracing and embraceable. —Leo Luke Marcello

Newman, Amy. *Order, or Disorder.* 75p. $15.00 (1-880834-

43-X); pap. $10.00 (1-880834-42-1). Cleveland, OH: Cleveland State University Poetry Center, Fall 1995. Winner of the 1994 CSU Poetry Center Prize. This is poetry of the first order, the work of an original, resourceful writer. The poems are passionate, they are intelligent, they are beautiful, marked equally by their haunting music and their sensuous, loss-touched images. Her language caresses and celebrates the contours and textures of the world as body, even as it reveals an unshakeable longing for something beyond it. —Wayne Dodd

Newman, Denise. *Why Pear?* 10p. $25.00 (0-9632085-9-4). Mill Valley, CA: Em Press, Fall 1996. "Why passion, why pear//Twice-born god." A ten-part poem letterpress printed in an accordion structure with handpainted cover. Signed edition of 250. —Em Press

Newman, Lesléa, ed. *My Lover Is a Woman: Contemporary Lesbian Love Poems.* 308p. $18.50 (0-345-39483-6). New York, NY: Ballantine Books, Spring 1996. Lesléa Newman has collected the work of both well-known and emerging poets (some of them published here for the first time) to create an anthology of some of the finest writers of any gender or sexual orientation writing poetry today. The probing fierceness of Adrienne Rich, the subtle longing in Joy Harjo, the intense sexual rhythm and tension in Olga Broumas, and the entrancing lament of June Jordan pay witness to the diverse and complex nature of women's sexuality. —Ballantine Books

Ní Chuilleanáin, Eiléan. *The Brazen Serpent*. 50p. $13.95 (0-916390-65-9); pap. $7.95 (0-916390-64-0). Winston-Salem, NC: Wake Forest University Press, Spring 1995. Her poetry resonates with ancient rites and presences from a spiritual otherworld. [She has] earned her place among the very best poets of her generation. —O'Shaughnessy Award Citation. Ní Chuilleanáin holds us captive by her luminous voice. —Molly Bendall, *Denver Quarterly*

Niederman, Sharon, and Miriam Sagan, eds. *New Mexico Poetry Renaissance*. 216p. pap. $14.95 (1-878610-41-4). Santa Fe, NM: Red Crane Books, Fall 1994. *New Mexico Poetry Renaissance* is an exemplary, high-quality collection that I heartily recommend to those who love poetry or New Mexico. This book is a necessity for those who love both. —Emilie Buckwald. The voices in *New Mexico Poetry Renaissance* offer beautiful music and wonderful stories that speak of experiences and emotions common to a wide audience of readers. Of course, they make New Mexico sound pretty appealing, too. —*Poet*

Nieman, Valerie. *How We Live*. 32p. pap. $6.00. Brockport, NY: State Street Press, Spring 1996. In these poems, a farm in West Virginia becomes a source for reflections about history, philosophy, psychology, science, and meditation. —State Street Press

Nikolayev, Philip. *Artery Lumen*. 37p. pap. $6.00 (0-9645516-1-6). Cambridge, MA: Barbara Matteau Editions, Fall 1996. Winner of the Barbara Matteau Editions Chapbook Prize. I can't recall any book of poetry of the last twenty years which has given me so much delight. Nikolayev really is a master of half rhymes, off-rhymes and assonance. —Joseph Green

Noguchi, Rick. *The Wave He Caught.* 40p. pap. $6.00 (0-9628094-7-0). Long Beach, CA: Pearl Editions, Spring 1995. Winner of the 1994 Pearl Chapbook Contest. The main character is a surfer looking for the great wave. A beginner at being and doing, his determination is as big as the sea, and as unruly. —Ann Menebroker

Noguere, Suzanne. *Whirling Round the Sun.* 96p. pap. $12.00 (1-877675-22-9). New York, NY: Midmarch Arts Press, Fall 1996. Noguere, winner of the 1996 Discovery/ *The Nation* Prize, here gathers the work of 20 years into a collection remarkably consistent in theme, voice, and style. Belonging to the company of the latter-day formalists, she is a celebrant, at times an ecstatic, of the experience of life—perception, memory, and mystery. —*Booklist*

Noriega, Carlos. *Espejo de Lluvia.* 57p. pap. $6.95 (0-8477-0262-6). San Juan, Puerto Rico: University of Puerto Rico Press, Fall 1996. In Spanish only.

Norris, Kathleen. *Little Girls in Church.* 79p. $24.95 (0-8229-3875-8); pap. $10.95 (0-8229-5556-3). Pittsburgh, PA: University of Pittsburgh Press, Spring 1995. Didn't Wordsworth dream of this: the dust of custom removed and our lives glowing with a visionary gleam—the ordinary and the holy revealed as the self-same thing? Subtle, beautiful, humorous, lucid—Norris's poems are inspired, inspiriting. —Gregory Orr. [Norris is] compassionate, observant, a poet of place. —*Village Voice Literary Supplement.* Poetry worth remembering . . . deft and incisive, with a strong wit. She is a spellbinder. —*Library Journal*

North, Rusty. *Little Old Lady in Tennis Shoes.* 20p. pap. $5.00. Port Townsend, WA: Sagittarius Press, 1990, reissued Spring 1996. Reprinted by Rusty North in the soggy spring of her 74th year. Type is hand set. —Sagittarius Press

North, Rusty. *Meeting House Poems.* 16p. pap. $5.00. Port Townsend, WA: Sagittarius Press, Fall 1995. From a journal kept during winter quarter at Pendle Hill, a center for Quaker study. —Sagittarius Press

Notley, Alice. *The Descent of Alette.* 150p. pap. $14.95 (0-14-058764-0). New York, NY: Penguin Books, Spring 1996. A remarkable achievement. —Robert Creeley. A major mythopoetic experimental work. —Anne Waldman. Notley's raw sensual language and imagery imbue the transformation of landscape with a startling psychological resonance. —*Publishers Weekly*

Nurkse, D. *Voices Over Water.* 96p. pap. $12.95 (1-884800-18-1). Marshfield, MA: Four Way Books, Fall 1996. These poems, which tell the story of an Estonian couple who emigrate to Canada in the early part of this century, work both as discrete, individually imagined lyrics and also as chapters in an ongoing narrative of genuinely engaging lives. There are no sag ging makeshifts here. A high proportion of the poems are gems of gravid simplicity, and Nurkse's rhetorical periods can be breathtaking. "We've hoarded our delights/like pennies in a sock/and they're heavy: our children/cry from dreams not hunger." —*The New Yorker*, Recommended Reading

Nye, Naomi Shihab. *Red Suitcase.* 109p. $20.00 (1-880238-14-4); pap. $12.50 (1-880238-15-2). Rochester, NY: BOA Editions, Fall 1994. Whether Nye writes of Madisonville or Jerusalem, the chalkdust of childhood or the mysteries of loss, these alert, attentive, largehearted poems awaken and enlarge the mind. —Chana Bloch. Her poetry is rich with the riddle of life. —Alicia Ostriker. She has a true, redeeming view. We need her poems. —Marvin Bell

Nye, Naomi Shihab, ed. *The Tree Is Older Than You Are: A Bilingual Gathering of Poems & Stories From Mexico.* 112p. $19.95 (0-689-80297-8). New York, NY: Simon & Schuster Books for Young Readers, Fall 1995. Through their work these sixty-four Mexican poets and painters—Rosario Castellanos, Alberto Blanco, Octavio Paz, Homero Aridjis, Julio Galán, Rodolfo Morales, and Leticia Tarragó among them—welcome us across their border as citizens of a shared world, inviting us to greet extended family and trade our ideas, visions, and dreams. —Simon & Schuster

Nye, Naomi Shihab, and Paul B. Janeczko, eds. *I Feel A Little Jumpy Around You: A Book of Her Poems and His Poems Collected in Pairs.* 256p. $17.00 (0-689-80518-7). New York, NY: Simon and Schuster Books for Young Readers, Spring 1996. This is an anthology about perspectives and the politics of gender, about the ways in which men and women view life and one another. These boyfriends and girl-friends, husbands, wives, grand-mothers, grandfathers, sisters and brothers speak to us in couples, from poems collected in pairs. A chance to explore what he said and what she said, as well as *how* and *why* they said it. —Simon & Schuster

O'Brien, Sean. *Ghost Train.* 54p. pap. $11.95 (0-19-283231-X). New York, NY: Oxford University Press, Spring 1996. O'Brien's fourth collection of poems investigates history, politics, autobiography, and the imaginative region where they meet. Sombre and expansive, elegiac and celebratory, *Ghost Train* is an ambitious and subtle book. —Oxford University Press

O'Grady, Tom. *Sun, Moon and Stars.* 64p. pap. $15.00 (1-884824-18-8). Chapel Hill, NC: Tryon Publishing Company, Spring 1996. This quietly intense, thoughtful poetry reads as if Tom O'Grady and the grass and the trees and the hills and the heavens grew up together as one, and as if they were speaking through him. —David Ignatow

O'Hara, Mark. *The Composer's Dream.* 32p. pap. $5.50 (0-9647127-2-5). Lawrenceville, GA: Coreopsis Books, Spring 1995. *The Composer's Dream* captures the great musicians in defining moments of their creative—and everyday—lives. It is a tour de force of imaginative biography. —Coreopsis Books. Mark O'Hara's poems take us where we would not have known to go on our own, and the movement is expert, the arrival affecting. The surprise in the images and in the words themselves is a truly exquisite pleasure. —Constance Pierce

O'Neil, Daniel X. *Memo To All Employees.* 48p. $12.00 (0-

9646137-2-7). Chicago, IL: Juggernaut, Spring 1995. A second book of poetry by the nationally-known performance poet out of Chicago. O'Neil bridges the gap between the thriving American Performance Poetry movement and the publishing world. —Juggernaut

O'Neil, Thomas. *Sex With God.* 120p. pap. $6.95 (0-9622398-1-X). New York, NY: Wexford Press, Revised Edition, Fall 1994. Winner of the Editor's Choice Award from *Lambda Book Report* and Editor's Pick Award from *Small Press Review.* Torn between forbidden gay love and love of God, a poet shouts to Heaven. In the original edition (1989) O'Neil scorned the vengeful God of the Bible to embark on a quest for love that was fulfilled when he met Brian. The lovers story now continues as they learn that Brian has AIDS in the *The Ashes of Eden* which is printed here along with the original text. —Wexford Press. Brilliant! O'Neil writes with such ease and fluid lucidity that it is a revelation. —*Dusty Dog Reviews.* Splendid! Beautiful! —*New York Native.* Ballsy and eloquent! —*Village Voice*

Oakes, Wayne. *Occur.* 63p. $20.00 (1-881471-06-3); pap. $10.00 (1-881471-07-3). New York City, NY: Spuyten Duyvil, Spring 1996. An interesting sequence of short-lined explorations, a number of which read like one page story-moments limned in the ink of intensity. —Edward Sanders

Ochester, Ed. *Allegheny.* 25p. pap. $8.00 (0-938566-67-9). Easthampton, MA: Adastra Press, Spring 1995. Hand-set letterpress edition, handsewn. A *Small Press Review* pick of the month, June 1995. Highly recommended. —*Small Press*

Offen, Ron. *Instead of Gifts: Poems for Poets.* 40p. pap. $6.95. Johnstown, OH: Pudding House Publications, Fall 1995.

Ogden, Hugh. *Windfalls.* 24p. pap. $5.00 (0-916897-22-2). Hartford, CT: Andrew Mountain Press, Spring 1996. Hugh Ogden's poems engage a lyric present that expands to evoke a rich sense of history and nature. These are poems of observant relationship, ripened waiting, intense fullness. —Patricia Eakins

Oisteanu, Valery. *Temporary Immortality.* 56p. pap. $10.00 (0-

9601870-1-8). New York, NY: Pass Press, Fall 1995. Valery is quickly becoming a Grand Master of the surrealist vein. —Gerard Malanga. Hilariously lewd, witty, juicy. —David Rattray

Oktenberg, Adrian. *The Bosnia Elegies.* 64p. pap. $10.95 (0-9638183-5-X). Williamsburg, MA: Paris Press, Fall 1996. These poems take the passion of anger and the clarity of narrative into the silences and evasions of history. They refuse to lie. They refuse to prevaricate. They disown the safety offered to the onlooker and accept instead the danger and pain of witness. They seek no peace. And, rightly, they allow the reader no peace. —Eavan Boland

Olds, Sharon. *The Wellspring.* 94p. $21.00 (0-679-44592-7); pap. $13.00 (0-679-76560-3). New York, NY: Alfred A. Knopf, Fall 1995. *The Wellspring* is a sequence of poems that takes us back to the womb, thence to childhood, adolescence, sexual awakening, and the depths of adult love. —Alfred A. Knopf

Olinka, Sharon. *A Face Not My Own.* 67p. pap. $8.95 (0-931122-82-1). Albuquerque, NM: West End Press, Spring 1995. *A Face Not My Own* is a spiritual search by a poet whose heart refuses to be crushed by the reality of class in America. —E. Ethelbert Miller

Olsen, William. *Vision of a Storm Cloud.* 88p. $35.00 (0-8101-5043-3); pap. $13.95 (0-8101-5044-1). Evanston, IL: Northwestern University Press/ TriQuarterly Books, Spring 1996. In moving beyond the "new formalists" and the "language poets," Olsen has crafted poems that are energetic, expansive, and romantic: his ability to manipulate language, image, and form harken back to the traditions of Blake and Whitman, while his range of subject and his use of metaphor forge his own unique artistic signature. These poems are a rich, dense, and polished example of the voice of a strong new poet. —TriQuarterly Books

Ooka, Makoto. Translated by Janine Beichman. *Beneath the Sleepless Tossing of the Planets: Selected Poems, 1972-1989.* 178p. $30.00 (0-942668-45-6); pap. $19.95 (0-942668-46-4). Honolulu, HI: University of Hawai'i Press, Spring 1996. Through the richness of Ooka's work we find once again the abundance of our spiritual and natural heritage. —Shuntaro Tanikawa

Orr, Gregory. *City of Salt.* 64p. $24.95 (0-8229-3876-6); pap. $10.95 (0-8229-5557-1). Pittsburgh, PA: University of Pittsburgh Press, Fall 1995. The heart of Orr's poetry . . . is the enigmatic image that is his signature. —Bill Christophersen, *San Francisco Review.* Orr enjoys the picture-making of the imagination and its autonomy, self-evidential even when appearing tamed. —John Robert Leo, *Poetry*

Ortiz, Simon J. *Woven Stone.* 367p. $45.00 (0-8165-1294-9); pap. $19.95 (0-8165-1330-9). Tucson, AZ: University of Arizona Press, 1992. This omnibus of three previous works— *Going for the Rain, A Good Journey,* and *Fight Back: For the Sake of the People, For the Sake of the Land*—offers old and new readers an appreciation of the thirty-year career of one of our most important Native American poets.—University of Arizona Press. A wise and prophetic book. —*El Palacio*

Ortiz Cofer, Judith. *Reaching for the Mainland and Selected New Poems.* 77p. pap. $9.00 (0-927534-55-X). Tempe, AZ: Bilingual Press, Fall 1995. A colorful, revealing portrait of Puerto Rican culture and domestic relationships. —*Publishers Weekly.* Cofer's warm, intimate use of language is always appealing. —*Library Journal*

Ostriker, Alicia Suskin. *The Crack in Everything.* 100p. $24.95 (0-8229-3936-3); pap. $10.95 (0-8229-5593-8). Pittsburgh, PA: University of Pittsburgh Press, Spring 1996. Alicia Ostriker has become one of those brilliantly provocative and imaginatively gifted contemporaries whose iconoclastic expression, whether in prose or poetry, is essential to understanding our American selves. —Joyce Carol Oates

Oswald, Alice. *The Thing in the Gap-stone Stile.* 64p. pap. $12.95 (0-19-282513-5). New York, NY: Oxford University Press, Spring 1996. Poetry Book Society Choice. The poems here are extraordinarily beautiful: intensely musical, strewn with emotion, and full of energy and warmth. Intensely musical, influenced by the rhythms of Hopkins, the poems in Oswald's first book speak passionately of nature and love. They have a religious sense of mystery and attempt to express the intangible in marvellously vivid language. —Oxford University Press. Alice Oswald's poetry possesses a startling originality. —Carol Ann Duffy, *Anvil New Poets 2*

P

Pack, Robert. *Minding the Sun.* 97p. $30.00 (0-226-64407-3); pap. $11.95 (0-226-64408-1). Chicago, IL: University of Chicago Press, Spring 1996. With characteristic sensitivity and intelligence, Robert Pack reflects on man's relation to and responsibilities toward nature. Throughout, his verses are informed by an ecological vigilance born of his devotion to the New England landscape. —University of Chicago Press. No one writes like Robert Pack. No one makes such central concerns so radically available. He is one of America's passionate originals. Not only

is he in a class by himself, he is his own school. —Mark Strand

Pack, Robert, and Jay Parini, eds. *Touchstones: American Poets on a Favorite Poem.* 352p. $45.00 (0-87451-722-2); pap. $19.95 (0-87451-723-0). Hanover, NH: University Press of New England, Spring 1996. Here fifty-nine of America's best poets select their favorite verse by another writer and explore its influence on their own writing. The result is an astonishing amalgam of deeply personal readings unfettered by critical jargon and, as the editors note, "unpredictable, witty, moving, and—almost always—celebratory." —University Press of New England

Packer, Eve. *Harmony Grits.* 43p. pap. $1.00. New York, NY: Eve Packer, Fall 1995. There is so much music here it dances off the pages. —Lawrence E. Johnson

Packer, Eve. *Show World.* 36p. pap. $3.00. New York, NY: Eve Packer, Fall 1996. This is the fierce/real/funny world of 42nd St. New York: the world of jazz, the world of love. —Eve Packer

Padgett, Ron. *New and Selected Poems.* 112 p. $20.95 (1-56792-038-1). Lincoln, MA: David R. Godine, Fall 1995. Ron Padgett's poems are remarkably clear, almost invisibly so, like a refreshing glass of cold water. —James Schuyler. [Padgett is] one of a kind and that's the first reason to read him. —*Harvard Book Review.* A genuine and admirable sensibility. —David Lehman, *Poetry*

Page, Carolyn. *Barn Flight.* 46p. $9.95 (0-942544-51-X). Mobile, AL: Negative Capability Press, Fall 1995.

Palgrave, Francis Turner, ed. *Palgrave's Golden Treasury.* 720p. $15.95 (0-19-282315-9). New York, NY: Oxford University Press, Sixth Edition, Fall 1995. [Updated by John Press,] Palgrave's anthology continues to map British verse from Shakespeare to the present. —Oxford University Press. The book is still a marvelous read, and Palgrave's claim that all the poems in it have a natural sweetness continues to ring true. —Derwent May, *The Times*

Palmer, Michael. *At Passages.* 128p. pap. $11.95 (0-8112-

1294-7). New York, NY: New Directions, Spring 1995. [Palmer's fourteenth collection of poems is] as exemplarily radical as ever, but tinged with a new dense lyricism and undercurrents of humor that make this his most exciting collection to date. —John Ashbery. Michael Palmer has been one of the most influential writers in recent years, perhaps because he fuses contemporary concerns about syntax and meaning-production with some very ancient poetic pleasures. —*The Village Voice Literary Supplement*

Paolucci, Anne. *Queensboro Bridge (and Other Poems).* 64p. pap. $10.00 (0-884754-27-9). Prairie Village, KS: Potpourri Publications, Fall 1995. Her unique style is a combination of thoughtful, observant commentary, self-knowledge and wisdom, the feeling of the feel of things and of feelings, and the language lean and apt and rich in culture. —Chandler Beall

Parini, Jay, ed. *The Columbia Anthology of American Poetry.* 757p. $29.95 (0-231-08122-7). Irvington, NY: Columbia University Press, Spring 1995. *The*

Columbia Anthology of American Poetry covers all of the canonical American poets, from the colonial to the contemporary. Parini has also selected a broad sampling of poetry from voices that have not been heard as widely over the years. Here, for the first time, is a thorough collection of nineteenth and twentieth-century poetry by women, Native Americans, and African Americans. —Columbia University Press

Parker, Alan Michael, and Mark Willhardt, eds. *The Routledge Anthology of Cross-Gendered Verse.* 216p. pap. $17.95 (0-415-11291-5). New York, NY: Routledge, Spring 1996. Over the course of centuries, many poets have explored the possibilities and power of assuming the voice of the opposite gender—from Geoffrey Chaucer writing as the Wife of Bath to Anne Sexton writing in the voice of Jesus. This fascinating anthology spans seven centuries of cross-gendered verse, incorporating the work of both canonical and lesser-known poets. Substantial introductions are included, placing each poet in a historical, literary, social and theoretical context. —Routledge

Parry, Betty. *Shake the Parrot Cage.* 114p. pap. $10.00 (0-932616-47-X). Balton, MD: New Poets Series, Fall 1994. These are exciting poems in a fresh and original voice. This vivid collection is worth reading for the sensuous use of color alone. —Josephine Jacobsen. Sensitive, and lyrical; and funny, often, in a mischievous way. —Gwendolyn Brooks

Parson-Nesbitt, Julie. *Finders.* 60p. pap. $8.95 (0-931122-83-X). Albuquerque, NM: West End Press, Spring 1996. Julie Parson-Nesbitt's first volume of poetry navigates the street-wise world of the personal; celebrates interracial love and marriage; and responds politically to her Jewish heritage. —West End Press. This work excites, via its venturesomeness, its contemporary energy, its refusal to wear blinders or dark glasses. —Gwendolyn Brooks

Paschen, Elise. *Infidelities.* 88p. $20.00 (1-885266-32-4); pap. $10.95 (1-885266-28-6). Brownsville, OR: Story Line Press, Fall 1996. Winner of the 1996 Nicholas Roerich Poetry Prize. These poems are passionate, lyrical episodes of precise and dangerous beauty. I'm proud to welcome this very accomplished first book of poetry. —Joy Harjo. In this impressive, skillful first collection Paschen assumes roles and dons masks to explore varieties of infidelity . . . these poems feature a strong female voice doing its best to articulate hard truths about love and betrayal. —*Publishers Weekly*

Pasolini, Pier Paolo. Translated by Pasquale Verdicchio. *A Desperate Vitality.* 20p. pap. $5.00 (1-879342-09-X). San Diego, CA: Parentheses Writing Series, Fall 1996. A deeply moving long poem that touches upon Pasolini's struggle with himself and the society in which he lived. —Parenthesis Writing Series

Pasolini, Pier Paolo. Translated by Norman MacAfee, with Luciano Martinengo. *Poems.* 231p. pap. $14.00 (0-374-52469-6). New York, NY: Farrar, Straus and Giroux/Noonday, Spring 1996. Pasolini seems to me indisputably the most remarkable figure to have emerged in Italian arts and letters since the Second World War. Whatever he did, once he did it, had the quality

of seeming necessary. His poetry is an important part of his passionate, proud, historically vulnerable body of work. —Susan Sontag. Of his copious writings, his poetry seems most likely to endure, translated now with clarity, ingenuity, and fidelity. —Edmund White, *The New York Times Book Review*

Passarella, Lee. *Asrael.* 24p. pap. $4.50 (0-9647127-1-7). Lawrenceville, CA: Coreopsis Books, Spring 1995. The world in general (not to mention the American South in particular) needs more good small presses that publish good poems. *Asrael* [contains some] impressive images and metaphors. It's a fine start for both Lee Passarella and Coreopsis Books. —Gilbert Allen, *Small Press Review*

Pastan, Linda. *An Early Afterlife.* 88p. $17.95 (0-393-03727-4). New York, NY: W.W. Norton & Company, Spring 1995. [Pastan has] fulfilled Emerson's dream—the revelation of the miraculous in the common. —*Jerusalem Post*

Patrick, William B. *These Upraised Hands.* $20.00 (1-880238-26-8); pap. $12.50 (1-

880238-27-6). Rochester, NY: BOA Editions, Fall 1995. William B. Patrick is a writer whose greatest strength is in making vocal portraits. Drawing from diaries, letters, memoirs and personal encounters, Patrick's poems and poetic narratives tell the intricate, painful and loving stories of people who once lived and those who now live on the North American continent. —BOA Editions

Peabody, Richard. *Buoyancy and Other Myths.* 70p. pap. $7.95 (0-945144-06-7). Cabin John, MD: Gut Punch Press, Spring 1995. Richard Peabody takes a hard look at himself and the contemporary world and comes up with poems alternately funny, sad, and tender. These poems remember childhood and sing of love—both lost and requited. *Buoyancy* has charm and insight in equal parts. —Miriam Sagan

Peacock, Molly. *Original Love.* 96p. $17.95 (0-393-03741-X); pap. $10.00 (0-393-31466-9). New York, NY: W.W. Norton & Company, Spring 1995. Peacock offers a new slant on the often misunderstood emotion, using rhyme, humor, and fierce honesty to convey passion

for love and all love's trappings. [These poems are] lyrical and beautiful, and [Peacock's] spirit shines through as brightly as love itself. —*Booklist.* She has a luxuriantly sensual imagination— and an equally sensual feel for the language. —*Washington Post.* Accomplished and witty, this anatomy of 'original' love is not for the fainthearted; it's for those who believe that it is still possible to feel deeply. —Frank Allen, *Library Journal*

Peacock, Molly. *The Wheel.* 8p. pap. $10.00. Anchorage, AK: Salmon Run Press, Spring 1995. In this gentle poem, poet Molly Peacock embraces the thawed Wheel of Fortune to find love and deep satisfaction in life's continuing cycle. —John E. Smelcer

Peacock, Molly; Elise Paschen, and Neil Neches, eds. *Poetry in Motion: 100 Poems From the Subways and Buses.* 157p. $18.95 (0-393-03977-3); pap. $11.00 (0-393-31458-8). New York, NY: W.W. Norton and Company, Spring 1996. This rich gathering emanates from the immensely popular poetry placards displayed in the subways and buses of New York

City. Starting in October 1992, when Poetry in Motion first appeared, and continuing with selections through August 1997, here are the first hundred poems of the program. —W.W. Norton & Company

Pearlberg, Gerry Gomez, ed. *The Zenith of Desire: Contemporary Lesbian Poems About Sex.* 64p. $12.00 (0-517-70281-9). New York, NY: Crown Publishers, Spring 1996. Riding the pulse of the lesbian experience, this book explores passion, desire, fantasy, and adventure through the work of such poets as Chrystos, May Swenson, Pat Califia, and Audre Lorde. —Crown Publishers

Pearson, Sela. *Sela's Sounds of Silence.* 61p. pap. $9.95 (0-9647742-0-8). Franklin, TN: Akanke Creations, Fall 1995. Sela's poems are extensions of her work as health care provider. They are caring, optimistic, sensitive, zealous. Her poems are personal, with the direct simplicity of a psalm. —Joe Speer & Gwynelle

Pease, Deborah. *All the Observable Grace.* 19p. pap. $3.00. Wakefield, RI: Monogram Editions, Fall 1996. Companion piece to *The Lost Voice of Silence.* —Monogram Editions

Pease, Deborah. *The Lost Voice of Silence.* 19p. pap. $3.00. Wakefield, RI: Monogram Editions, Fall 1996. The stroll through Pease's world is an intriguing and engaging one; I recommend that you take it. —Carl Little

Peck, John. *M and Other Poems.* 104p. pap. $12.95 (0-8101-5056-5). Evanston, IL: Northwestern University Press/Triquarterly Books, Fall 1996. Peck has established himself as a major poet, opening up territory no one else has attempted. —Clive Wilmer, *Times Literary Supplement*

Peckenpaugh, Angela. *Singing a Circle of Seasons.* 20p. pap. $5.50. Milwaukee, WI: Sackbut Press, Fall 1995. Pagan poems for all the pagan holidays with a calendar explaining the meaning of the seasons of the pagan year. —Sackbut Press

Pegram, Amelia Blossom. *Echoes Across a Thousand Hills.* 102p. $29.95 (0-86543-417-4); pap. $9.95 (0-86543-418-2). Trenton, NJ: Africa World Press,

Fall 1995. Amelia Blossom Pegram is one of my favorite poets! Her poems of life remembered in South Africa and life lived in the States are a bridge 'across a thousand hills' of Black sisterhood. —Stephanie Stokes Oliver

Perdomo, Willie. *Where a Nickel Costs a Dime.* 78p. pap. $13.00 (0-393-31383-2). New York, NY: W.W. Norton & Company, Spring 1996. Packaged with a CD of the author performing his poems. Willie Perdomo's poems have grace and power and don't waste their time. —Ai. Willie Perdomo is a new and important voice, a *Djali* (Griot). —Amiri Baraka. Drawing on rap, jazz, Langston Hughes and the rhythms of the streets, this collection bristles with congas, timbales, police sirens and wino oracles. [His poems are] scalding, toxic and dizzying. —*Publishers Weekly*

Perillo, Lucia. *The Body Mutinies.* 114p. pap. $12.95 (1-55753-083-1). West Lafayette, IN: Purdue University Press, Fall 1996. Winner of the 1995 Verna Emery Contest. Perillo tells stories with a grim eye for the comic and an ear tuned to language's highest pitch.

—Purdue University Press. These dazzling and powerful poems hold nothing back. Perillo commits herself wholeheartedly to the passions, pleasures, and griefs of a body that is dying and subject to all the violations of a violent world. —Andrew Hudgins

Perreault, George. *Trying To Be Round.* 64p. pap. $9.50 (1-880286-20-3). Canton, CT: Singular Speech Press, Fall 1994. George Perreault's poetry is always a delight to read because he captures the rhythms of our language in wonderfully modulated, musical phrases. He puts down the sounds of words in lean, clearly imaged poems that hunger for more life, and which, in turn, make us more alive. —Len Roberts

Peters, Robert. *"Twin Peaks" Cherry Pie: New Poems.* 12p. pap. $6.00. Pocatello, ID: Redneck Press, Fall 1995.

Peterson, Nils. *The Comedy of Desire.* 70p. pap. $10.00 (0-9638722-0-6). Saint Paul, MN: Blue Sofa Press/Ally Press Center, Fall 1994. Peterson writes lively narrative comedy with a fine flair for embarrassing situations of the idealistic lover. This is a book of humor and grace. —Robert Bly

Peterson, Robert. *All the Time in the World.* 67p. $20.00 (1-882413-33-4); pap. $12.00 (1-882413-32-6). Brooklyn, NY: Hanging Loose Press. If the great Japanese haiku poet Kobayashi Issa were to resurface, he would take the name of Robert Peterson and write this book. In fact, this *is* Issa—Issa in modern dress. Issa having ridden a Harley, listened to a CD of Puccini, and blown his nose on a Kleenex. —Clemens Starck. With his zipped-up wit and timing, perfect phrasing, delivery, and control, manic style, and high polish, one hardly cares what Peterson is writing about, because one more than suspects he can write about anything. —*Publishers Weekly*

Pettet, Simon. *Selected Poems.* 120p. $29.95 (1-883689-31-7); pap. $9.95 (1-883689-30-9). Jersey City, NJ: Talisman House, Publishers, Fall 1995. Like Beethoven's Bagatelles, Simon Pettet's short poems have a great deal to say, and their seemingly modest dimensions help rather than hinder his saying it. An unorthodox

lucidity reminiscent of Schuyler, a certain English dappleness and an oriental concision blend in poetry whose sweet, complex fragrance is Pettet's secret. —John Ashbery

Pettit, Michael, ed. *The Writing Path 1: Poetry and Prose from Writers' Conferences.* 243p. $32.95 (0-87745-508-2); pap. $14.95 (0-87745-509-0). Iowa City, IA: University of Iowa Press, Spring 1995. Published in conjunction with Writers' Conferences and Festivals. In this first volume of a projected series, established writers introduce new writers they believe show promise. Selections from both the established and new writers are included. —University of Iowa Press. For anyone curious about the stumbling, the groping, and the glimmers of brilliance of our most established and newest talents, *The Writing Path 1* is a delightful romp. —*Bloomsbury Review*

Pettit, Michael, ed. *The Writing Path 2: Poetry and Prose from Writers' Conferences.* 285p. $32.95 (0-87745-552-X); pap. $14.95 (0-87745-548-1). Iowa City, IA: University of Iowa Press, Spring 1996.

Peyser, Carolyn. *Walking in Traffic*. 21p. pap. $5.00. San Francisco, CA: Carolyn Peyser, Spring 1996.

Pfrenum, Richard Ionnsonn. *For a Few Downers More*. 27p. pap. $2.50. Los Angeles, CA: Undulating Bedsheets Productions, Fall 1995. Somewhere drowning in the room of radiation-sick souls lie these poems. Slag the cinder blocks off your weary bones, and scream down the elevator shaft. A hard candy shell becomes your best available defense. . . . —Undulating Bedsheets

Pfrenum, Richard Ionnsonn. *When it Pains it Roars*. 20p. pap. $2.00. Los Angeles, CA: Undulating Bedsheets Productions, Spring 1996. Dark, thudding sounds reverberate underwater; here's a nice soft pillow for your head after the guillotine falls. Keeps it from rolling away too. . . . —Undulating Bedsheets

Philip, Neil, ed. *Poems for Christmas*. 92p. $14.95 (0-312-13339-1). New York, NY: St. Martin's Press, Fall 1995. Everyone's favorites are here, including e. e. cummings's *Little*

Tree, the traditional *Cherry Tree Carol*, Charles Causley's tender lullaby *Sleep, King Jesus*, Thomas Hardy's well-loved *The Oxen* and Robert Frost's *Stopping by Woods on a Snowy Evening.* —St. Martin's Press

Phillips, Carl. *Cortége*. 96p. pap. $12.95 (1-55597-230-6). St. Paul, MN: Graywolf Press, Fall 1995. [Phillips is] an African-American poet with mandarin grace and surpassing elegance of form married to unflinchingly bold and discerning content. —Marilyn Hacker. These are some of the most sensitive homoerotic poems to be found in contemporary literature. —*Library Journal*

Phillips, Louis. *Savage Steps to the House of Meaning*. 96p. pap. $9.95. New York, NY: Prologue Press, Spring 1995.

Phillips, Louis, ed. *The Random House Treasury of Light Verse*. 320p. $10.00 (0-679-76316-3). New York, NY: Random House, Fall 1995.

Piccione, Anthony. *For the Kingdom*. 80p. $20.00 (1-880238-22-5); pap. $12.50 (1-880238-23-3). Rochester, NY: BOA Editions, Spring 1995. In the tradition of Pablo Neruda, Robert Bly and James Wright, Anthony Piccione writes rich, imagistic poems that jar the reader with their brilliant simplicity. —BOA Editions. These poems . . . give the reader a sense of rare, true, wondrous discovery. —Lucien Stryk

Pickles, Sheila, ed. *Bridal Bouquet: A Treasury of Verse and Prose Scented by Penhaligon's.* 64p. $6.50 (0-517-70374-2). New York, NY: Crown Publishers/Harmony Books, Spring 1996. From Harmony's series of miniature books edited by the managing director of the exclusive English perfume house, this book contains passages from well-loved writers and poets, such as Hardy, Donne and Collette, and is scented with the floral perfume Orange Blossom. Others in the series, all of which are edited by Sheila Pickles and scented by Penhaligon's, include: *Mother and Child* (1996, 0-517-70355-6); and *The Language of Wildflowers.* —Crown Publishers

Pinckney, Diana. *Fishing With Tall Women.* 32p. pap. $15.00 (1-879009-24-2). Whispering Pines, NC: Persephone Press, Fall 1996. Winner of the 1996 Persephone Press Book Award. *Fishing With Tall Women* is outstanding, relating its personal terrors and exultations to history, to the crimes, banalities and bigotries of our culture. Its poems end where they should, leaving properly unwritten lines in the reader's imagination. —Donald W. Baker

Pinkerton, Helen. *Bright Fictions.* 36p. Edgewood, KY: Robert L. Barth (R.L.B.), Spring 1996.

Plumpp, Sterling. *Hornman.* 70p. pap. $8.00 (0-88378-177-8). Chicago, IL: Third World Press, Spring 1996. *Hornman* officiates the pauses, whirlwinds and baptismal journey of saxophonist Von Freeman through the distinctive cadence of blues verse. Plumpp provides lyrical access to the inner soul of Black-and-blues folk. —Third World Press. Plumpp is that rarity: a poet who looks with his ears. —*Publishers Weekly*

Poe, Edgar Allan. Edited by Peter Washington. *Poems and Prose.* 255p. $10.95 (0-679-44505-6). New York, NY: Alfred A. Knopf/Everyman's Library Pocket Poet, Fall 1995.

Poe, Edgar Allan. *The Raven, with The Philosophy of Composition.* 40p. pap. $7.95 (1-55921-178-4). Wakefield, RI: Moyer Bell, Fall 1996. First published in 1845, "The Raven" exemplifies Poe's knack for evoking the eerie and wretched. The poem is here illustrated by nine woodcuts by Alan James Robinson that brilliantly depict the fierce, ominous presence of the ungainly fowl. It is accompanied by Poe's eloquent *modus operandi,* "The Philosophy of Composition." —Moyer Bell

Polito, Robert. *Doubles.* 72p. $20.00 (0226-67337-5); pap. $8.95 (0226-67338-3). Chicago, IL: University of Chicago Press, Fall 1995. The narrative poems in *Doubles* inhabit a space of unquiet desperation and even lurid hallucination—a space in which crime and passion and anger and awe get all confused. These poems lurk in the jagged edges of experience, and at the same time one feels in them a pull in the opposite direction, toward lyricism and the joining together of fragments. This is a terrific book. —David Lehman

Polkinhorn, Harry. *Mount Soledad.* 112p. pap. $9.00 (1-880516-19-5). Barrytown, NY: Left Hand Books, Spring 1996. In *Mount Soledad* Harry Polkinhorn uses his ill-fated romance with a Cuban-American woman to illuminate the themes of love and money, employing in the opening pages the conceits associated with the language of love before shifting these rhetorical tropes into a kind of vacillating syntax. —Left Hand Books

Ponge, Francis. Translated by Lee Fahnestock. *The Nature of Things.* 52p. pap. $6.95 (0-87376-080-8). New York, NY: Red Dust, Fall 1995. Published in 1942 and considered the keystone of Francis Ponge's large body of work, *Le parti pris des choses* appears here in its entirety. Ponge's first full volume, it reveals his preoccupation with nature and its metaphoric transformation through the creative ambiguity of language. —Red Dust

Pope, Deborah. *Mortal World.* 67p. $17.95 (0-8071-1983-0); pap. $9.95 (0-8071-1984-9). Baton Rouge, LA: Louisiana State University Press, Fall 1995. Pope's poems have been widely published and they deserve to be. This book is one to own, and to give to someone you love or admire. —*Virginia Quarterly Review*

Porta, Antonio. Translated by Pasquale Verdicchio. *Salomè.* 20p. pap. $5.00 (1-879342-08-1). San Diego, CA: Parentheses Writing Series, Spring 1996.

Porter, Bern. *Symbols.* 42p. pap. $3.00 (1-57141-15-5). Port Charlotte, FL: Runaway Spoon Press, Spring 1995. Simple-seeming but eye-opening verbo-visual collages. —Runaway Spoon Press

Poster, Carol. *Surrounded by Dangerous Things.* 48p. pap. $7.00 (1-880286-17-3). Canton, CT: Singular Speech Press, Fall 1995. Greatly gifted, the poet Carol Poster keeps getting better and better as the tightly focused, clean-lined, always various poems in *Surrounded by Dangerous Things* prove. This is an admirable collection. —George Garrett

Potter, Carol. *Upside Down in the Dark.* 73p. pap. $9.95 (1-882295-05-6). Farmington, ME: Alice James Books, Spring 1995. The sense of dislocation—of homelessness—that is at the heart of this collection func-

tions, paradoxically, as the source of intimate observation and recognition of the dramas of 'home' everywhere. —Linda McCarriston

Pound, Ezra. *The Cantos of Ezra Pound.* 832p. pap. $22.95 (0-8112-1326-9). New York, NY: New Directions, Spring 1996. Now available for the first time in paperback, the *Cantos* is the most important epic poem of the twentieth century. —New Directions. They are one of the touchstones of modern poetry. He discloses history by its odor, by the feel of it—in the words; fuses it with the words, present and past, to MAKE his *Cantos*. Make them. —William Carlos Williams

Powell, Jeanne. *Cadences.* 28p. pap. $8.00 (0-9653587-0-4). San Francisco, CA: Meridien PressWorks, Spring 1996. Illustrated with photographs of the American Southwest by Clarence Towers. —Meridien PressWorks

Powell, Jeanne. *February Voices: First Poems.* 28p. pap. $8.00 (0-932693-08-3). San Francisco, CA: Jukebox Press, Fall 1995. She writes with the honesty of a survivor and the elegance of a stylist. Whether satirizing or keening or offering her own story with irony and gracefulness, her *Voices* are promising poems. I recommend that readers read them, and that she write more. —Christopher Bernard

Powell, Kevin. *Recognize.* 79p. pap. $11.00 (0-86316-324-6). New York, NY: Writers and Readers Publishing/Harlem River Press, Fall 1995. Here's the vital, voluble, vulnerable Kevin Powell, biting into print with *Recognize*, so rejoice ye seekers. The intersection of the personal, the political and art is dancing with the bebop-hiphop-nonstop antitradition tradition. —Bob Holman. Kevin Powell approaches the contemporary experience of the African American by a number of avenues: he leads the reader through dark ghettos, through the maze of the mass media, through his own personal history. —Sonia Sanchez

Powell, Lynn. *Old & New Testaments.* 82p. $17.95 (0-299-14900-5); pap. $10.95 (0-299-14904-8). Madison, WI: University of Wisconsin Press, Fall 1995. Winner of the 1995 Brittingham Prize in Poetry.

These poems explore Lynn Powell's Southern Baptist upbringing and how that history echoes through her adult experiences. —University of Wisconsin Press. These are poems of the recovery of spiritual desire. This is an extraordinary book, and an extraordinary new talent. —Robert Morgan. The intensity of the opening poems in *Old & New Testaments* builds throughout the book until, almost intolerable, it transforms into profound acceptance, the quietness that comes of acknowledging both life and death. —A. R. Ammons

Presfield, Christopher. *Dark Rose Dialogue.* 24p. Mena, AR: Cedar Hill Publications, Spring 1996.

Presnell, Barbara. *Snake Dreams.* 24p. pap. $6.00 (1-879205-54-8). Troy, ME: Nightshade Press, Fall 1994. Narrative poems from this powerful, tender Kentucky poet. —Nightshade Press

Purpura, Lia. *The Brighter the Veil.* 80p. pap. $12.95 (0-914061-56-9). Alexandria, VA: Orchises Press, Spring 1996. Lia Purpura is a master of the particular. She is a realist and one step beyond. She is a recorder of the soul as it rests comfortably, or uncomfortably, inside us and our things. She is honest and true. And moving. —Gerald Stern

Pursifull, Carmen M. *The Many Faces of Passion.* 109p. pap. $10.00 (1-881900-04-5). Champaign, IL: Hawk Productions, Spring 1996. Carmen Pursifull's poems have always combined bright imagery with a highly personalized directness, tinged with audacity. There is much vintage Carmen in *The Many Faces of Passion*, but she goes farther here, entering the realms of the surreal and the macabre. —Charles Suhor

Putnam, Seth. *Cessation.* 16p. $11.00; pap. $6.00. Jackson, MS: Semiquasi Press, Fall 1996. *Cessation* is an experimental "word-bridging" chapbook from the Prague Infant chapbook series (dedicated to making 'accessible' avant-garde material widely available and inexpensive). *Cessation* introduces performance-reader Seth Putnam's half cut-up / half automatic texts. Di Michele's collages throughout the book reflect the same disjointed-holistic approach to random and archetypal visual information. —Semiquasi Press

Qa, Laura. *Tribute to the Hound.* 64p. pap. $11.95 (0-9637704-2-X). Alexandria, VA: Red Dragon Press, Fall 1995. This second collection of verse by Laura Qa exemplifies the ability to blend sensuality and thought with literary innovation. The title pays homage to the dog that guards the gates of Hell, and here are verses that venture into the realm of the soul. —Red Dragon Press

Qabbani, Nizar. Translated by Lena Jayyusi and Sharif Elmusa. *On Entering the Sea: The Erotic and Other Poetry of Nizar Qabbani.* 184p. $22.95 (1-56656-186-8); pap. $15.00 (1-56656-193-0). Northampton, MA: Interlink Publishing, Fall 1996. Qabbani has succeeded in re-establishing the vitality of the erotic tradition in Arabic poetry, and has enriched it with the experience of a modern man deeply aware of the imperative of a woman's right to assume control over her body and emotions. —Interlink Publishing. Qabbani is one of the greatest love poets of all time. [This is a] beautiful collection. —*Booklist*

Quillen, Rita Sims. *Counting the Sums.* 64p. $20.00 (1-885912-07-2); pap. $12.00 (1-885912-04-8). Abingdon, VA: Sow's Ear Press, Fall 1995. These are poems about paths: individual, rocky, secret; linking, connecting, creating families, communities across time . . . —Robert Morgan. Rita Sims Quillen's words shine with truth, even in her darkest lines, and what she says is as true as the world's unceasing breath. —Fred Chappell

Quinn, Fran. *The Goblet Crying for Wine.* 73p. pap. $10.00 (0-9638722-1-4). Saint Paul, MN: Blue Sofa Press/Ally Press Center, Spring 1995. Quinn's poetry is related to William Carlos Williams' in its inclusion of coffee cups and door-stoops next to intense feeling and elegant turns of phrase. In a time of coolness, he has written marvelous love poems. In a time of neo-cortex language

poetry, his words are clear and weighty. —Robert Bly

Quinn, James P. *Grandpa Was No Saint.* 112p. pap. $8.95 (1-56474-136-2). Santa Barbara, CA: Fithian Press, Fall 1995. A lyrical view of Ireland, family and friendship, love and death, from an Irish-American poet. —Fithian Press

Quiñones, Magaly. *Sueños de Papel.* 126p. pap. $6.95 (0-8477-0261-8). San Juan, PR: University of Puerto Rico Press, Fall 1996. A feminine perspective of the creative process, gleaning insights through her interactions with the day-to-day world. In Spanish only. —University of Puerto Rico Press

Quintana, Leroy V. *My Hair Turning Gray Among Strangers.* 88p. pap. $9.00 (0-927534-57-6). Tempe, AZ: Bilingual Press, Spring 1996. Quintana transforms the mundane events of homecoming into a serious grappling with a universal phenomenon. —*Publishers Weekly*

R

Radon, Lisa. *The Super Deluxe with Everything and Other Poems.* 38p. pap. $6.95 (0-9654684-8-8). Capitola, CA: Big Star Press, Fall 1996.

Rafferty, Charles. *The Man on the Tower.* 64p. $14.00 (1-55728-339-7); pap. $8.00 (1-55728-340-0). Fayetteville, AR: University of Arkansas Press, Spring 1995. This new collection of poems—winner of the fifth annual Arkansas Poetry Award—is composed of dramatic monologues and fables about "the man"—the many incarnations of our lives that are not allowed, cannot be lived, or are kept darkly hidden. —University of Arkansas Press. These poems are so right I sometimes had to catch my breath before going on to the next one. —Miller William

Raimund, Hans. Translated by Robert Dassanowsky. *Verses of a Marriage.* 112p. pap. $16.95 (1-880391-16-3). Desert Hot Springs, CA: Event Horizon Press, Fall 1996. A major Austrian writer, Hans Raimund is considered one of the important voices of his generation. —Event Horizon Press

Rakosi, Carl. Edited by Andrew Crozier. *Poems 1923-1941.* 210p. pap. $12.95 (1-55713-185-6). Los Angeles, CA: Sun & Moon Press, Fall 1995. This volume brings together for the first time all the poems Rakosi wrote as an "Objectivist," together with others of his poems from the 1920s and 1930s. Working with Rakosi, Crozier has produced a carefully edited volume of Rakosi's early writing. —Sun & Moon Press

Ramke, Bin. *Massacre of the Innocents.* 96p. pap. $10.95 (0-87745-492-2). Iowa City, IA: University of Iowa Press, Spring 1995. Winner of the 1994 Iowa Poetry Prize.

Ransom, Bill. *Learning the Ropes: A Creative Autobiography.* 192p. pap. $19.95 (0-87421-190-5). Logan, UT: Utah State University Press, Fall 1995. A collection of Ransom's finest work from the last 25 years, including poems, fiction, and essays. —Utah State University Press. With mind-language as rapier and heart-language as salve, Bill Ransom duels the

Beast—and soothes its noisy wounds. —Tom Robbins

Ranzoni, Patricia. *Claiming.* 82p. pap. $8.95 (0-913006-59-9). Orono, ME: Puckerbrush Press, Fall 1995. The poems of Patricia Ranzoni have the pizzazz [and inventiveness] of real country speakers, close to the earth and each other. Her voice adds significantly to the [record of the] imaginative expressiveness of New England. —Hayden Carruth

Ratcliffe, Stephen. *Present Tense.* 104p. pap. $12.00 (0-935724-71-0). Great Barrington, MA: The Figures, Fall 1995.

Ratner, Rochelle. *Zodiac Arrest.* 20p. pap. (1-56439-042-0). Roseville, MI: Ridgeway Press, Fall 1995.

Rautenberg, Arne. *Dislimitation.* 30p. pap. $5.00 (1-57141-009-0). Port Charlotte, FL: Runaway Spoon Press, Spring 1995. A collection of visual poetry from Germany. —Runaway Spoon Press

Rav-Hon, Orna. Translated by Karen Alkalay-Gut, Stanley H. Barkan, and Riva Rubin. *Firebird.* 48p. $15.00 (0-89304-492-8); pap. (0-89304-493-X). Merrick, NY: Cross-Cultural Communications, Spring 1996. Bilingual edition, Hebrew and English.

Raworth, Tom. *Clean & Well Lit: Selected Poems 1987-1995.* 106p. pap. $10.95 (0-937804-64-6). New York, NY: Roof Books, Fall 1996. For more than thirty years, Tom Raworth has been at the forefront of English language writing. . . . There is no better introduction to Raworth than *Clean & Well Lit.* —Charles Bernstein

Ray, David. *Kangaroo Paws: Poems Written in Australia.* 143p. $19.95 (0-943549-35-3); pap. $9.95 (0-943549-34-5). Kirksville, MO: Thomas Jefferson University Press, Spring 1995. I've always been touched by David Ray's poetry, and it's clear that it is deepening all the time. He speaks eloquently of the depth possible in private life. —Robert Bly

Reader, Willie. *Fishing a Whirlpool.* 32p. pap. $6.00. Brockport, NY: State Street Press, Spring 1996. Personal and family history caught in poems about the precarious balance of rural life. —State Street Press

Rebolledo, Tey Diana, and Eliana S. Rivero, eds. *Infinite Divisions: An Anthology of Chicana Literature*. 387p. pap. $19.95 (0-8165-1384-8). Tucson, AZ: University of Arizona Press, 1993. There is simply no better anthology for readers wondering how to enter those borderlands Chicana writers have been occupying for the past decades. . . . A superb selection of poems, stories, essays and plays by fifty authors. —*Women's Review of Books*. This undoubtedly will be the definitive text for some time to come on the subject of Chicana writers. —*Bloomsbury Review*

Rector, Liam. *American Prodigal*. 64p. $19.95 (0-934257-21-3); pap. $11.95 (0-934257-22-1). Brownsville, OR: Story Line Press, Fall 1994. This collection of verse monologues extends and refines the ever-evolving American character. The divide between those-who-go and those-who-stay informs the structure of the book. Rector addresses our travel, our transience, our broken homes, our broken polity, our work, our money, and our American dreams. —Story Line Press. [Rector's] Americans are caught on a 'tide' that carries them away from, then toward, home. —*Publishers Weekly*. In his second book of poems . . . [Rector] approaches with a slightly angry edge to his voice and an observant eye, like some contemporary prodigal returning to a homeland he once doubted he'd want to see again. —Elizabeth Gunderson, *Booklist*

Red Hawk. *The Way of Power*. 86p. pap. $10.00 (0-934252-64-5). Prescott, AZ: Hohm Press, Fall 1996. Red Hawk traces the path to power, or spiritual realization, the path of the broken heart. —Hohm Press. Red Hawk is like Whitman because he can contain multitudes and yet he is always so authentically himself. Behind all these (poems) there is always one single simple thing, which is Red Hawk's own voice. Haunting and stark, ironic and spare. —William Packard

Redel, Victoria. *Already the World*. 68p. $17.00 (0-87338-530-6); pap. $9.50 (0-87338-531-4). Kent, OH: Kent State University Press, Fall 1995. I like Redel's poems because of their braveness and their lucidity. The music is lovely and the tone, distinctive. —Gerald Stern. Redel is writing the love poems of a new generation of women. Sensual and daring, there are possibilities in these poems that all of us are discovering. —Toi Derricotte

RedKitchen Poets' Performance Troupe. *Hey, Good Lookin'!* 42p. pap. $7.95. Johnstown, OH: Pudding House Publications, Spring 1995. Poems from six diverse Columbus area performance poets: Steve Abbott, Jennifer Bosveld, Chris Conti, Sandra J. Feen, MJ Abell, and William Merricle. —Pudding House Publications

Reed, Helen G. *Riding the Bubbles Down.* 72p. pap. $12.00 (0-939121-08-5). Shreveport, LA: Cooper House Publishing, Fall 1995. Winner of the 1994 American Chapbook Award from Cooper House Publishing and *Poet Magazine*. Reed's images are powerful, her poems delicate and nostalgic, evocative. —Marcia Gale Kester

Reed, John R. *Great Lake.* 72p. pap. $9.95 (1-56439-044-6). Roseville, MI: Ridgeway Press, Fall 1995. These poems demonstrate how painfully close are the worlds we relish and the

world we fear. Its author has a superb talent for fashioning language compelling enough to transport us. Laurence Goldstein, *The Michigan Quarterly*

Reed, John R. *Life Sentences.* 86p. pap. $14.95 (0-8143-2629-3). Detroit, MI: Wayne State University Press, Fall 1996. Some of the most innovative poems in this book are dramatic monologues in the voices of famous literary figures, including Oscar Wilde, Charles Baudelaire, Ernest Dowson, Paul Verlaine, and Gabriele d'Annunzio. Reed's poetry reveals the effort we all make to resist the reduction of our private life stories to insignificance through the imaginative construction of our "life sentences." —Wayne State University Press

Rehder, Robert. *The Compromises Will Be Different.* 78p. pap. $12.95 (1-85754-127-8). Riverdale-on-Hudson, NY: Sheep Meadow Press, Fall 1995. Rehder contemplates the splendors and miseries of everyday life with an eye to foibles and absurdities, including our own. —Marjorie Perloff

Rehm, Pam. *To Give It Up.* 80p. pap. $9.95 (1-55713-212-7).

Los Angeles, CA: Sun & Moon Press, Fall 1995. Winner of the 1994 National Poetry Series Award. How fine, how original, humbling in the purity of its tone, is *To Give It Up*. And the creative intensity in which her poems struggle until a calm descends in which the spirit thrives. —Barbara Guest

Reinhard, John. *On the Road to Patsy Cline.* 88p. pap. $11.95 (0-89823-171-X). Minneapolis, MN: New Rivers Press, Fall 1996. John Reinhard travels a landscape of cornfield and river, small town, highway and city to celebrate growing up in America. He is a true troubadour whose candor and generosity of spirit allow us to believe in heroes again. —Judith Minty. Both a riveting storyteller and a poet of lyric intensities, John Reinhard writes with charm, depth, and uncommon sense. His lovely, often funny poems make room for jukeboxes, herons, Emily Dickinson's ankle, and notes from the dead. His work is just a little bit heartbreaking. It has the power to revise your skepticism and your faith. —Alice Fulton

Reiss, James. *The Parable of Fire.* 64p. $20.95 (0-88748-238-4);

pap. $11.95 (0-88748-239-2). Pittsburgh, PA: Carnegie Mellon University, Spring 1996. Pursued by the same phantoms, which reappear on the telephone, in sequential rooms, in snapshots, in slides, Reiss writes them down in an accomplished plain style, with a momentum carrying whole poems along on the humming acceleration of a single sentence. —Helen Vendler, *The New York Times Book Review*. Reiss writes with urgency and zing. There isn't a dull page in the book. —*Library Journal*

Reiter, Thomas. *Crossovers.* $23.00 (0-910055-19-X); pap. $12.50 (0-910055-20-3). Cheney, WA: Eastern Washington University Press, Spring 1995. Reiter is someone I would like to call up (along with Holden Caulfield) to see what his next poem will be. —Frank Allen, *Poet Lore*. There is no doubt in reading these poems that Reiter loves craft in its largest sense. The subjects he chooses return again and again to the idea [of craft]: carpenters, fishermen, painters, handymen; [he celebrates] anyone who performs a task with wisdom and grace. —*Quarterly West*

Retallack, Joan. *Afterrimages.* 115p. $25.00 (0-8195-2219-8); pap. $12.95 (0-8195-1223-0). Middletown, CT: Wesleyan/ University Press of New England, Spring 1995. Joan Retallack offers readers a book of forms, like the medieval *Book of Hours*, intended to provide a meditative experience of time, space, language, and the many humors of chance and design as they intersect and leave their traces on the page. —Wesleyan University Press. For readers interested in the best contemporary writing, Joan Retallack's *Afterimages* is a good place to begin, continue, or end. . . . A work which is rewarding on every level. —Ann Lauterbach

Revell, Donald. *Beautiful Shirt.* 67p. $22.50 (0-8195-2216-3); pap. $10.95 (0-8195-1219-2). Middletown, CT: Wesleyan/ University Press of New England, Fall 1994. This is a poetry of often blunt, gnomic statements, but also an abundance of thought and dazzling wordplay. —*Publishers Weekly*

Rhodes, Martha. *At the Gate.* 60p. $35.00 (0-944854-19-2); pap. $10.00 (0-944854-18-4). Provincetown, MA: Provinc-etown Arts Press, Spring 1995. Rhodes cleaves to no fixed perspective—this is a single speaker, eccentric, various, [persuasive] because it imitates and preserves the child's helplessly reactive mind as it survives into adulthood. These short poems, by turns savage, wry, mordantly witty, read like a series of fragments; they duplicate on the page the sense of a past's being, piece by piece, recovered; they convey, devastatingly, the moment of a pattern's emerging; cohere heart-stoppingly into a narrative which fuses the damaged body to the divided heart. [Reading these poems] we are in the presence of a wild, stubborn, unkillable life. —Louise Glück, *The Threepenny Review*

Rice, Felicia, ed. *Contextos: poemas.* 20p. pap. $3.50 (0-939952-18-1). Santa Cruz, CA: Moving Parts Press, Fall 1994. *Contextos: poemas* includes poems by Juvenal Acosta, Mario Angel Quintero, Arthur Arteaga and Carmen Rosello; with drawings by Jennifer Cordery. Bilingual edition published in conjunction with the 1994 MACLA Broadside Series. —Moving Parts Press

Rice, Felicia, ed. *Lenguas Sueltas: poemas.* 32p. pap. $3.75 (0-939952-19-X). Santa Cruz, CA: Moving Parts Press, Fall 1994. This anthology of 17 poets was produced in association with the Bay Tree Bookstore, to accompany an evening of poetry, curated by Elba Rosario Sánchez, at Oakes College, USSC. Drawings by Robert Chianto. —Moving Parts Press

Rice, Stan. *Fear Itself.* 93p. $20.00 (0-679-44441-6). New York, NY: Alfred A. Knopf, Fall 1995. Stan Rice's new book of poems is faithful to the strong, expressionist thrust of his [earlier work]. *Fear Itself* is equally arresting in the ominous visions it invokes—as though the book's title is to be taken literally, and the reader to be both engaged and disquieted. —Alfred A. Knopf

Rich, Adrienne. *Collected Early Poems 1950-1970.* 435p. pap. $15.00 (0-393-31385-9). New York, NY: W.W. Norton & Company, Fall 1995. This important volume charts the radical transformation of one of America's most significant poets. —*Publishers Weekly*

Rich, Adrienne. *Dark Fields of the Republic: Poems 1991-1995.* 86p. $25.00 (0-393-03868-8); pap. $10.00 (0-393-31398-0). W.W. Norton & Company, Fall 1995. In her vision of warning and her celebration of life, Adrienne Rich is the Blake of American letters. —Nadine Gordimer

Rich, Adrienne. *Diving into the Wreck: Poems 1971-1972.* 72p. pap. $8.95 (0-393-31163-5). New York, NY: W.W. Norton & Company, Fall 1994. *Diving into the Wreck* is one of those rare books that force you to decide not just what you think of it, but what you think about yourself. It is a book that takes risks, and forces the reader to take them also. . . . You feel about her best images, her best myths, that nobody else writes quite like this. —Margaret Atwood, *New York Times Book Review*

Rich, Adrienne, and David Lehman, eds. *The Best American Poetry 1996.* 318p. $27.50 (0-684-81455-2); pap. $13.00 (0-684-81451-X). New York, NY: Scribner/Simon & Schuster, Fall 1996. Culled from over forty periodicals that range from leading journals like *The New*

Yorker and *The Paris Review* to vibrant little magazines like *Lingo* and *Many Mountains Moving*, Rich's selections reflect her strong commitment to social justice, human community, and the voices of poets outside the literary mainstream. —Scribner

Richman, Jan. *Because the Brain Can Be Talked Into Anything.* 48p. $15.95 (0-8071-1993-8); pap. $8.95 (0-8071-1994-6). Baton Rouge, LA: Louisiana State University Press, Spring 1995. Winner of the 1994 Walt Whitman Award. Underlying the attractive, flamboyant, often comic rhetoric of this splendid first book is the untamed seriousness of art. —Robert Pinsky. Richman's collection is dazzling from the first lines and never lets up. —*Booklist*. Richman's work explodes with electricity that is like a Fourth of July celebration, not of liberty but of a lively mind transforming disappointment into ingenious (and sometimes goofy) metaphor. —Frank Allen, *Library Journal*

Richter, Harvena. *Green Girls: Poems Early and Late.* 48p. pap. $6.00. Albuquerque, NM: North Valley Press, Fall 1996.

This is an eclectic, powerful collection with New York City and New Mexico origins. Traditional and experimental forms are used, from the sonnet to the fugue. —North Valley Press

Richter, Harvena. *The Yaddo Elegies and Other Poems.* 40p. pap. $6.00. Albuquerue, NM: North Valley Press, Spring 1995. [These poems are] full of darkness and richness. —William L. Weber. Pristine poems, to be admired for their elegance; delectable poems, to be savored for their eloquence. —Geraldine Sanford

Riddle, Rita Sizemore. *Aluminum Balloons and Other Poems.* 44p. pap. $5.50 (0-936015-65-9). Blacksburg, VA: Pocahontas Press, Spring 1996. *Aluminum Balloons* is a powerful collection of poems about infidelity, suicide and domestic violence. —Pocahontas Press. The poems are edgy and nervous and angry—as they should be. —Richard Hague

Rifbjerg, Klaus. Translated by Steven T. Murray and Tiina Nunnally. *War.* 78p. pap. $10.00 (0-940242-66-4). Seattle, WA: Fjord Press, Spring

1995. With insight, irony and lyricism, Denmark's foremost contemporary poet delivers a powerful indictment of the marketing of war and its incidious effect on the daily lives of ordinary people. Rifbjerg shows us how war is woven inextricably into the fabric of our lives. —Fjord Press

Riley, James Whitcomb. *Little Orphant Annie and Other Poems.* 76p. pap. $1.00 (0-486-28260-0). Mineola, NY: Dover Publications, Fall 1994.

Rilke, Rainer Maria. Translated by Stephen Mitchell. *Orpheus, Eurydice, Hermes: Notations on a Landscape.* 35p. $150.00 (0-89304-058-4); Deluxe ed. $500.00 (0-89304-057-6); Merrick, NY: Cross-Cultural Communications, Fall 1995. Deluxe edition includes an original carborundum print. —Cross-Cultural Communications

Rilke, Rainer Maria. Edited by Peter Washington. *Poems.* 254p. $12.50 (0-679-45098-X). New York, NY: Alfred A. Knopf/Everyman's Library Pocket Poets, Spring 1996.

Rilke, Rainer Maria. Translated by M. D. Herter Norton. *Translations from the Poetry of Rainer Maria Rilke.* 245p. pap. $9.95 (0-393-31038-8). New York, NY: W.W. Norton & Company, Fall 1994.

Rilke, Rainer Maria. Translated by Edward Snow. *Uncollected Poems.* 266p. $22.00 (0-86547-482-6). New York, NY: Farrar Straus and Giroux/North Point Press, Spring 1996. The Snow translation of these little-known Rilke poems is brilliant. —Mark Strand. It is wonderful to have a whole new (and sizable) volume of Rilke poems given us by Edward Snow, who is far and away Rilke's best contemporary translator—one who never imposes his own personality or idiosyncrasies of style between us and the original, but gives to it that respect which proves him worthy of the task. —Denise Levertov

Ringold-Johnson, Francine Leffler. *The Trouble with Voices: Selected Poetry.* 56p. pap. $9.95 (1-57178-022-X). Tulsa, OK: Council Oak Books, Fall 1995. Winner of the Oklahoma Book Award for Poetry. From Francine Ringold-Johnson, editor of *Nimrod*, come these haunting, querulous and loving voices that will not let us rest. —Council Oak Books

Ríos, Andrés Castro. *La noche y la poesía Tienen algo que decir.* 48p. pap. $6.95 (0-8477-0265-0). San Juan, PR: University of Puerto Rico Press, Fall 1996. In Spanish only.

Ritterbusch, Dale. *Lessons Learned.* 88p. pap. $12.00 (1-885215-08-8). Woodbridge, CT: Viet Nam Generation/Burning Cities Press, Fall 1995. These are poems of great power and marvelous sensibility, haunting and beautiful, alive with outrage and decency and a sadness deeper than dreams. *Lessons Learned* is a blessing, and only fools turn their backs on blessings. —W. D. Ehrhart

Roberson, Ed. *Voices Cast Out to Talk Us In.* 182p. pap. $10.95 (0-87745-510-4). Iowa City, IA: University of Iowa Press, Spring 1995. Winner of the 1994 Iowa Poetry Prize. The ebb and flow of words, phrases, and caesuras in Roberson's work convey an oceanic roll, a largesse of possibilities, how to write and how to live. —Lewis Warsh

Robertson, Kirk. *Just Past Labor Day: Selected and New Poems 1969-1996.* 296p. pap. $16.00 (0-87417-284-5). Reno, NV: University of Nevada Press, Fall 1996. One of Nevada's best known poets, Kirk Robertson's lean verses powerfully express the realities of life in the modern West—its irony, disconnection and relentless quest for meaning and a sense of place. —University of Nevada Press. The American West is beginning to discover its next generation of voices. Kirk Robertson, when it all shakes down, is sure to be one of the writers we listen to with gratitude. He helps us make sense of our own selves, what we want, and helps us get started down the road toward defining what we maybe *ought* to want. —William Kittredge

Robertson, Kirk. *Music.* 56p. pap. $10.00 (0-912449-51-9). Cedarville, CA: Floating Island Publications, Spring 1995. These poems go to the heart of it: the urgent task before us now is finding once more our home among the elements. Robertson's poems show how it's done, in the light and wind of the desert, and in the weather of his own feelings. His is the straight, honest, and hardest way, and for that reason, indispensable. —Andrei Codrescu

Robins, Corinne. *Facing It.* 62p. pap. $9.00 (0930557-01-8). New York, NY: Pratt Press, Spring 1996. *Facing It* is a moving and sometimes devastating account of a mother's discovery of and reaction to a daughter's drug addiction. The poems are at once impressionistic and deeply cutting in tone. They are distinguished by their images—Corinne Robins is a well known contemporary art historian and curator of shows of women's paintings—which work a collage effect on the book as a whole. *Facing It* is therefore not a direct, narrative account of painful events, but painful events revealed in imagery, art made from the underlife. —Molly Peacock

Robinson, Edwin Arlington. *The Torrent and the Night Before.* 50p. $12.95 (0-88448-183-2). Gardiner, ME: Tilbury House, Publishers, Spring 1996. Centennial facsimile edition of his first book, self-published in 1896 by the three-time Pulitzer Prize-winning poet from Gardiner, Maine. Afterword by Donald Justice. —Tilbury House

Robinson, Jen. *Ten Poems.* 10p. pap. $4.00. Brooklyn, NY: Mundungus Productions, Fall 1995.

Rodriquez, Andres. *Night Song.* 78p. pap. $7.95 (1-882688-05-8). Chicago, IL: Tia Chucha Press, Fall 1994. Andres Rodriguez's poetry combines severity and sweetness in fresh ways. He writes about love, family, place and culture with a natural dignity that is both self-questioning and restorative. —W. S. Di Piero

Roeske, Paulette. *Divine Attention.* 69p. $17.95 (0-8071-1950-4); pap. $9.95 (0-8071-1951-2). Baton Rouge, LA: Louisiana State University Press, Fall 1995. Texture, density, grit and gravity—I feel in Paulette Roeske's *Divine Attention* the force of experience fully absorbed and the power of poetry to organize our attention. —Marvin Bell. [Roeske's] open form poems are incidents accompanied by analysis, a thoughtful form of telling which gives equal weight to the occasion of the poem and the poet's meditation. —*Poetry East*

Rogers, Bertha, ed. *Iroquois Voices, Iroquois Visions: A Celebration of Contemporary Six Nations Arts.* 130p. pap. $12.00

(0-9646844-3-8). Treadwell, NY: Bright Hill Press, Spring 1996. An anthology of literary and visual works by over 60 contemporary Iroquois artists, among them Maurice Kenny, Alex Jacobs, Diane Schenandoah, and Tom Huff. Includes poetry, fiction, essays, and two-and-three-dimensional art. —Bright Hill Press

Rogers, Bertha, ed. *The Word Thursdays Anthology of Poetry and Fiction.* 198p. pap. (0-9646844-1-1). Treadwell, NY: Bright Hill Press, Spring 1995. This new collection focuses on the work of 75 poets and writers who read their work at Word Thursdays annual tour and festival. The anthology includes the work of several regional high-school students. —Bright Hill Press

Rogers, Pattiann. *Fire-Keeper.* 260p. pap. $12.95 (1-57131-400-8). Minneapolis, MN: Milkweed Editions, Fall 1994. Rogers combines the detail of a field guide with the vision of a physics book and the reverence of a hymnal. —Milkweed Editions

Rogoff, Jay. *The Cutoff.* 64p. pap. $10.00 (0-915380-31-5). Wash-ington, DC: The Word Works, Spring 1995. Winner of the 1994 Word Works Washington Prize. A sequence of lyrical monologues set in the world of minor league baseball. —The Word Works. A terrific book. —Marilyn Hacker. Caught up in Rogoff's touching story, his exuberance for baseball, and the verve and grace of his writing, it's easy to overlook, at first, the virtuoso brilliance of his poetry. For readers who love baseball, poetry, or another human being, *The Cutoff* is rich in pleasures. —Andrew Hudgins

Rohrer, Matthew. *A Hummock in the Malookas.* 74p. $17.95 (0-393-03798-3); pap. $11.00 (0-393-31548-7). New York, NY: W.W. Norton & Company, Fall 1995. Winner of the 1994 National Poetry Series. A *Publishers Weekly* Best Book of the Year. Everything is animate and startling in this surrealistic, hip, and firmly controlled collection. —*Publishers Weekly.* The gathering intelligence in the book is omnivorous and generous. Poems with this much energy are always a pleasure. —Anthony Robbins, *American Book Review*

Rolfe, Edwin. Edited by Cary Nelson and Jefferson Hendricks. *Trees Became Torches: Selected Poems.* 152p. pap. $13.95 (0-252-06417-8). Champaign, IL: University of Illinois, Fall 1995. Rolfe's voice is one that many of us feared was buried forever in the graveyard dug simultaneously by McCarthyism and by those academics who established the canon of elite modernism. He stands in the forefront of an entire 'lost generation' of left-wing writers who fused artistic craft with irrepressible political commitment. —Alan Wald. Rolfe writes with artistic and philosophical authority, great skill, powerful feeling, and considerable appeal. —Reginald Gibbons

Romtvedt, David. *Certainty.* 88p. pap. $12.00 (1-877727-59-8). Fredonia, NY: White Pine Press, Spring 1996. The poems in *Certainty* ambush numbness, despair and grief with quiet and powerful compassion. —Mekeel McBride. In these beautiful, unusual pieces, David Romtvedt strips his voice to that which he can say with certainty. The results are meditations and transformations—heart, magic, insights, irony, comedy, surrealism, the deepest storytelling, and a surprising, very moving

masculinity. —Sharon Doubiago

Ronk, Martha. *State of Mind.* 76p. pap. $10.95 (1-55713-236-4). Los Angeles, CA: Sun & Moon Press, Fall 1995. The poems in *State of Mind* are in transit as geographies (especially Californian) slide into states of mind, statements of "fact" into memory or metaphor. —Sun & Moon Press

Rosalee. *The Moon Saw Me Happy.* 36p. pap. $6.95 (1-56315-044-1). Pittsburgh, PA: Sterling House, Spring 1996.

Rose, Aaron. *Meanderings.* 71p. Miami, FL: Arco Publishing Company, Spring 1996. Traditional, family-oriented poetry. —Arco Publishing Company

Rose, Wendy. *Bone Dance: New and Selected Poems, 1965-1993.* 108p. $19.95 (0-8165-1428-3); pap. $10.95 (0-8165-1412-7). Tucson, AZ: University of Arizona Press, Fall 1995. This is one of the most important collections of poems by an American Indian writer. Rose's best poems are as good as any written in the last twenty years by *any* poet. —Carter Revard

Rose, Wilga. *Black Swan to Currawong.* 20p. pap. Free for Postage (55¢ and 6x9″ SASE). Arlington, VA: Bogg Publications, Fall 1995. A clear and memorable voice firmly rooted in the Australian experience. —Robert Boyce

Rosenstock, S.X. *United Artists.* 64p. $15.95 (1-57003-130-4); pap. $9.95 (1-57003-131-2). Columbia, SC: University of South Carolina Press, Spring 1996. Rosenstock has created her own quirky nomenclature of experience, her own wise-cracking erotics of art. —Edward Hirsch. Imagine the *Divine Comedy, Goblin Market, Divine Comedies,* and Brock-Broido's *Hunger,* then join with them Rosenstock's prismatic music, and you will have *United Artists.* —Cynthia Macdonald

Ross, Clifton. *Fables for an Open Field.* 34p. pap. $4.00 (0-915117-07-X). Berkeley, CA: New Earth Publications, Fall 1995.

Rossetti, Christina. *Poems of Christina Rossetti.* 112p. $8.99 (0-517-11851-3). Avenel, NJ: Gramercy Books, Fall 1994.

Rossiter, Charles. *No, I Didn't Steal This Baby, I'm the Daddy.* 20p. pap. $3.00. Albany, NY: A. P. D., Spring 1995. As a dad who works at home while mom holds down the traditional 9 to 5, Charlie's the one in his household who spends more time on "the frontlines of childcare." This collection of poems from the first three years of that experience tells a little bit about what it's like. —A. P. D.

Rossiter, Charles. *On Reading the Thousand-Year-Old Sorrows in a Book of Chinese Poems.* 12p. pap. $2.00. Delmar, NY: Esker Press, Spring 1996. Excellent. —James Laughlin

Rotella, Alexis K., and Florence Miller. *A String of Monarchs: Thirteen Linked Poems.* 52p. pap. $12.95 (0-917951-49-2). Los Gatos, CA: Jade Mountain Press, Fall 1995. [In these renga there is] no emotion too shameful, no thought shielded from their honesty and no cow too sacred. —Jane Reichhold, *Mirrors*

Rothenberg, Jerome. *Seedings & Other Poems.* 128p. pap. $10.95 (0-8112-1331-5). New York, NY: New Directions, reissued

Fall 1996. By equating archaic and experimental, primitive and complex, Rothenberg has offered contemporary poets an opportunity to conceive of their roots as deeper and wider than any narrowly defined academic lineage. —Geoffrey O'Brien, *Voice Literary Supplement*

Rothenberg, Jerome, and Pierre Joris, eds. *Poems for the Millennuim: The University of California Book of Modern & Postmodern Poetry, Vol. 1: From Fin-de-Siècle to Negritude.* 800p. $60.00 (0-520-07225-1); pap. $24.95 (0-520-07227-8). Berkely, CA: University of California Press, Fall 1995. This invaluable collection, rather than gathering the most fully realized poetry of this century's first four decades, maps poetic possibility, thus demonstrating how poetry was literally remade during this period. —*Publishers Weekly.* This ambitious documentary history should take its place in most poetry collections, large and small. —Fred Muratori, *Library Journal*

Roumain, Jacques. Translated by Joanne Fungaroli and Ronald Sauer. *When the Tom-Tom Beats: Selected Prose and Poems.* 109p.

pap. $11.95 (0-9632363-8-5). Washington, DC: Azul Editions, Fall 1995. Jacques Roumain is to Haitian literature what Langston Hughes is to American literature. Throughout his life, he searched for ways to advance the cause of justice and human solidarity. —Azul Editions

Rowe, Vernon. *Sea Creatures and Other Poems.* 64p. pap. $9.95 (0-9647053-0-3). Overland Park, KS: Whirlybird Press, Fall 1995. Love of family, of earth and its wonders, of the patients he helps as a doctor, make Vernon Rowe's first book worth our attention. William Carlos Williams would greet a disciple. —David Ray

Roy, Camille. *The Rosy Medallions: Selected Work.* 69p. pap. $10.00 (0-932716-35-0). Berkeley, CA: Kelsey St. Press, Spring 1995. Roy's nasty, luscious stories and poems make up a dyke coming-of-age novel, set not in the American family, but in our traveling explosion of body-race-class-gender. —Robert Gluck. This author's perspective ranges back and forth over her life and memories like a hungry camera, doggily attracted to instances of beauty, cruelty and aeons of female privacy. Roy's a pioneer of new literature. —Eileen Myles

Roy, Lucinda. *The Humming Birds.* 88p. pap. $12.95 (0-933377-38-X). Portland, OR: Eighth Mountain Press, Fall 1995. Her beautifully crafted poems invite the reader to inhabit the world she is looking at, whether it is through the eyes of a slave on a Virginia plantation or the eyes of a contemporary woman remembering Africa, remembering her dead mother, remembering nights of passionate love. —Eighth Mountain Press. These poems are honest and unflinching, familiar yet startling and new. They are a wonderful telling of the stories of women. —Lucille Clifton

Royet-Journoud, Claude. Translated by Keith Waldrop. *A Descriptive Method.* 18p. pap. $7.00 (0-942996-23-2). Sausalito, CA: Post-Apollo Press, Spring 1995. Waldrop, who has already translated a number of Royet-Journoud's books of poems, gives us a beautiful rendering. Royet-Journoud's is a poetry as dense as it is spare, as concise as it is explosive—a

poetry of the literal made strange. —Marjorie Perloff

Royet-Journoud, Claude. Translated by Keith Waldrop. *i.e.* 20p. pap. $5.00 (1-886224-08-0). Providence, RI: Burning Deck, Fall 1995. One of the most exciting poets of the new generation in France—highly original, elegant, controlled and extremely moving. [This is a] superb translation. —Paul Auster

Rubin, Diana Kwiatkowski. *Dinosauria: Poems of the Prehistoric World.* 31p. pap. $3.00 (0-929688-66-X). Eureka Springs, AR: Bear House Publishing, Fall 1995.

Rubin, Robert Alden, ed. *Poetry Out Loud.* 215p. pap. $9.95 (1-56512-122-8). Chapel Hill, NC: Algonquin Books of Chapel Hill, Fall 1995. Here are more than 100 short, vivid and dramatic poems that come alive when read aloud; with background notes, explanations, and cues on reading poetry out loud. —Algonquin Books. A timeless selection. Each poem, read aloud, reverberates. —*Writer's Digest.* Something for everybody. A collection for reading without any skipping, or, even better, for random browsing. —*The Virginian-Pilot & Ledger-Star*

Rucker, Robert L. *Lex • i • con.* 10p. pap. $2.50 (0-916155-33-1). Parkdale, OR: Trout Creek Press, Fall 1996.

Ruddick, Bruce. *Poems.* 48p. pap. $10.95 (1-878818-26-0). Riverdale-on-Hudson, NY: Sheep Meadow Press, Fall 1994. This collection is informed by Ruddick's special knowledge of the Canadian bush and wilderness and by his preoccupation with the art, magic, and customs of native Canadians. —Sheep Meadow Press

Rudman, Mark. *The Millennium Hotel.* 186p. $25.00 (0-8195-2229-5); pap. $11.95 (0-8195-2230-9). Middletown, CT: Wesleyan/University Press of New England, Fall 1996. *The Millennium Hotel* enlarges upon the themes that appear in *Rider* and includes several of the same players and personae. The books build upon each other to create an increasingly rich linguistic world. Rudman is writing a sophisticated poetry of polyphonic voices. He engages the question of the construc-

tion of the self obliquely, in poems that "think on their feet." —Alice Fulton

Ruefle, Mary. *Cold Pluto.* 72p. $20.95 (0-88748-220-1); pap. $11.95 (0-88748-221-X). Pittsburgh, PA: Carnegie Mellon University Press, Spring 1996

Ruffin, Paul. *Circling.* 77p. pap. (1-889150-00-2). Dallas, TX: Browder Springs Press, Spring 1996. A masterful storyteller, Paul Ruffin proves himself in *Circling* to be a rare lyricist as well. These are powerful poems that challenge a reader's emotions. —X. J. Kennedy

Rukeyser, Muriel. Edited by Jan Heller Levi. *A Muriel Rukeyser Reader.* 320p. $15.00 (0-393-31323-9). New York, NY: W. W. Norton & Company, Spring 1995. A visionary poet, Muriel Rukeyser speaks to us today in the name of courage, full consciousness, and the making of connections. This is a life-giving collection. —Jane Cooper. A lucid and accessible volume introducing new readers to one of the twentieth century's germinal writers. —Marilyn Hacker. Now we may begin to take measure of this American genius. —June Jordan

Rumi, Jelaluddin. Translated by Camille and Kabir Helminski. *Daylight: A Daybook of Spiritual Guidance.* 208p. pap. $15.00 (0-939660-35-0). Brattleboro, VT: Threshold Books, Fall 1994. 365 selections from Rumi's *Mathnawi*, the greatest spiritual masterpiece ever written. —Threshold Books

Rumi, Jelaluddin. Translated by Camille and Kabir Helminski. *Jewels of Remembrance: A Daybook of Spiritual Guidance.* 202p. $22.00 (0-939660-50-4). Brattleboro, VT: Threshold Books, Spring 1996. Having been immersed in the Sufi tradition for many years, Camille and Kabir Helminski offer translations which preserve the subtlety, tone, and depth of the original texts. —Threshold Books

Rumi, Jelaluddin. Translated by Shahram T. Shiva. *Rending the Veil: Literal and Poetic Translations of Rumi.* 280p. $27.95 (0-934252-46-7). Prescott, AZ: Hohm Press, Spring 1995. A beguiling addition to the current Rumi vogue in the West. Shahram Shiva leaps the cross-

cultural chasm with engaging panache. [These are] faithfully polished translations. —*Publishers Weekly*

Rumi, Jelaluddin. Translated by Coleman Barks and John Moyne. *Say I Am You: Poetry Interspersed With Stories of Rumi and Shams.* 128p. pap. $12.00 (1-884237-00-2). Athens, GA: Maypop Books, Fall 1994. Included here are poems and stories and bits of discourse springing from Rumi's relationship with his teacher, Shams. This poetry remembers their friendship and conversations. —Maypop Books

Russell, Frazier. *Fweivel: The Day Will Come.* 40p. pap. $8.00 (1-56439-059-4). Roseville, MI: Ridgeway Press, Fall 1996. *Fweivel* is a long prose poem written in the form of letters, which move through emotion after emotion with surrealistic imagery and a sense for Magic Realism. —Ridgeway Press

Rustomji-Kerns, Roshni, ed. *Living in America: Poetry and Fiction by South Asian American Writers.* 277p. $71.50 (0-8133-2379-7); pap. $20.95 (0-8133-2378-9). Boulder, CO: Westview Press, Fall 1995. A host of strong voices telling wonderfully poignant stories of the struggles to accommodate Old World customs to New World expectations. An important volume in expanding the corpus of Asian American literature and illuminating the variety and richness of South Asian Americans. —Amy Ling

Rutkowski, Thaddeus. *Beautiful Youth.* 28p. pap. $4.00. Talent, OR: Talent House Press, Fall 1994.

Rutkowski, Thaddeus. *Sex-Fiend Monologues.* 36p. pap. $4.00. New York, NY: Venom Press, Fall 1994.

Rutkowski, Thaddeus. *Super Nature.* 16p. pap. $2.00. New York, NY: Power Trio Press, Fall 1994. Poems written for performance including a Nuyorican Poets Cafe poetry slam winner. —Power Trio Press

Ryan, Kay. *Elephant Rocks.* 84p. $18.00 (0-8021-1586-1). New York, NY: Grove Press, Spring 1996. These are fine poems that inspire us with poetry's greatest gifts: the music of language and the force of wisdom. —Annie Dillard

S

Saenz, Gil. *Moments in Time.* 77p. pap. $8.00 (0-9635681-4-0). Dearborn, MI: Saenz Publishing, Fall 1995.

Saffioti, Judith Dingle. *Emotions.* 48p. pap. $6.95. Philadelphia, PA: Judith Dingle Saffioti, Spring 1995. Poems dealing with the raptures and agonies of women who follow the traditional erotic path. —Judith Dingle Saffioti

Saint, Assotto. *Wishing for Wings.* 96p. pap. $10.00 (0-9621675-3-3). Staten Island, NY: Galiens Press, Spring 1995. *Wishing for Wings* is the culmination of an extraordinary legacy from a very gifted man of letters. The poems in this final collection were written over a short year—from the time of his lover's death in late March of 1993 through March, 1994 when his own physical strength was severely diminished. Written during a time of great hardship, these poems bear witness to the tragic and yet fully realized life of a gay, HIV-positive artist. —Walter Holland

Sala, Jerome. *Raw Deal: New and Selected Poems 1981–94*. 152p. pap. $10.95 (0-929968-47-6). Chicago, IL: Another Chicago Press, Fall 1995. This is poetry in the Pop Populist tradition, and Jerome Sala is the best at it since Frank O'Hara. Read him now or the French will discover him, and you know how you feel when that happens. —Bill Knott. Jerome Sala's sharp-minded and rapier-tongued poems seem to have digested our culture in a way that gives a new, enlarged meaning to the phrase "wise guy." Sala's work is not only sardonic and funny, edgy, illuminating and grim— it's also elegant and brilliant. —Amy Gerstler

Salach, Cin. *Looking for a Soft Place to Land*. 69p. pap. $10.95 (1-882688-11-2). Chicago, IL: Tia Chucha Press, Spring 1996. Cin Salach, that glorious griot, sings the lesson we should have learned by now—that "spoken word" is not simply the sound that spills from an open mouth. This shimmering writer leaps off the page with a soft and startling gospel. Her talent refuses to be contained or compromised, and once you have closed this book you will have been changed for-ever. —Patricia Smith

Salas, Floyd. *The Color of My Living Heart*. 80p. pap. $8.00 (1-5585-171-2). Houston, TX: Arte Publico Press, Fall 1996.

Salerno, Mark. *Hate*. 62p. pap. $8.95 (0-9644269-0-0). Los Angeles, CA: 96 Tears Press, Fall 1995. Obdurate and un-sentimental, this book is as much a harrowing journey through a landscape of shifting value and affection as it is an extended struggle between po-etic form and poetic content. —96 Tears Press. [*Hate* is] an almost breathless testament to love. —Douglas Messerli. Strong, bittersweet poems poignant with existential questioning. Recommended. —Carl Rakosi

Salter, Mary Jo. *Sunday Skaters*. 102p. $20.00 (0-679-43109-8); pap. $13.00 (0-679-76567-0). New York, NY: Alfred A. Knopf, Fall 1994. The poems in *Sunday Skaters* are clear and exact as prose, but they have the compactness and sonic ap-peal of poetry. A powerful ethi-cal dimension is active every-where in this book, where human conflict is rendered through an art that adopts good will as one of its critical touchstones. —Alfred Corn,

Boston *Globe*. A winning book. —*Washington Post Book World*

Saltman, Benjamin. *The Sun Takes Us Away: New and Selected Poems 1968–1996.* 192p. pap. $12.95 (0-9639528-7-0). Palmdale, CA: Red Hen Press, Spring 1996. The consistant humanity and grace of these poems—nearly thirty years work—should be a double lesson: to those who have settled for less, and to those who have presumed more. —Jim Krusoe. He's a fine poet, a genuine one—which is saying a great deal. Lovely plainness— apparent plainness. With that depth beyond it. —W. S. Merwin

Samyn, Mary Ann. *Rooms by the Sea.* 50p. pap. $3.00 (0-87338-514-4). Kent, OH: Kent State University Press, Fall 1994. An exciting new voice. These poems are haunting, delicate, and full of care and wonder at life's exigencies. [There is] music here, embodying the richness and anguish of being alive. —Tom Andrews

Sanchez, Carol Lee. *She) Poems.* 41p. pap. $7.95 (0-9619111-9-0). Goshen, CT: Chicory Blue Press, Spring 1995. A multi-sectioned poem about

the seeking, restless, creative shape-shifter a woman is: "She) moved forward because / She) could no longer hold the surfaces together / Around her." —Chicory Blue Press

Sánchez, Ricardo. *Canto Y Grito Mi Liberación/The Liberation of a Chicano Mind Soul.* 198p. pap. $13.95 (0-87422-125-0). Pullman, WA: Washington State University Press, Fall 1995. To say [Sánchez] is a poet is little. [He] is the poet not only of poetry, but of life. —Yevgeny Yevtushenko. Richardo Sánchez is like any great poet. He's at once a preacher, a teacher, a priest, a rabbi. He's a guru, he's a master. And because he is that he's also a rebel. He's a maverick. Every great teacher is a maverick. —Maya Angelou, *Spokesman Review*

Sanchez, Sonia. *Wounded in the House of a Friend.* 128p. $15.00 (0-8070-6826-8). Boston, MA: Beacon Press, Spring 1995. Only a poet with an innocent heart can exorcise so much pain with so much beauty. —Isabel Allende. The poetry of Sonia Sanchez . . . makes you wish you had thought those thoughts . . . and expressed them so effortlessly and so well.

—Chinua Achebe. Sanchez gives voice to the emotions of many; she is compassionate, proud, angry, and determined as she writes about betrayals both private and public. —*Booklist*

Sandburg, Carl. Edited by George and Willene Hendrick. *Selected Poems.* 350p. pap. $15.00 (0-15-600396-1). San Diego, CA: Harcourt Brace/ Harvest Books, Spring 1996. This new collection of Sandburg's finest and most representative poetry draws on all of his previous volumes and includes four unpublished poems about Lincoln. —Harcourt Brace

Sanders, Edward. *Chekhov.* 240p. $25.00 (0-87685-966-X); pap. $13.50 (0-87685-965-1). Santa Rosa, CA: Black Sparrow Press, Spring 1995. A groundbreaking experiment in verse biography, *Chekhov* adapts the millennial language of Ed Sanders' unique performance-poetry voice to the life story of the great Russian writer Anton Chekhov. Chekhov's life here becomes a mirror that reflects Sanders' own concerns as a writer. —Black Sparrow Press

Sanders, Tony. *Partial Eclipse.* 75p. $15.95 (0-929398-79-3); pap. $10.95 (0-929398-81-5). Denton, TX: University of North Texas Press, Fall 1994. Winner of the Vassar Miller Prize in Poetry. Tony Sanders possesses a steady rhythm and a lyrical inclination that make of every poem a balance and occasionally a battle of harmony and melody. . . . Sanders displays his ability to sing on paper. —*Booklist*

Sandy, Stephen. *Vale of Academe: A Prose Poem for Bernard Malamud.* 10p. pap. $5.00 (0-9638731-9-9). Spartanburg, SC: Holocene Publishing, Spring 1996.

Santa Maria, A. V. *Seasons of Sentire.* 80p. $15.95 (0-944957-80-3). New York, NY: Rivercross Publishing, Spring 1996. The word "sentire" is from the Latin, to perceive, to feel. These are revelations of this poet's innermost being, the record of a man's deep love. —Rivercross Publishing

Sapphire. *American Dreams.* 177p. pap. $12.00 (0-679-76799-1). New York, NY: Vintage Books, Spring 1996. Sapphire knows more than the rap stars, more than the sociologists, about the inner city. She knows how people talk: abused children, prostitutes, tired domestic workers, white bigots, lesbians in love. She does their voices in a way that breaks your heart. —*Entertainment Weekly*. This angry yet hopeful collection speaks not of dreams deferred but of nightmares lived. Sapphire's poetry takes the stuff America's illusory dreams are made of, and turns it inside out. —*The New York Times Book Review*

Sardella, Sandro. Translated by Jack Hirschman. *Coloredpaperbits.* 48p. pap. $6.00 (1-879342-11-1). San Diego, CA: Parentheses Writing Series, Spring 1996. A fragmented socio-sexual view of contemporary life. —Parentheses Writing Series

Sargent, Robert. *The Cartographer.* 89p. pap. $10.00 (0-938572-09-1). Hedgesville, WV: The Bunny and the Crocodile Press/ Forest Woods Media, Fall 1994. Sargent is a patient and canny cartographer of our emotional world. He has come to a graceful relaxation of the line, with a comfortable turning to

the ever more colloquial and plain in his language. —Roland Flint

Sarton, May. *A Private Mythology.* 113p. pap. $11.00 (0-393-31552-5). New York, NY: W.W. Norton & Company, Spring 1996. In these poems, Sarton reflects on a journey undertaken to celebrate her fiftieth birthday, a journey that took her around the world to Greece via Japan and India. The trip marked a new direction in her life—a sense of fresh horizons both without and within, new suppleness and fluidity in her writing. Lucid, ardent, and contemplative, May Sarton was one of America's best-loved writers. —W.W. Norton & Company

Sarton, May. *Coming Into Eighty.* 72p. $15.95 (0-393-03689-8). New York, NY: W.W. Norton & Company, Fall 1994. Sarton's voice is still disarmingly fresh and buoyant, whether she is rejoicing in the appearance of a scarlet tanager or describing the challenge of getting dressed in the morning: "I am still whole and merry/ And when all's said and done/ Rejoice in my strange story,/ Ardent and alone." —*Library Journal*

Sarton, May. Selection and Photographs by Edith Royce Schade. *From May Sarton's Well: Writings of May Sarton.* 158p. $20.00 (0-918949-52-1); pap. $12.00 (0-918949-51-3). Watsonville, CA: Papier-Mache Press, November 1994. Schade has composed a set of her impressive photographs to communicate the light and shadow of my view of life, and accompanies the photographs with a text culled from my works to communicate this vision. I am grateful. —May Sarton, June 29, 1994

Sasanov, Catherine. *Traditions of Bread and Violence.* 64p. pap. $12.95 (1-884800-09-2). Marshfield, MA: Foor Way Books, Fall 1996. This book is animated by an extraordinary sense of jeopardy and alienation that results in alert, almost startled acts of imagination. These short-lined lyrics probe unerringly toward heart's truth. —Gregory Orr. Compassion and vulnerability can be the raw material of poetry. Catherine Sasanov breathes spirit into flesh and blood and turns tears into our daily bread. Her poems should be said out loud like prayers. It has been years since I have read poems of such humanity. —Elena Poniatowska

Sato, Hiroaki, ed. *One Hundred Frogs.* 128p. pap. $7.95 (0-8348-0335-6). New York, NY: Weatherhill, Spring 1995. Sato has collected some 130 translations, versions, parodies, and inspired renditions of Basho's famous haiku, "Old pond/Frog jumps in/The sound of water." —Weatherhill

Saunders, Sally Love. *Quiet Thoughts and Gentle Feelings.* 126p. Phoenixville, PA: Peggy Judge Arnold, Spring 1996. These poems speak of love and friendship, pain and death. This is a book to be read many times in many moods. —Peggy Judge Arnold

Savageau, Cheryl. *Dirt Road Home.* 78p. pap. $11.00 (1-880684-30-6). Willimantic, CT: Curbstone Press, Fall 1995. Savageau writes of poverty, mixed ancestry, nature and family in poems that are simultaneously tough and tender. —Curbstone Press. Savageau's poetry is stirring, imagistic and powerful. —*Ms. Magazine*

Scalapino, Leslie. *The Front Matter, Dead Souls.* 104p. $25.00

(0-8195-5290-9); pap. $11.95 (0-8195-6295-5). Middletown, CT: Wesleyan/University Press of New England, Spring 1996. This extraordinary new book is essay-fiction-poetry, an experiment in form that collapses the distinctions between documentary and fiction, fiction and poetry. —Wesleyan University Press. Leslie Scalapino's undulating phrasal rhythms are in turn psychedelic, analytic, notational, pointillistic, and narrational, balancing the unbalanceable poetic accounts of social justice and aesthetic insistence. —Charles Bernstein

Schapiro, Jane. *Tapping This Stone.* 65p. pap. $10.00 (0-931846-47-1). Washington, DC: Washington Writers' Publishing House, Spring 1995. Winner of the 1994 Washington Writers' Publishing House poetry contest. Read the poem "Carcinoma" and discover how she can infuse the domestic with ferocity and terror. Read "in my other life" for how she can find the poetry in pain, the sympathy in the imaginary. And "Postpartum" for how life can still be touched by myth in our dim, sad age. A fine book. —C.K. Williams

Scheele, Roy. *To See How It Tallies.* 22p. pap. $3.00. Las Cruces, NM: Whole Notes Press, Fall 1995.

Schelling, Andrew, and Anne Waldman, trans. *Songs of the Sons and Daughters of Buddha.* 112p. pap. $10.00 (1-57062-172-1). Boston, MA: Shambhala Publications, Spring 1996. These are earthy, courageous translations of the most ancient Buddhist poems. How honest the struggle of these practitioners with death and lust and self-doubt (just like us): how beautiful their moments of release. —Jack Kornfield. These enlightenment songs of the earliest disciples of the Buddha are vibrant, celebratory, and very human. —Sharon Salzberg

Schevill, James. *Winter Channels.* 56p. pap. $8.00 (0-912449-49-7). Cedarville, CA: Floating Island Publications, Fall 1994. Schevill knows that the essence of a modern poem is speed. His metaphors take in objects from our daily lives and by comparing them to the eternities of sky and sea brings us up with a start. It is always a mark of a poet that he has eyes that are never still and a mind that is constantly searching for a place to alight. . . . In Schevill's world we feel this restlessness. —William Carlos Williams. Mr. Schevill combines the scholar's instinct for meaningful detail with the poet's subjective insight. —M.L. Rosenthal

Schmitt, Peter. *Hazard Duty.* 64p. pap. $9.95 (0-914278-65-7). Providence, RI: Copper Beech Press, Fall 1995. *Hazard Duty* is a radiantly humane and lyric volume no reader will easily forget. —Dana Gioia. Peter Schmitt's voice is a quiet one, but it is weighty with honesty and wisdom. He is a bard of the everyday, writing of ordinary people leading their daily, extraordinary lives. —Linda Pastan

Schorn, Brian. *Strabismus.* 64p. pap. $8.00 (0-930901-98-3). Providence, RI: Burning Deck, Fall 1995. An eye wanders off course because a visual stimulus has lept from the picture frame, insisting on the journey into words. The distinctions between I and non-I, psychological and physical dissolve. —Burning Deck

Schulman, Grace. *For That Day Only.* 70p. $19.95 (1-878818-

29-5); pap. $12.95 (1-878818-35-X). Riverdale-on-Hudson, NY: The Sheep Meadow Press, Fall 1995. Winner of the 1995 Delmore Schwartz Award.

Schuyler, James. *Collected Poems.* 430p. $35.00 (0-374-12618-6); pap. $14.00 (0-374-52403-3). New York, NY: Farrar, Straus and Giroux/Noonday, Fall 1993. As far as Schuyler explores form and language— and he does so profoundly— the results are (and I use the word carefully) great. —Lawrence Joseph, *Poetry East.* There is no better way to come to [Schuyler's] poetry than to come to it all at once . . . One sees at a sweep his life's work in all its comic elegance, its sad grandeur and wit, the gushing-forth of confessed love affairs and chemical addictions, restraints and subtleties. —Liz Rosenberg, *The Boston Globe.* [He is] quietly Whitmanic; a planetary celebrator. —David Lehman, *The Washington Post Book World*

Schwartz, Leonard, Joseph Donahue and Edward Foster, eds. *Primary Trouble: An Anthology of Contemporary American Poetry.* 498p. $45.95 (1-883689-29-5); pap. $24.95

(1-883689-28-7). Jersey City, NJ: Talisman House, Publishers, Spring 1996. *Primary Trouble* brings together work by more than sixty poets central to the current radical reformulation of the nature and function of poetry. These poets also represent not only well acknowledged groups and practices such as the New York school, language writing, and multicultural traditions but also gnostic and hermetic poetries that are increasingly identified among the most experimental and innovative work being published today. —Talisman House, Publishers

Schwartz, Ruth L. *Accordion Breathing and Dancing.* 85p. $24.95 (0-8229-3898-7); pap. $10.95 (0-8229-5571-7). Pittsburgh, PA: University of Pittsburgh Press, Fall 1995. This is a powerful first collection about AIDS, Central America, poverty, cruelty, and love shining through in unexpected places. Ruth Schwartz's poems are lucid, hard-hitting, and yet compassionate. —Maxine Kumin. I think this book may well find many grateful readers. . . . Its great distinction lies in its fierce, erotic loyalty to the possibility

of song, in any light, in any shadow. —William Matthews

Schweik, Joanne, ed. *Penelope Flowers.* 56p. pap. $6.00. Buffalo, NY: Weird Sisters Press, Spring 1995. This anthology contains work by women of the Penelope Group as well as winners of the 1994 Betty Hall Cobb Memorial Poetry Contest. —Weird Sisters Press

Scott, Peter Dale. *Crossing Borders: Selected Shorter Poems.* 144p. pap. $11.95 (0-8112-1284-x). New York, NY: New Directions, Fall 1994. A poet capable of true invention. —Thom Gunn

Scully, James. *Raging Beauty.* 214p. pap. $13.95. Washington, DC: Azul Editions, Spring 1995.

Seagram, Blair. *News Brief and Broken: Pocketful of Why.* 8p. pap. $5.00. New York, NY: Blair Seagram, Fall 1994.

Seaton, Jerome P., and Dennis Maloney, eds. *A Drifting Boat: An Anthology of Chinese Zen Poetry.* 200p. pap. $15.00 (1-877727-37-7). Fredonia, NY: White Pine Press, Fall 1994. This valuable collection brings together a broad range of work by Chinese poets both familiar and less well-known to Western readers. In its pages, myriad voices intertwine. —Jane Hirshfield

Seaton, Maureen. *Furious Cooking.* 76p. pap. $10.95 (0-87745-541-4). Iowa City, IA: University of Iowa Press, Spring 1996. Seaton's writing is extravagant, rich in texture and tenor and substance, a joyous spill, a rapid, unstoppable boiling over. —Deborah Digges. Female sexuality, Catholic iconography, and the New Jersey Turnpike take mischievous spins in Seaton's wry, fervent, and mercurial third book of poetry. A streetwise, postmodern alchemist, Seaton. . . . calls on a subtle but firm command of craft (most poems are in free-verse couplets or triplets) and an agile sense of play. —*Publishers Weekly* (starred review)

Sedgwick, Eve Kosofsky. *Fat Art, Thin Art.* 166p. $45.95 (0-8223-1501-7); pap. $15.95 (0-8223-1512-2). Durham, NC: Duke University Press, Fall 1994. Sedgwick's first volume of poetry opens up another dimension of her continuing project of crossing and re-crossing the electrified boundaries between theory, lyric, and narrative. In her poems, characters, sexualities and fates are made and unmade. —Duke University Press. *Fat Art, Thin Art* is a wrenchingly honest account of a writer's relation to her gift. . . . filled with hesitations, self-cancellations, erasures, and gratifying fireworks. —Wayne Koestenbaum

Seferis, George. Translated by Edmund Keeley and Philip Sherrard. *George Seferis: Collected Poems.* 296p. $39.50 (0-691-06861-5); pap. $14.95 (0-691-01491-4). Princeton, NJ: Princeton University Press, Revised edition, Fall 1995. [This is a] translation worthy of Seferis, which is to praise it as highly as it could be praised. —Archibald MacLeish

Seffron, Richard A. Edited by Leonard J. Cirino. *The Selected Poems.* 60p. pap. $9.00 (944550-40-1). Albion, CA: Pygmy Forest Press, Spring 1996. Hard-hitting poems about the inner city by a generation X, hip-hop poet, who committed suicide in 1993. —Pygmy Forest Press

Seibles, Tim. *Kerosene.* 43p. pap. $5.00 (0-935331-16-6). Bristol, RI: Ampersand Press, Spring 1995. *Kerosene,* the author's third collection, moves between the polarities of delight and rage. These poems explore the sense of alienation that accompanies being non-white in the United States. —Ampersand Press

Seidman, Hugh. *Selected Poems: 1965–1995.* 231p. $20.95 (1-881163-10-5); pap. $14.95 (1-881163-11-3). Oxford, OH: Miami University Press, Spring 1995. [His] poetry speaks with a delicate, troubling, growing urgency. —W.S. Merwin. Fine, uncompromising, fierce. —Stanley Kunitz

Selby, Spencer. *Malleable Cast.* 80p. pap. $10.00 (0-945112-20-3). Cleveland, OH: Generator Press, Spring 1995. Verbovisual poetry combining found images with found texts. —Generator Press. There is an undertone of unquiet in this work, an unsettled, restless energy, which speaks with a compelling urgency about the ongoing struggle to make sense of ordinary life. But there is a quality of innocence and hu-

mor as well—a wonder at the forms which life takes in this late, strange culture we inhabit. —Johanna Drucker

Selman, Robyn. *Directions to My House.* 60p. $24.95 (0-8229-3894-4); pap. $10.95 (0-8229-5568-7). Pittsburgh, PA: University of Pittsburgh Press, Fall 1995. I love Robyn Selman's knack of making life's intractable facts obey the hard rules of her forms—aesthetic stringencies that magnanimously accommodate sex, whim, and back talk. —Wayne Koestenbaum. Robyn Selman's exact, hilarious, and often heartbreaking lyrics are . . . hot-headed, warm-hearted, astringent, peppery, and even . . . burning. —Richard Howard. Robyn Selman's poems are sure to have a healthy survival rate. People who discover her work will remain impatient for more. —*The Boston Review*

Sensei, Kamishiura. Translated by Gary Crounse. *Pathways: Restful Meditations.* 64p. pap. $6.95 (0-87905-669-X). Layton, UT: Gibbs Smith, Publisher/Peregrine Smith Books, Spring 1995. Translations of Sensei's haiku constituting a cycle of leaving and returning home. —Gibbs Smith, Publishers

Seshadri, Vijay. *Wild Kingdom.* 64p. pap. $12.95 (1-55597-236-5). St. Paul, MN: Graywolf Press, Spring 1996. Vijay Seshadri is a lyric poet who can mix elegy and affirmation within a few stanzas of one another. He makes the landscape and the cityscape into one challenging and heartbreaking place where the old transformations of language can still happen. —Eavan Boland. In a compassionate, perceptive spirit, Seshadri offers us works that belong among the broadest, most intelligent new poetry of this decade. —*Publishers Weekly*, starred review

Sewell, Marilyn, ed. *Claiming the Spirit Within: A Sourcebook of Women's Poetry.* 384p. $35.00 (0-8070-6834-9); pap. $18.00 (0-8070-6835-7). Boston, MA: Beacon Press, Fall 1996. More than 300 poems, by internationally known poets and others who are appearing here for the first time in book form, explore how women claim the sacredness of their lives through relationships, thoughts, and actions. —Beacon Press

Sexton, Tom. *King Island.* 8p. pap. $10.00. Anchorage, AK: Salmon Run Press, Fall 1994. A single poem meditating on a carving of a whale. A spare and moving piece. —Salmon Run Press

Shanken, Zev. *Al Het.* pap. $10.00 (0-91128720-5). Yakima, WA: Blue Begonia Press, Fall 1996. The Hebrew words *Al Het* mean *for the sin.* The prayer, *Al Het*, is the Jewish confessional prayer, recited collectively many times on *Yom Kippur*, the Day of Atonement. In five poems written over a twenty year period, Zev Shanken faces themes of Israel, the Holocaust, and the Sabbath. In the title poem, *Al Het*, Shanken uses a traditional Jewish liturgical form as a starting point for a work of imagination, wit and courage. —Blue Begonia Press

Shapiro, Alan. *Mixed Company.* 96p. $35.00 (0-226-75030-2); pap. $11.95 (0-226-75031-0). Chicago, IL: University of Chicago Press, Spring 1996. What draws us into Alan Shapiro's *Mixed Company* is the quiet, undaunted way he goes after the truth of human feeling and motive. The poems are full of astonishing insights, a rare articulateness, and what another age called "knowledge of the human heart." —Richard Wilbur. Shapiro is a shrewd and sympathetic moralist. He never trivializes his subjects with high-minded flourishes or stylistic gimmicks. . . . These poems are not likely to be forgotten. —J.D. McClatchy, *The New York Times Book Review*

Shapiro, Myra. *I'll See You Thursday*. 62p. pap. $10.00 (0-9638722-2-2). Saint Paul, MN: Blue Sofa Press/Ally Press Center, Spring 1996. Shapiro possesses a human vision that is as excited to reveal to us the precious flaw as the perfectly wrought, the impeccably sealed. Thus, to be touched by these poems is to be touched by a life that is as complicated as yours or mine, as unresolved, as scarred by the fire, as watermarked, as ready. —Deborah Digges. There is an urgency of the soul here, that it will be heard. That urgency and careful sound work bind together all sorts of emotion: her longings for the Romantic, her mourning for the political life of the old city, love of her husband, suffering of the exiled soul and sexual delight. —Robert Bly

Sharkey, Lee. *To a Vanished World*. 92p. pap. $8.95 (0-913006-58-0). Orono, ME: Puckerbrush Press, Spring 1996. Each of the poems in this collection was written in response to a photograph from *A Vanished World*, Roman Vishniac's photographic record of his people and their culture, the Jews of Eastern Europe, between 1933 and 1939, who lived under Hitler's threat of annihilation. —Puckerbrush Press

Sheck, Laurie. *The Willow Grove*. 70p. $21.00 (0-679-44714-8). New York, NY: Alfred A. Knopf, Spring 1996. Laurie Sheck interweaves the contemporary with the mythic, creating a realm in which such things as radios, skyscrapers, expressways, and mannequins are at once familiar and strange; immediate, yet tinged with the light of distance and myth. —Alfred A. Knopf

Shelley, Percy Bysshe. *Percy Bysshe Shelley: Selected Poems*. 256p. $7.99 (0-517-11831-9). Avenel, NJ: Gramercy Books, Fall 1994.

Shepherd, Reginald. *Some Are Drowning*. 76p. $24.95 (0-8229-3867-7); pap. $10.95 (0-

8229-5547-4). Pittsburgh, PA: University of Pittsburgh Press, Fall 1996. Winner of the 1993 AWP Award Series in Poetry. This first collection of poems enacts the struggle of a young black gay man in his search for identity. Many voices haunt these poems: black and white, male and female, the oppressor's voice as well as that of the oppressed. The poet's aim, finally, is to rescue some portion of the drowned and the drowning. —University of Pittsburgh Press. Passionate, brainy, and sad, Shepherd's poems chronicle the mysteries of emotional and intellectual life. —Chase Twichell

Shiels, Bill. *Blown White.* 36p. pap. $6.00 (0-930502-25-6). Landisburg, PA: Pine Press, Spring 1996.

Shinder, Jason, ed. *Eternal Light: Grandparent Poems.* 144p. pap. $10.00 (0-15-600099-7). San Diego, CA: Hartcourt Brace/ Harvest Books, Spring 1995. Shinder's our preeminent anthologist. —Allen Ginsberg

Shinder, Jason, ed. *Lights, Camera, Poetry! American Poets Write About the Movies.* 192p. pap. $13.00 (0-15-600115-2). San

Diego, CA: Harcourt Brace/ Harvest Books, Fall 1995. Here are more than 100 poems inspired by the movies. There's May Swenson on James Bond, Delmore Schwartz on Marilyn Monroe, Jack Kerouac on Harpo Marx, and so on. —Harcourt Brace. This collection is bliss. —Donna Seaman, *Booklist*

Shipley, Vivian. *Devil's Lane.* 88p. pap. $15.95 (0-942544-52-8). Mobile, AL: Negative Capability Press, Fall 1996. Vivian Shipley is, in the best poetry tradition, a border figure. Her object in living—as one Frostian epigraph suggests—is to unite diverse realms, which she does here in poem after poem, by dint of the most accurate and persuasive language. *Devil's Lane* is a triumph. —Sydney Lea. Family has always been a focus in Vivian Shipley's writing and this powerful collection is no exception. Shipley is not a poet of easy answers or facile diction. She takes no short cuts along the way, yet her poems cut a line straight into the heart. —Joseph Bruchac

Shively, Bill. *Terminal Bar.* 26p. pap. $5.00. Portland, OR: 26

Books, Spring 1995. Rhythmic oral poetry involving bars, travel, love, intestinal disorders and slugs. —26 Books

Short, Gary. *Flying Over Sonny Liston.* 80p. pap. $10.00 (0-87417-285-3). Reno, NV: University of Nevada Press, Fall 1996. 1996 Winner of the Western States Book Award for Poetry. Gary Short's poems live dangerously. They look hard at love and life and give us, finally, the gifts of beauty, honesty, and wisdom. Reading this tender and powerful book, we are ourselves made more human, and more humane. —Western States Book Award Jury

Shugrue, Jim. *Small Things Screaming.* 26p. pap. $5.00. Portland, OR: 26 Books, Fall 1995. These are intense urban meditations—seeing through dark windows, viewing religion, landfills and learning from others. —26 Books

Shuttle, Penelope. *Building a City for Jamie.* 64p. pap. $12.95 (0-19-282517-8). New York, NY: Oxford University Press, Fall 1996. Penelope Shuttle is a law unto herself. She writes strange, brilliant, sometimes outrageous, funny, sad, poetry, which suddenly moves one with its utter clarity. This is her sixth collection. —Oxford University Press

Siegel, Donald R. *A Life in Poetry.* 69p. pap. $12.95 (0-9644769-0-8). New City, NY: Donald R. Siegel, Fall 1995. A self-published collection of biographically-inclined poems that dote on everyday experience by the owner of Don's T-V Service. —Donald R. Siegel

Siegel, Donald R, and Jeanne R. Siegel. *More Life in Poetry.* 62p. pap. $12.95 (0-9644769-1-6). New City, NY: Donald R. Siegel, Spring 1996.

Siegen-Smith, Nikki, ed. *Welcome to the World: A Celebration of Birth and Babies From Many Cultures.* 48p. $17.95 (0-531-36006-7). New York, NY: Orchard Books. In this anthology, poets and photographers from cultures all over the world celebrate the mysterious, vulnerable, and awesome world of new babies. With the work of artists and writers from Africa, Bosnia, India, the USA, the Czech Republic, China, New Zealand, South Africa, and elsewhere, *Welcome to the World* has been created not only to extend a welcome to our new brothers and sisters, but also to remind us that it is our responsibility to ensure their welfare. —Orchard Books

Silex, Edgar Gabriel. *Through All the Displacements*. 78p. pap. $10.95 (1-880684-25-X). Willimantic, CT: Curbstone Press, Fall 1995. Highly original poems dealing with the historic and contemporary damage inflicted on Native American people and culture in the United States. Silex's poetry is forceful and effective. —*Publishers Weekly*

Silliman, Ron. *N/O*. 107p. pap. $10.95 (0-937804-56-8). New York, NY: Roof Books, Fall 1994. Long a national leader of the Language-centered writing movement, Ron Silliman's poetry and criticism have influenced an entire generation of poets. *N/O* is two letters of his ongoing poem, "The Alphabet." —Roof Books. There is something incredibly moving about Silliman's capacity and capability, his will and willfulness—his hunger to know and absorb—as he rants, records, juxtaposes, declares, riffs, puns, pans. —Tom Beck-

ett. Ron Silliman lives the most passionate life of the mind in America! He is a political poet par excellence. —Samuel R. Delany

Silva, Sam. *Art as Anyone's Salvation*. 24p. pap. $3.00 (0-916155-29-3). Parkdale, OR: Trout Creek Press, Spring 1995.

Silver, Nina. *Birthing*. 55p. pap. $15.00 (0-934172-39-0). San Jose, CA: Woman in the Moon Publications, Fall 1995. These are juicy poems, full of sap. Nina Silver engages us in the passions of a life lived with a full heart and a brimming soul. This is strong, spirited work. Loved it! —Patricia Monagahan

Simic, Charles. *Walking the Black Cat*. 96p. $24.00 (0-15-100219-3); pap. $13.00 (0-15-600481-X). San Diego, CA: Harcourt Brace/Harvest Books, Fall 1996. Few contemporary poets have been as influential—or as inimitable— as Charles Simic. For more than thirty years his work has claimed citizenship to its own dreamlike land. —*The New York Times Book Review*. [He is] one of our very finest and most truly original poets. —*Harvard Book Review*

Simola, Robert. *In Raspberry Gulch.* 20p. pap. $3.75. Kew Gardens, NY: New Spirit Press, Spring 1995. Winner of the New Spirit Press Quarterly Chapbook Contest.

Simon, Maurya. *The Golden Labyrinth.* 64p. pap. $12.95 (0-8262-0995-5). Columbia, MO: University of Missouri Press, Spring 1995. Not only does Simon describe the colorful jangle of the markets and streets, but she recognizes what is behind them. —*Library Journal*

Simon, Seymour, ed. *Star Walk.* 29p. $15.00 (0-688-11887-9). New York, NY: William Morrow & Company/Morrow Junior Books, Fall 1995. Illustrated with remarkable full-color photographs, this poetry collection contains works by a host of authors, ranging from William Wordsworth and Walt Whitman to Archibald MacLeish and Diane Ackerman. There are poems about Saturn and Mars, space flight, constellations, and the majestic dance of the planets in their orbits. —Morrow Junior

Books. It would be hard to imagine a better introduction to our little corner of the universe. —*Kirkus Reviews* (pointered review)

Simpson, Lewis P. *The Circus by the Cemetery.* 28p. $15.00 (1-884725-08-2); pap. $8.00 (1-884725-08-2). Thibodaux, LA: Blue Heron Press, Fall 1995. In his first collection of poems, this senior scholar of Southern letters looks back on the boy he was, growing up in northwest Texas. Simpson's poems are condensed, sometimes elliptical, variations on themes that have been central in his criticism: the relation between memory and history and the distance between what he has called the "Christian fable" and the existential loneliness of modern Americans, especially Southerners. —Grady Ballenger, *Louisiana Literature*

Simpson, Louis. *There You Are.* 100p. $16.95 (1-885266-15-4); pap. $10.00 (1-885266-17-0). Brownsville, OR: Story Line Press, Fall 1995. A distinguished poet and essayist who won the Pulitzer Prize in 1964, Louis Simpson remains allusive, antielitist, mellow, and keenly observant. Highly recommended. —Frank Allen, *Library Journal*. Louis Simpson is one of the best poets now writing in English. *There You Are* is full of poems one wants to read aloud to friends. —*The Washington Times*

Simsic, Wayne. *Garden Prayers: Planting the Seeds of Your Inner Life*. 96p. pap. $5.95 (0-88489-360-X). Winona, MN: Saint Mary's Press/Christian Brothers Publications, Fall 1995. The forty-one prayers in this book help us meet God walking in the gardens of the world and the garden of the soul. —Saint Mary's Press

Sindall, Susan. *Graces*. 20p. pap. $6.00. New York, NY: Firm Ground Press, Spring 1996.

Singer, Davida. *Shelter Island Poems*. 54p. pap. $11.00 (1-886435-01-4). Sag Harbor, NY: Canio's Editions, Fall 1995.

Sirowitz, Hal. *Mother Said*. 128p. cloth $15.00 (0-517-70497-8). New York NY: Crown Publishers, Spring 1996. Hal Sirowitz's poems are indelible because they're incredibly funny, totally genuine, and because they're rooted in a complicated

sympathy for the ambitions of the American family. This book will make you laugh out loud at the truth. —Rick Moody. Sirowitz's poems might be the channeled voice of Philip Roth in a state of catatonic dementia. —*The Village Voice*

Sisson, C. H. *Selected Poems*. 96p. pap. $9.95 (0-8112-1327-7). New York, NY: New Directions, Spring 1996. [Sisson's] poems move in service of the loved landscapes of England and France; they sing (and growl) in love of argument, in love of seeing through, in love of the firm descriptions of moral self-disgust; they move in love of the old lost life by which the new life is condemned. —Donald Hall, *New York Review of Books*

Sjöberg, Leif, and William Jay Smith, trans. *The Forest of Childhood: Poems From Sweden*. 176p. pap. $14.95 (0-89823-135-3). Minneapolis, MN: New Rivers Press, Fall 1996.

Sklar, Morty, and Joseph Barbato, eds. *Patchwork of Dreams: Voices from the Heart of the New America*. 224p. pap. $12.50 (0-930370-43-0). Jackson Heights, Queens, NY: The Spirit That Moves Us Press, Fall 1996. The first book ever of writing from the most ethnically diverse area in the nation, Queens, the borough (in New York City) of nations and neighborhoods where people from 120 countries speak most of the languages of the world. Selections include stories, poems, essays, drama, photographs and interviews from new and established writers. —The Spirit That Moves Us Press

Sklarew, Myra. *Lithuania: New and Selected Poems.* 141p. pap. $12.95 (1-885214-02-2). Washington, DC: Azul Editions, Fall 1995. The poem, "Lithuania," is based upon the firsthand accounts of elderly Lithuanians and surviving Lithuanian Jews, on letters written from Lithuania to my family on the eve of World War II, on diaries secretly kept, on conversations with a family member, and on evidence still visible—massacre pits in every town and village that I visited. It is based on the felt absence of Jews in a place that had once been the center of world Jewry. —Myra Sklarew

Slaughter, Adèle. *What the Body Remembers.* 96p. pap. $11.95 (0-934257-99-X). Brownsville, OR: Story Line Press, Spring 1995. Here are poems of great dignity, reserve, and control on matters that rarely call forth such responses: a violent, abusive upbringing as a 'military brat,' persistent familial alcoholism, and a failed marriage all figure in them, presenting occasions, never subjects, for Slaughter. Her subject is, instead, the perceiving and surviving self. Her quest is to understand the ways in which the outer life forms the inner and, conversely, how the inner life can be sustained despite emotional travail. A stunning debut volume. —*Booklist*

Slaughter, William. *The Politics of My Heart.* 81p. pap. $12.95 (0-9651413-0-6). Port Angeles, WA: Pleasure Boat Studio, Fall 1996. *The Politics of My Heart* stands apart from all other China books that have mushroomed in the West before and after the Tiananmen tragedy. Neither academic nor journalistic, it is the pilgrim's progress of a poet-scholar to the Gate of Heavenly Peace. —Wu Ningkun

Slavitt, David R. *A Gift: The Life of da Ponte.* 55p. $16.95 (0-8071-2047-2); pap. $9.95 (0-8071-2048-0). Baton Rouge, LA: Louisiana State University Press, Spring 1996. In [this] book-length poem . . . Slavitt revives the restless, embattled, occasionally triumphant story of [Lorenzo] Da Ponte's (Mozart's librettist) life. —*The Philadelphia Inquirer*

Sleigh, Tom. *The Chain.* 104p. $30.00 (0-226-76240-8); pap. $11.95 (0-226-76241-6). Chicago, IL: University of Chicago Press, Spring 1996. In a series of elegies, portraits, and love poems, the poet movingly dramatizes the ambiguous nature of truth and the difficulties the moral imagination must overcome in recalling, understanding, and judging the past. —University of Chicago Press. Tom Sleigh's precision marks him as the diamond cutter of poetry; his verse has a tense musicality, and his ability to convey exact emotions . . . is unerring. —*The New York Times Book Review.* Notable Books of the Year, 1990–1991.

Smith, Arthur. *Orders of Affection.* 72p. $20.95 (0-88748-222-8); pap. $11.95 (0-88748-223-6).
Pittsburgh, PA: Carnegie Mellon University, Spring 1996.

Smith, Charlie. *Before and After.* 62p. $21.00 (0-393-03775-4). New York, NY: W.W. Norton & Company, Spring 1995. With the unadorned acuity that is his signature, novelist and poet Smith describes the ruins of family life in contemporary America. A glittering, forceful collection. —*Publishers Weekly*

Smith, Dave. *Fate's Kite: Poems, 1991–1995.* 104p. $19.95 (0-8071-2040-5); pap. $10.95 (0-8071-2041-3). Baton Rouge, LA: Louisiana State University Press, Fall 1995. This sequence of near-sonnets (13 lines each) records his flight toward redemptive meaning in the American South, Italy, Seamus Heaney's Ireland, and the landscapes of memory. —*Library Journal.* Like Mike Tyson with an M.F.A., Smith delivers his poetry with such force that there's no point in resisting it. —*Publishers Weekly*

Smith, Dave. *Floating on Solitude: Three Volumes of Poetry.* 331p. pap. $19.99 (0-252-06584-0). Urbana, IL: University of Illinois Press, Fall 1996. This volume collects three of Smith's previously published work: *Goshawk, Antelope*; *Dream Flights*; and *Cumberland Station*. [Smith] is a poet of the utmost ambition and utmost care; his poems make other poems seem loose, unfinished. —Helen Vendler, *Parnassus*. His voice retains a youthful, almost adolescent energy that hardly seems to know what it is to sound tired, to stop caring that one has lost hope, or tailored one's ambitions to conform with reality. —Phoebe Pettingell, *Poetry*

Smith, Gary E., ed. *Awakened From the Forest: Meditations on Ministry*. 54p. pap. (1-55896-335-9). Boston, MA: Skinner House Books, Spring 1995. A "meditation manual" of poems by Unitarian ministers and poets. —Skinner House Books

Smith, Joan Jobe, ed. *Das ist Alles: Charles Bukowski Recollected*. 76p. pap. $10.00 (0-9628094-8-9). Long Beach, CA: Pearl Editions, Fall 1994. A tribute to the late Charles Bukowski by the poets and women who loved him. Essays by Joan Jobe Smith and Gerald Locklin; poems by FrancEyE (Frances E. Smith), Ann Mene-broker, Linda King, Edward Field, Marvin Malone, and others. —Pearl Editions

Smith, Patti. *Early Work*. 192p. pap. $10.00 (0-393-31301-8). New York, NY: W.W. Norton & Company, Spring 1995. [Patti Smith's] mix of vulnerability and chutzpah, idolatry-cum-appropriation of culture heroes, and risky originality still resonates with great heart. —Gary Indiana, *Details*. [*Early Work*] establishes Smith as a visionary belletrist who believed in rock as a spiritual outlet and haven for black sheep. —Evelyn McDonnell, *Rolling Stone*

Smith, Patti. *The Coral Sea*. 71p. $18.00 (0-393-03908-0). New York, NY: W.W. Norton & Company, Spring 1996. Patti Smith has written of a great spiritual journey in words drawn from nature and mythology. For anyone who has known a terrible loss, this poem in prose will come as a consolation. She was once our savage Rimbaud, but suffering has turned her into our St. John of the Cross, a mystic full of compassion. —Edmund White. Through these poems, a singular, glowing vision of

Robert Mapplethorpe emerges.
—William S. Burroughs

Smith, Philip, ed. *100 Best-Loved Poems*. 96p. pap. $1.00 (0-486-28553-7). Mineola, NY: Dover Publications.

Smith, R.T. *Hunter–Gatherer*. 69p. $19.95 (0-942979-33-8); pap. $9.95 (0-942979-34-6). Livingston, AL: Livingston Press, Fall 1996. R.T. Smith's poems have so honed the vision of nature that even the palest of urbanites might appreciate the philosophy his poems espouse. —Livingston Press

Smith, R.T. *Trespasser*. 65p. $16.95 (0-8071-2047-2); pap. $9.95 (0-8071-2048-0). Baton Rouge, LA: Louisiana State University Press, Spring 1996. With craggy Celtic metaphysics and perfect linguistic pitch, R.T. Smith evokes the landscape, culture, and history of Ireland and the New World through the eyes and ears of an outsider. —Louisiana State University Press. R.T. Smith may be a trespasser, but he is a holy trespasser, one who loves the natural world that he violates with both careful thought and rapturous, word-driven song. —Andrew Hudgins

Smith, Rolland G. *Quiet Musings*. 96p. pap. $12.95 (0-919842-22-4). Stamford, CT: Sun-Scape Publications, Fall 1995. Rolland Smith is a journalist with integrity . . . a compassionate poet with the spirit of a sage. —John Denver. Spirited, pensive, revealing. —*The Book Reader*

Smith, Thomas R. *Horse of Earth*. 75p. pap. $8.95 (0-930100-55-7). Duluth, MN: Holy Cow! Press, Fall 1994. These poems seem both effortless and profound, as if they have sprung from a life in which reverence for the moment has become habitual. Not since discovering Neruda in the 1960s, W. S. Merwin in the 1970s and Rumi in the 1980s have I been so moved by reading a collection of poetry. —Jim Heynen. Some of the finest American love poems of recent decades are here. —Robert Bly

Smith, Winthrop. *The Weigh-In: Collected Poems*. 172p. pap. $12.95 (1-879194-20-1). San Francisco, CA: GLB Publishers, Spring 1996. *The Weigh-In* offers a view of the underside of gay experience that uses incantatory techniques borrowed from Gertrude Stein and contemporary minimalist music to convey the repetition-compulsion of promiscuity. In these poems words are snapped in half like breadsticks and sentences enjambed between lines to fashion a jagged argot of Smith's very own, one well suited to portray anonymous lives bent on ecstasy at any cost, to whom he brings the protection of poetry. —Alfred Corn

Smukler, Linda. *Home in Three Days. Don't Wash*. 96p. Multimedia Edition, $24.95 (1-889097-00-4); pap. $12.95 (0-9638433-8-9). West Stockbridge, MA: Hard Press, Fall 1996. Multimedia edition includes a CD-ROM with dreamscapes designed by the author. Like Gertrude Stein, her modernist forbear, Smukler uses the most direct American idiom to render the complexity, anguish, and humor of desire. —Rebecca Brown. Linda Smukler has reinvented butch desire as a passionate amalgam of abjection, power and trembling knees. She is the Percy Sledge of lesbian butch-femme cri-de-coeur écriture. —Kevin Killian. If sex has a flag, this is it. —Eileen Myles

Snodgrass, W.D.. *The Fuehrer Bunker: The Complete Cycle*. 209p. $24.00 (1-880238-18-7); pap. $15.00 (1-880238-19-5). Rochester, NY: BOA Editions, Spring 1995. Eminent American poet-translator Snodgrass, who won the Pulitzer in 1960, offers the "complete cycle" of a work first published in 1977. With over 65 monologs by 15 speakers and a variety of supporting poems in collage format, Snodgrass achieves remarkable historical breadth. The action takes place in one month (April 1945) in the Berlin Bunker where Hitler and other Nazis died, and each doomed speaker has poetic forms appropriate to his or her character. —Frank Allen, *Library Journal*

Snow, Carol. *Breath As*. 44p. pap. $55.00 (0-9632085-6-X). Mill Valley, CA: Em Press, Fall 1994. Signed letterpress edition of 100 on handmade papers, hand sewn. —Em Press

Snyder, Dee. *Wake Me Up and F*** Me*. 20p. pap. $3.00 (0-9637704-3-8). Alexandria, VA: Red Dragon Press, Spring 1996. First published in 1993, this popular collection of poems and lyrics is laced with the author's trademark sex and humor. —Red Dragon Press

Sobel, Carolyn. *Intermissions.* 50p. pap. $12.00 (0-9637483-7-8). St. Augustine, FL: Kings Estate Press, Spring 1995. A first collection of warm, elegant poems, with line drawings by Margo Hammond. —Kings Estate Press

Sobelman, 'Annah. *The Tulip Sacrament.* 96p. $25.00 (0-8195-2223-6); pap. $11.95 (0-8195-1227-3). Middletown, CT: Wesleyan/University Press of New England, Fall 1995. As fresh as a handful of well-water, fluid, compassionate, bearing a grave resonance, 'Annah Sobelman's poetry worries the world along uncommon paths of love and sorrow. A wondrous first book. —Marvin Bell. Luminous, bizarre, elegant, hilarious . . . Sobelman's invention plays a perfect counterpoint to grief. —Toi Derricotte

Sober, Richard. *Because the House Is Wild and Empty.* 58p. pap. $5.00. Baltimore, MD: Apathy Press, Fall 1995.

Sobin, Gustaf. *Breaths' Burials.* 112p. pap. $11.95 (0-8112-1299-8). New York, NY: New Directions, Spring 1995. Gustaf Sobin enters the subtle substance of words with such profound caring reading him one becomes immersed in language, swims in a physical sea of *meaning* which can only have breath for its sustenance. He is a consummate poet and *Breaths' Burials* is the farthest reach yet of his unique powers. —Robert Creeley. He is a landscape artist whose terrain is language. —*Village Voice Literary Supplement*

Södergran, Edith. Translated by Stina Katchadourian. *Love and Solitude: Selected Poems 1916–1923.* 185p. pap. $14.00 (0-940242-14-1). Seattle, WA: Fjord Press, reissued Spring 1996. Bilingual edition first published in 1981. The poignant beauty of Edith Södergran—in her art as in her person—is unforgettable. This is a poet to be read over and over again, with awe at her magic, and with the tenderness one feels towards an intimate friend. —Carolyn Kizer. Before her death at 31, Södergran left a body of work reminiscent of Dickinson—as eternally new, as unforgettable. —Jayne Anne Phillips

Solomon, Sandy. *Pears, Lake, Sun.* 96p. $24.95; pap. $10.95 (0-8229-5615-2). Pittsburgh, PA: University of Pittsburgh Press, Fall 1996. Winner of the 1995 Agnes Lynch Starrett Poetry Prize. In the brilliant surfaces and reflections of *Pears, Lake, Sun*, Sandy Solomon catches the moods and ambiguities of the very late twentieth century where harrowing events exist side by side with ghostly flashes of beauty. These are tough-minded poems, impeccably crafted, full of passionate stillness and disciplined commotion, that refuse to look away from the barbarities of our high civilizations. —Maura Stanton

Sornberger, Judith. *Open Heart.* 98p. $19.95 (0-934971-31-5); pap. $9.95 (0-934971-32-3). Corvallis, OR: Calyx Books, Fall 1995. Sornberger's superb first collection of poems is about the fracture of conventional wisdom under the pressure of women's experience . . . The poet's control of form holds her readers in place while Sornberger steals, retells, and resignifies women's stories. —Hilda Raz. A caring poet-heart struggling to illuminate for us the tangled

bonds of family and love, the memorable in the perishable, and the dear significance in the everyday. —Tillie Olsen

Sorrentino, Gilbert. *The Orangery.* 102p. pap. $10.95 (1-55713-225-9). Los Angeles, CA: Sun & Moon Press, Fall 1995. First published in 1978, *The Orangery* is one of Gilbert Sorrentino's most memorable collections of poetry. Each poem is a variation on "orange," which appears and reappears as a color, a fruit, a memory, an intrusion, a word seeking a rhyme, a presence expected and awaited. —Sun & Moon Press

Soto, Gary. *Gary Soto: New Selected Poems.* 180p. $22.95 (0-8818-0761-4); pap. $12.95 (0-8118-0758-4). San Francisco, CA: Chronicle Books, Spring 1995. Soto writes with a pure sweetness free of sentimentality that is almost extraordinary in modern American poetry. —Andrew Hudgins. Soto insists on the possibility of a redemptive power, and he celebrates the heroic, quixotic capacity for survival in human beings and the natural world. —*Publishers Weekly*. Soto has it all—the learned craft, the intrinsic abilities with language, a fascinating autobiography, and the storyteller's ability to manipulate memories into folklore. —*Library Journal*

Souders, Bruce. *Fitting the Pieces Together*. 96p. pap. $10.95 (1-880016-20-6). Painter, VA: Road Publishers, Spring 1995. This latest collection reflects Bruce Souders' hallmarks—deep ethical concern, delight in quotidian images, wide reading and travel, and historical perspective. —Warren De Arment. A most ample and rich collection. —X.J. Kennedy

Spencer, Jon Michael. *Self-Made and Blues-Rich*. 130p. $32.95 (0-86543-502-2); pap. $11.95 (0-86543-503-0). Trenton, NJ: Africa World Press, Fall 1996. This collection is like a finely compressed jewel of African American meanings. The graphics of the volume are a wonderful complement to the resonant poetry. The spirit of African American song and instrumentation is stunningly captured in an appropriately tailored space. —Houston A. Baker, Jr.

Sperber, Barbara. *In the Garden of Our Own Making*. 116p. pap.

$9.00 (0-918949-69-6). Watsonville, CA: Papier-Mache Press, October 1995. These tactful, passionate poems, written with a mature clarity, tell a large story—a daughter's exploration, by way of her mother's death, of her own abandoned role as a mother, and her successful search to reclaim responsibility for that unacknowledged area of her life. This is a stunningly human document and I find myself deeply moved by the odyssey this skillful poet brings before us. —Michael Dennis Browne

Spiegel, Rich. *Transcendental Relics*. 8p. pap. $3.00. Staten Island, NY: Rich Spiegel, Fall 1995.

Spires, Elizabeth. *With One White Wing*. 32p. $14.00 (0-689-50622-8). New York, NY: Margaret K. McElderly Books, Fall 1995.

Spires, Elizabeth. *Worldling*. 72p. $18.95 (0-393-03855-6). New York, NY: W.W. Norton & Company, Fall 1995. If poetry exists to turn the ordinary into the memorable, to transform profane into sacred space, then Elizabeth Spires is one of the best poets of her generation.

—*Booklist*. Her meticulous craft, sensuous language, incisive intelligence and resonant feeling establish Spires as one of our very best poets. —*Choice*

Spring, Justin. *Polaroid Poems*. 24p. pap. $5.95. Fox River Grove, IL: White Eagle Coffee Store Press, Spring 1996. [Justin Spring's work is] as real as the spliced narrative he finds himself in, as real as the gaps in our attempts to understand ourselves. There's courage in it, integrity. I enjoyed the ride. —David Craig

St. Germain, Cindi. *Time Is Not Linear*. 42p. pap. $6.00 (1-56439-046-2). Detroit, MI: Ridgeway Press, Fall 1995. Poetry by one of Detroit's finest performance poets. Ms. St. Germain's poetry is stunning in performance and very much alive on the page. —Ridgeway Press

St. Germain, Sheryl. *The Journals of Scheherazade*. 78p. pap. $10.95 (1-57441-010-5). Denton, TX: University of North Texas Press, Spring 1996. Sheryl St. Germain is a courageous, wild, and disciplined poet. In this book she faces the erotic, of body and mind—

passionately, precisely, delineating "the damage that is beautiful." —Alicia Ostriker

St. Jacques, Elizabeth. *Landings Soft: Haiku*. 16p. pap. $5.00 (0-936545-21-6). Bakersfield, CA: Amelia Press, Spring 1995.

Stafford, William. *Even in Quiet Places*. 122p. $20.00 (1-881090-19-1); pap. $11.00 (1-881090-16-7). Lewiston, ID: Confluence Press, Spring 1996. This first full-length volume since Stafford's death three years ago at age 79 gathers the work of four chapbooks published between 1990 and 1993. —Confluence Press. A major contribution to 20th-century American poetry, his work transforms "commonest things" into universal truth. Highly recommended. —Frank Allen, *Library Journal*

Stafford, William. *The Methow River Poems*. 20p. pap. $6.00 (1-881090-18-3). Lewiston, ID: Confluence Press, Spring 1995. In 1994, award winning poet William Stafford was commissioned by the Winthrop Ranger District to write seven poems to be placed at pullouts along the North Cascades Highway in Washington State, throughout the Methow Valley. This hand-held booklet is a duplication of those seven poems. —Confluence Press

Stahlecker, Beth. *Three Flights Up.* 52p. pap. $11.95 (1-884800-04-1). Marshfield, MA: Four Way Books, Spring 1996. *Three Flights Up*, a posthumous poetry collection, established a series in the author's name. (There is a) sense in these poems of something under pressure, and shimmering. —Ellen Bryant Voigt

Staley, Harry C. *The Lives of a Shell-Shocked Chaplain.* 62p. pap. $8.95 (1-879934-43-4). Laurinburg, NC: St. Andrews College Press, Fall 1995. What a marvelous poetic biography Harry Staley has given us! He follows the life of a chaplain who comes of age, matures, grows old in wars real and imagined: the Great War that preceded his birth, World War Two, Korea, Vietnam. The coherence, the wit, and the power of Staley's first published work are formidable. A virtuoso performance. —William Kennedy

Standing, Sue. *Gravida.* 75p. pap. $11.95 (1-884800-02-5). Marshfield, MA: Four Way Books, Spring 1995. [Standing's poems affirm] that every process and object is pregnant with meaning. . . . *Gravida* presents a compelling view of life, persuasively and elegantly. —Robert Pinsky

Starck, Clemens. *Journeyman's Wages.* 68p. pap. $10.95 (1-885266-02-2). Brownsville, OR: Story Line Press, Fall 1995. Winner of the 1996 William Stafford Memorial Book Award. Clem Starck presents the life of a working man in scenes and language taken directly from life. This is the kind of poetry Whitman called for: an expression of the individual—original, moving, refreshingly unacademic. —Louis Simpson. These poems celebrate not only work itself, but also the journeyman who can see, as Starck does, the sublime grace of hanging out at an auto parts store chatting about Chevies or of loose tools rattling in the back of the truck. Starck is an expert workman, building his original lines nail by nail. —*Booklist*

Steele, Frank, ed. *Quiet Music: A Plainsong Reader.* 54p. pap. $4.00. Bowling Green, KY: Plainsong Press, Spring 1996.

The poems included here represent fifteen years worth of work from the poetry journal *Plainsong*, which is committed to publishing short poems which reflect the restrained, undisturbed surfaces of language (often with turbulent feelings going on somewhere beneath). —Plainsong Press

Steele, Frank, ed. *The Valley Beneath Words: The Best of Plainsong.* 60p. pap. $4.00. Bowling Green, KY: Plainsong Press, Spring 1996. Designed for use as a teaching tool and writing text, this anthology includes poems which are accessible to students who have basic reading skills but not a lot of knowledge about poetry. —Plainsong Press

Steele, Timothy. *Sapphics and Uncertainties: Poems, 1970–1986.* 96p. $20.00 (1-55728-376-1); pap. $12.00 (1-55728-375-3). Fayetteville, AR: University of Arkansas Press, Fall 1995. This volume brings together two previous works, *Uncertainties and Rest* (1979) and *Sapphics Against Anger and Other Poems* (1986). [Timothy Steele is] one of the finest contemporary poets to write in meter and traditional forms. —*Publishers Weekly*

Stefanile, Felix. *The Dance at St. Gabriel's.* 80p. pap. $12.95 (1-885266-08-1). Brownsville, OR: Story Line Press and Peterloo Poets (UK), Fall 1995. His luminous intelligence, unillusioned emotion, and delicious humor capture the immigrant experience with unmatched immediacy. —Dana Gioia. The book's intersecting and intertwining themes include delight in memories uncorrupted by eventual outcome; celebration of the common man, who seeks morality and friendship rather than fame; and exploration of the emotional components of living during World War II. Stefanile peoples his work with immigrants, boccie players, rowdy recruits, and restless veterans, bringing all to life with compassion and eloquence. —*Booklist*

Stein, Kevin. *Bruised Paradise.* 88p. pap. $12.95 (0-252-06537-9). Champaign, IL: University of Illinois Press, Fall 1996. Kevin Stein is a superb storyteller who braves the insidious, the irrational, the unpredictable and the dangerous in our common lives.

What is amazing about the poems in his *Bruised Paradise* is the compassion that survives in them against all odds. —John Knoepfle. Stein is a poet who knows how to transcribe not just the melodies and timbres of the physical world but also the "throaty cry, our cry that comes as we witness the gradual dispatch of the world we trust." —Curt Rode, *American Book Review*

Steingraber, Sandra. *Post-Diagnosis.* 104p. $20.95 (1-56341-058-3); pap. $9.95 (1-56341-057-5), Ithaca, NY: Firebrand Books, Spring 1995. A gifted young poet—a survivor of cancer in her twenties, a biologist with an environmental bent committed to cancer activism—writes about hope and renunciation, desire and determination. —Firebrand Books

Steinman, Lisa M. *Ordinary Songs.* 26p. pap. $5.00. Portland OR: 26 Books, Fall 1996. *Ordinary Songs* finds the music in daily life and the magic in ordinary things. —26 Books

Stelmach, Marjorie. *Night Drawings.* 88p. pap. $9.95 (1-884235-12-3). Kansas City,

MO: Helicon Nine Editions, Spring 1995. Winner of the 1994 Marianne Moore Poetry Prize. *Night Drawings* is a prayerful book. In it ordinary, everyday speech is transformed as a medium of reverence towards experience. A highly original and perceptive first book, *Night Drawings* is a signal achievement. —David Ignatow.

Stern, Gerald. *Lucky Life.* 88p. pap. $11.95 (0-88748-207-4). Pittsburgh, PA: Carnegie Mellon University Press/Classic Contemporary Series, Fall 1995. These are the powerful, haunting poems of a grown man—rare in America, where we are more familiar with the questions of protracted adolescence. —Muriel Rukeyser. Stern is one of those rare poetic souls who makes it almost impossible to remember what our world was like before his poetry came to exalt it. —C.K. Williams

Stern, Gerald. *Odd Mercy.* 122p. $18.95 (0-393-03879-3). New York, NY: W.W. Norton & Company, Fall 1995. What's so liberating about Stern's poems is the lyrical restlessness, the zany jigs, the yearning, that are inseparable from the lifetime he declares he's spent "grieving and arguing." —Gail Mazur, *Boston Sunday Globe.* Gerald Stern's presence in our midst is an enormous, indestructible blossom. One of the funniest, most moving, elusive poets writing in English. —Richard Katrovas, *Times-Picayune.* For over two decades, no one has equaled [Stern's] compassionate, surreal parables about the burden of and the exaltation at being alive. Highly recommended. —Frank Allen, *Library Journal*

Stevens, A. Wilber. *From the Still Empty Grave: Collected Poems.* 144p. pap. $12.95 (0-87417-272-1). Reno, NV: University of Nevada Press, Fall 1995. In this masterful collection, Stevens explores the complex connections between place and experience; life and death; the world of books and the quotidian world of work, pain, and loss. —University of Nevada Press

Stevens, Elisabeth. *The Night Lover.* 56p. pap. $11.50 (0-913559-26-1). Delhi, NY: Birch Brook Press, Fall 1995.

Letterpress edition. Erotic love poems from a woman's point of view—beautiful and brave. —Grace Cavalieri

Stewart, Pamela. *What Goes On.* 32p. pap. $6.00. Brockport, NY: State Street Press, Spring 1996.

Stewart, Susan. *The Forest.* 80p. $25.00 (0-226-77409-0); pap. $10.95 (0-226-77410-4). Chicago, IL: University of Chicago Press, Fall 1995. Susan Stewart plumbs human history in an attempt to articulate the way language, memory, and art join in evoking consciousness. *The Forest* is about violence and memory: the violence we do to our surroundings and to ourselves; and the propensity of the human mind to exploit and rationalize in its longing for truth. —University of Chicago Press. It is rare, very rare, when a book combines so successfully both the emotional reverberance and the depth and range of intelligence that is found here. This is a very beautiful book. —Thomas Lux

Stillman, Peter. *Planting by the Moon: On Life in a Mountain Hamlet.* 105p. pap. $10.95 (0-86709-347-1). Portsmouth,

NH: Heinemann-Boynton/Cook Publishers, Spring 1995. *Planting by the Moon* provides a rollicking yet poignant portrait of hardscrabble America. He *is* the things he writes about: logger, firefighter, horseman, cabin dweller, loiterer at the general store. These essays and poems give readers a close-up view of Gilead, "the most wonderful community on earth," its people, its miseries, its exquisite beauty. —Heinemann-Boynton/Cook

Stock, Thomas Allen. *Cone Poems: Celebrating the Long Island Pine Barron.* 16p. pap. $2.50. Smithtown, NY: Thomas Allen Stock, Fall 1995. A chapbook of thirteen poems about Long Island's 50,000 acre forest preserve. —Thomas Allen Stock

Stockwell, Samn. *Theater of Animals.* 64p. pap. $10.95 (0-252-06476-3). Champaign, IL: University of Illinois Press, Fall 1995. I have found in this collection what I seek in any literary work, unprecedented voice, in this case stern, elliptical, erotic, and relentlessly intelligent. No poem in Samn Stockwell's first collection exceeds forty lines, yet the impression created is one of eerie

gravity and substance, simultaneously austere and sensual. —Louise Glück

Stone, Ruth. *Simplicity.* 128p. pap. $12.95 (0-9638183-1-7). Northampton, MA: Paris Press, Spring 1995. By turns sly, subtle, exuberant, poignant, bawdy and bitter—and always unflinchingly honest— Ruth Stone's *Simplicity* is anything but simple. She is one of poetry's wise women and one of our age's fiercest, purest, most original poets. —Sandra M. Gilbert. [She is] America's Akhmatova. —Willis Barnstone. What a pleasure it is to come across a poet who tells stories, whose wit and voice is always uniquely recognizable, and whose poems taken together create the outline, the flesh, scars, laughter and quiet meditation of a great spirit. —T. Barnstone, *Poetry Flash*

Strahan, Bradley R., ed. *Balkan Visions.* pap. (0-938872-20-6). Falls Church, VA: Black Buzzard Press/Visions-International, Spring 1995. This collection contains some of the best recent poetry from the Balkans, including a fair sampling from each of the major national groups and translations from

Bosnian, Albanian, Croation, Macedonian, Greek and Romanian. —Black Buzzard Press

Straus, Marc J. *One Word.* 80p. $29.95 (0-8101-5010-7); pap. $11.95 (0-8101-5035-2). Evanston, IL: Northwestern University Press/Triquarterly Books, Fall 1994. Wilfred Owen once asserted that his poetry was in the pity. He could well have described the impressive, direct, blood-stained poems of physician Marc Straus in the same way. —Dannie Abse. *One Word* is the most powerful and original book I have read in long time. —Thomas Lux

Strickland, Stephanie, and Anneliese Wagner, eds. *River Poems.* 56p. pap. $8.00 (0-9624178-1-5). Tarrytown, NY: Slapering Hol Press, 1992.

Stuart, Dabney. *Light Years: New and Selected Poems.* 196p. $24.95 (0-8071-1898-2); pap. $14.95 (0-8071-1899-0). Baton Rouge, LA: Louisiana State University Press, Fall 1994. In this selection, Dabney Stuart's formal variety and range are wonderfully displayed. But dazzling as these changes are, it is his constancy that is most memorable. His story is the oldest quest, made new in terms as ambiguous and true as our own lives. —Betty Adcock. [This collection] establishes Virginian Dabney Stuart's place among the modern poets. A retrospective of thirty years of lucid writing, *Light Years* shows the poet's growth in voice, technique and self-awareness. —*The Virginian Pilot* and *The Ledger Star*

Studebaker, William. *Falling From the Sky.* 12p. pap. $6.00. Pocatello, ID: Redneck Press, Fall 1994. Idaho's foremost native poet explores dreams and fantasies of stoical hedonism, platonic love, androgyny and human wholeness. —Redneck Press

Stuefen, Fern. *Circle of Love.* 68p. pap. $7.00 (1-877649-24-4). Canton, SD: Tesseract Publications, Fall 1995.

Suarez, Lou. *Losses of Moment.* 32p. pap. $4.75 (0-87338-534-9). Kent, OH: Kent State University Press, Spring 1996. Lou Suarez's poems are about what we can and can't see. Watch, look, see—usually these verbs are the pivots of his poems. Even our inner lives are visible [in] these carefully made poems.

—William Mathews. Lou Suarez's poems look into the beauty, loss and redemption of relationships and the relational world with a clarity of vision and voice that both astounds and carries us. —Gary Margolis

Sullivan, Charles, ed. *America in Poetry.* 208p. pap. $16.95 (0-8109-2650-4). New York, NY: Harry N. Abrams, Spring 1996. With paintings, drawings, photographs and other works of art—100 illustrations in all, including 50 full color plates. —Harry N. Abrams. The happy idea of uniting visual images and verbal makes a unique contribution in which one art form enhances another. —James A. Michener. A powerful, varied collection of classic and contemporary poems. —*Booklist*

Sullivan, Charles, ed. *Fathers and Children in Literature and Art.* 162p. (0-8109-3329-2). New York, NY: Harry N. Abrams, Fall 1995. Sullivan has selected over 100 poems, quotations, and passages of prose and paired them with paintings, drawings, photographs, and sculptures to illustrate the broad range of thoughts and feelings that may be experi-

enced by fathers and their children, as they take part in one of the most basic, yet complex, human relationships. —Harry N. Abrams

Sullivan, Charles, ed. *Imaginary Animals.* 114p. (0-8109-3470-1). New York, NY: Harry N. Abrams, Fall 1996. This volume brings together a remarkable selection of over eighty poems and juxtaposes them with paintings, photographs, drawings, and sculpture to stimulate the reader's own imagination. Here, the enigmatic Sphinx, the Trojan Horse, the scary-looking Crackbeak, and the elusive Loch Ness Monster cavort with dancing bears, talking fish, and birds of all feathers. —Harry N. Abrams

Sullivan, Kevin Patrick. *First Sight.* 64p. pap. $8.95 (0-9638843-4-4). Santa Barbara, CA: Mille Grazie Press, Fall 1994. Sullivan's poems are an adventure out of the self; these poems have dirt under their nails, they are exposed to the weather. —Benjamin Saltman. Sullivan is a meticulous minimalist . . . a poet of submerged feelings who can mop up the mythical with the best of them. —Ray Clark Dickson, *Small Press Review*

Sund, Robert. *As Though the Word Blue Had Been Dropped into the Water.* 28p. pap. $5.00. Port Townsend, WA: Sagittarius Press, 1986, reissued 1996. Handset, limited edition.

Survant, Joe. *We Will All Be Changed.* 28p. pap. $6.00. Brockport, NY: State Street Press Chapbooks, Spring 1995.

Susko, Mario. *Mothers, Shoes, and Other Mortal Songs.* 104p. pap. $11.95 (0-938999-07-9). Stamford, CT: Yuganta Press, Fall 1995. Mario Susko is retelling the oldest tales of brutality and human unkindness with unmediated honesty. There is in these poems a kind of epic finality—this is how we were if any archaeologist asks. . . . This is a work of delicacy and brutal fact, of poetic preciseness and logic, an elegy, a requiem. Yet it is about life, living and the things of existence. —Robert Karmon

Sutphen, Joyce. *Straight Out of View.* 128p. $22.00 (0-8070-6824-1); pap. $12.00 (0-8070-6825-X). Boston, MA: Beacon Press, Spring 1995. Winner of the 1994 Barnard New Women Poets Prize. This is a compelling voice, resonant with passionate candor. —Patricia Hampl. Sutphen's first collection . . . reveals a poet of place whose assured, straightforward style seems sprung from the Minnesota farmlands where she was raised. —*Publishers Weekly*

Sutton, Eve. *Laryngitis and Other Poems To Read Aloud.* 34p. pap. Palo Alto, CA: Perma Press Books, Fall 1995.

Sutton, Maureen. *To Encourage the Dawn.* 32p. pap. $12.00. Whispering Pines, NC: Persephone Press, Fall 1995.

Svoboda, Terese. *Mere Mortals.* 152p. pap. $14.95 (0-8203-1710-1). Athens, GA: University of Georgia Press, Spring 1995. Negotiating a "wacked-out" path to rueful wisdom, [Svoboda] casts a cold eye at love beyond innocence at the end of the 20th century. —Frank Allen, *Library Journal*. [Svoboda has] guts, grist, balls, heart, lungs and a world view horrifically, uniquely [her] own. —Mark Richard, *Vogue*. Svoboda delicately balances a harsh, yet convincing indictment of Western culture with an equally ardent belief in the possibility of human compassion and responsibility. —*Publishers Weekly*

Swander, Mary. *Heaven-and-Earth House*. 84p. $20.00 (0-679-42984-0); pap. $13.00 (0-679-76568-9). New York, NY: Alfred A. Knopf, Fall 1994. [Swander's new book of narrative poems] deals with her insights into her rural home among the Amish community at Kalona where she gardens and raises various animals. Though this volume has immense appeal to Iowa people, these poems transcend the specific and time-locked. —Ann Struthers, Des Moines *Sunday Register*. A poet of substance and fine craft in earlier volumes here steps up into the big leagues of her art. This is a marvellously joy-filled book. —Pat Monaghan, *Booklist*

Swanger, David. *This Waking Unafraid*. 64p. pap. $12.95 (0-8262-0987-4). Columbia, MO: University of Missouri Press, Spring 1995. Often provocative and occasionally outrageous, these poems inevitably make thematic connections that jolt the reader into view-

ing the ordinary in a new way. —University of Missouri Press

Swann, Brian, ed. *Wearing the Morning Star: Native American Song-poems*. 180p. $23.00 (0-679-44827-6). New York, NY: Random House, Fall 1996. This new collection celebrating the vibrant oral traditions of indigenous North American peoples includes songs of the earth and sky, songs of mourning and love, ritual songs, songs of derision and threat, ribaldry, hunting chants and the song sung by an Inuit about the first airplane he ever saw. This collection illuminates the complexities and the unique perspectives of Native American cultures. —Random House

Swensen, Cole. *Numen*. 80p. pap. $8.00 (1-886224-00-5). Providence, RI: Burning Deck, Fall 1995. Her poetry is like Dickinson without the syncopation, but with something of Traherne's sublime orderliness: numinous, in fact. —John Ashbery, *TLS*

Swenson, May. Edited by R.R. Knudson. *May Out West*. 72p. $15.95 (0-87421-200-6). Logan, UT: Utah State University Press, Spring 1996. This new collection of May Swenson's poems takes the West as its focus and field of vision. Some of Swenson's best-known poems are included, along with some that have never been collected before. Others reflect revisions made by the poet after previous publication. —Utah State University Press. May Swenson was a poet of dazzling gifts. . . . quite simply, one of the most inventive, imaginative, intelligent and provocative poets of the era. —Joyce Carol Oates

Swir, Anna. Translated by Czeslaw Milosz and Leonard Nathan. *Talking to My Body.* 160p. pap. $14.00 (1-55659-108-X). Port Townsend, WA: Copper Canyon Press, Spring 1996. What is the central theme of these poems? Answer: Flesh. Flesh in love and ecstasy, in pain, in terror, flesh afraid of loneliness, giving birth, resting, feeling the flow of time or reducing time to one instant. Anna Swir achieves in her sensual, fierce poetry a nearly calligraphic neatness. —Czeslaw Milosz

Swist, Wally. *Blowing Reeds.* 28p. pap. $7.50 (0-944048-06-4).

Fulton, MO: Timberline Press, Spring 1995. A collection of 80 haiku that explore the natural world and our place in it. New England shapes the imagery and echoes in every poem as the haiku cycle through the seasons. —Timberline Press

Swist, Wally. *The Mown Meadow.* 80p. pap. $9.95 (1-879603-19-5). San Diego, CA: Los Hombres Press, Spring 1996. Haiku and poetic sequences. The astonishment, the mystery, the solitude, the admiration of nature are all suggested in a few words, with the distillation of the poet's emotions rendered impersonally, according to haiku aesthetics. —*Abatross*

Sylvester, William. *War and Lechery: The Poem.* 101p. pap. $12.00 (0-912592-39-7). Ashland, OH: The Ashland Poetry Press, Fall 1995. This is a great poem! —Andrei Codrescu. William Sylvester's brilliant recovery of our great classical sources makes a playful collage of the present world and all that it thinks it came from. His generous wit and inventiveness keep the old stories alive. —Robert Creeley

Sze, Arthur. *Archipelago.* 86p. pap. $12.00 (1-55659-100-4).

Port Townsend, WA: Copper Canyon Press, Fall 1995. Here is surrealism, Japanese style: "water is the koan of water"; [Sze's] vivid imagery proves we can indeed achieve unity through diversity. —*Library Journal*

Szirtes, George. *Selected Poems, 1976-1996*. 128p. pap. $15.95 (0-19-283223-9). New York, NY: Oxford University Press, Spring 1996. Depth of feeling, a compassionate discerning intelligence, and a commitment to truthfulness—a combination of qualities hard to find simultaneously in any other contemporary British poet. —Richard Burns, *Jewish Chronicle*

Szymborska, Wislawa. Translated by Stanislaw Barańczak and Clare Cavanagh. *View With a Grain of Sand*. 240p. $20.00 (0-15-100153-7); pap. $12.00 (0-15-600217-5). San Diego, CA: Harcourt Brace/Harvest Books, Spring 1995. Winner of the 1996 Nobel Prize. Szymborska portrays a world in which nature is wise and prodigal and fate unpredictable, if not mischievous. With acute irony tempered by a generous curiosity, she documents life's improbability and its transient beauty. —Harcourt Brace

T

Tabasso, Gina M. *From Between My Legs*. 23p. pap. $4.00. Kew Gardens, NY: New Spirit Press, Fall 1995. Winner of the 1995 New Spirit Press Quarterly Chapbook Contest. An engrossing and cathartic collection about childhood incest and sexual abuse. —New Spirit Press

Tan Lin. *Lotion Bullwhip Giraffe*. 184p. pap. $10.95 (1-55713-258-5). Los Angeles, CA: Sun & Moon Press, Spring 1996. This young American Chinese poet "sets tooth on the treetops," lets language twist and tumble over itself like a "Chickory Lickery Bock." In this marvelous celebration of language, Tan Lin explores "a meditation backwards," inventing new poetic structures and forms as he creates a dialogue between himself and the significant other Reader. —Sun & Moon Press

Tanikawa, Shuntaro. Translated by Kazuo Kawamura and William I. Elliott. *Naked*. 64p. pap. $10.95 (1-880656-25-6). Berkeley, CA: Stone Bridge Press, Spring 1996. These evocative hymns of childhood recreate the world of first lies, first loves, piano lessons, playmates, wonder and foreboding. —Stone Bridge Press

Tapscott, Stephen, ed. *Twentieth Century Latin American Poetry: A Bilingual Anthology*. 448p. $55.00 (0-292-78140-7); pap. $24.95 (0-292-78138-5). Austin, TX: University of Texas Press, Spring 1996. Tapscott's collection sets a standard likely to last well into the next century. —*Publishers Weekly*

Tekavex, Valerie. *Peacocks & Beans*. 44p. pap. $8.00 (1-56439-051-9). Roseville, MI: Ridgeway Press, Spring 1996. Unqiue, strange, Carveresque prose poems that form haunting little stories that sink deep within the soul of the reader. Tekavex is a truly original poet/writer from the Catskill Mountains in upstate New York. —Ridgeway Press

Tellman, Susan. Artwork by Marilynn Derwenskus. *Words and Images*. 56p. pap. (0-937994-31-6). Muncie, IN: Ball State University, Spring 1996.

Terranova, Elaine. *Damages*. 78p. pap. $12.00 (1-55659-105-5). Port Townsend, WA: Copper Canyon Press, Spring 1996. Elegant metaphors and sure-footed cadences dazzle as the poet guides us through her dark cross-cuts and interstices. Subtle as oracles and as demanding of respect, Terranova's fearless poems call for our wonder and admiration. —Colette Inez

Terris, Susan. *Killing in the Comfort Zone*. 32p. pap. $7.95. Johnstown, OH: Pudding House Publications, Spring 1995.

Theriault, Jeri. *Corn Dance*. 32p. pap. $6.95 (1-879205-53-X). Troy, ME: Nightshade Press, Fall 1994. Evocative images, skillful use of language. —Gene M. Koehler, *The Leaflet*

Thilleman, Tod. *Wave-Run*. 55p. $20.00 (1-881471-10-1); pap. $7.95 (1-881471-10-X). New York, NY: Spuyten Duyvil, Fall 1995. [In this collection,

Thilleman] does something special, unique even, something that links *Wave-Run* to the greatest American, Walt Whitman: it returns the city of New York to water. . . . —Joe Napora, *Taproot Reviews*

Thomas, Laurence W. *The Face in the Mirror.* 55p. pap. $12.00. Ypsilanti, MI: Laurence W. Thomas, Fall 1996.

Thompson, Dorothy Perry. *Fly With the Puffin.* 67p. pap. $10.00. Greenville, SC: Ninety-Six Press, Spring 1995. *Fly With the Puffin* is a spirited collection that celebrates the African American experience with emotional intensity, humor, and grace. —Ninety-Six Press

Thompson, Jeanie. *Witness.* 96p. $17.00 (1-881320-48-0). Montgomery, AL: Black Belt Press, Fall 1995. Her resilience in the face of pain and loss, her affection for Southern landscape, and above all, her deep, abiding sonority place Thompson in the first rank of poets writing today. To read this book is to experience first hand hope, redemption and grace. —Peter Cooley, *North American Review*

Tibbon, George. *Love Poems & Others.* 176p. pap. $16.95

(1-885896-00-X). San Diego, CA: Libraries Publishing Company, Fall 1994.

Tillinghast, Richard. *The Stonecutter's Hand.* 61p. $19.95 (1-56792-011-X). Lincoln, MA: David R. Godine, Spring 1995. [This collection] solidifies and deepens the considerable achievements of his earlier work. —*Ploughshares.* Tillinghast's talent for combining prosaic and imagistic styles produces fresh, lucid verse and reaffirms his status as a major talent. —Mark Jackson, *Boston Book Review*

Todd, J. C. *Nightshade.* 36p. pap. $6.00 (0-930502-16-7). Landisburg, PA: Pine Press, Spring 1996. [In these] lyric poems, requiem and lullaby are merged. —Eleanor Wilner

Tomé, Jesús. *Como el caer del agua Sobre el agua.* 78p. pap. $6.95 (0-8477-0259-6). San Juan, PR: University of Puerto Rico Press, Fall 1996. In Spanish only.

Tomlinson, Charles. *Jubilation.* 65p. pap. $11.95 (0-19-282451-1). New York, NY: Oxford University Press, Spring 1995. This book, a fourth collection since Charles Tomlinson's *Collected Poems* (1987), is about staying young while getting older. The title is a pun on the Spanish word *jubilación*, which means 'retirement'. —Oxford University Press

Tomlinson, Rawden. *Deep Red.* 100p. $19.95 (0-81310-1346-1); pap. $10.95 (0-81310-1347-X). Gainesville, FL: University Press of Florida, Spring 1995.

Torra, Joseph. *Keep Watching the Sky.* 128p. pap. $11.95 (0-944072-56-9). Cambridge, MA: Zoland Books, Spring 1996. Joseph Torra recognizes the world cannot be neatly divided into oppositions of good and evil, dream and reality. Knowing that the sky in his dreams and the one overhead can pass through each other, Torra registers both the shifts of the world and the mind's flux and all the sites where they intersect. —John Yau

Torrence-Thompson, Juanita. *Spanning the Years.* 76p. pap. $9.00 (0-9652892-0-6). Forest Hills, NY: Torderwarz Publishing Company, Fall 1996. The speaker of these little narratives faithfully records those

tender moments others often cast aside. Celebrating friends, family, and extended family, Juanita Torrence-Thompson's poems are a refreshing antidote to those of a self-centered generation. —Rochelle Ratner

Torrence-Thompson, Juanita. *Wings Span to Eternity.* 35p. pap. $4.95. Flushing, NY: Juanita Torrence-Thompson, Spring 1995. *Wings Span to Eternity* is a serviceable piece of work. The themes are not lightweight—African American and Indian history and cultures. Thompson writes, not about victims, but about a resilient people. —*Point of View*

Torres, Edwin. *Lung Poetry.* 28p. New York, NY: Soncino Books, Fall 1994. Modern, sometimes experimental poems accompanied by photographs. —Soncino Books

Trachtenberg, Jordan N., ed. *Monster Trucks.* 16p. New York, NY: David Lantow and Jordan Trachtenberg, Spring 1996. Conceived as a collaborative venture between visual and literary disciplines, *Monster Trucks* is composed of the work of sixteen poets coupled with that of sixteen artists. —Lantow and Trachtenberg

Tranströmer, Tomas. Edited by Daniel Halpern. *For the Living and the Dead: New Poems and a Memoir.* 71p. $22.00 (0-88001-436-9). Hopewell, NJ: Ecco Press, Fall 1995. Perhaps more than any other living poet, Tranströmer conveys a sense of what it is to be a private citizen anywhere. [His is] an uncannily sensitive imagination doing the work of a religious temperament in a secular and dangerous age. —Robert Hass

Trask, Haunani-Kay. *Light in the Crevice Never Seen.* 128p. $21.95 (0-934971-38-2); pap. $11.95 (0-934971-37-4). Corvallis, OR: Calyx Books, Fall 1994. Trask is known most for her role in leading her people on a path towards justice with her eloquent and sharply truthful voice. Her poetry springs from this fight, which is born of a love for her native Hawaii. —Joy Harjo. Grounded in the rhythms of the old chants, Trask's poems range from lament to celebration, from exposé to exorcism. —Joseph Bruchac

Trawick, Leonard. *Beastmorfs.* 59p. pap. $5.00 (0-914946-60-9). Cleveland, OH: Cleveland State University Poetry Center, Fall 1994. Visual poems that are, as Edmund Spenser says, "full of great lumps of flesh and gobbets raw . . . of books and papers, deformed monsters, fowle, and blacke as inke." —Cleveland State University Poetry Center

Trott, Jon. *Trees and Roots and Growing Things.* 51p. pap. $5.00 (0-940895-33-1). Chicago, IL: Cornerstone Press Chicago, Fall 1994.

Troupe, Quincy. *Avalanche.* 126p. $19.95 (1-56689-045-4); pap. $11.95 (1-56689-044-6). Minneapolis, MN: Coffee House Press, Spring 1996. The typical Troupe poem comes at the reader like a locomotive on fire, full of blazing and powerful imagery. —Ishmael Reed, *The San Diego Reader*

Trowbridge, William. *O Paradise.* 120p. $18.00 (1-55728-341-9); pap. $10.00 (1-55728-342-7). Fayetteville, AR: University of Arkansas Press, Spring 1995. William Trowbridge is very much up on the peculiarities of our little time in the world. He is both funny and serious, seriously funny—probably the best, if not the only, way of dealing with our complex predicament. —Howard Nemerov

Trudell, Dennis. *Fragments in Us: Recent and Earlier Poems.* 94p. $17.95 (0-299-15210-3); pap. $10.95 (0-299-15214-6). Madison, WI: University of Wisconsin Press, Fall 1996. Winner of the 1996 Felix Pollak Prize in Poetry. In *Fragments in Us*, Dennis Trudell writes, above all, about the humility and humanity we gain from recognizing our ties to all our fellow sojourners on this earth, noticing that strangers and neighbors are often brave and resilient and lovely beyond reason. —University of Wisconsin Press

Tsujii, Takashi. Edited by Thomas Fitzsimmons. Translated by R. Brady and A. Wegmüller. *Disappearance of the Butterfly.* 96p. $24.95 (0-942668-43-X); pap. $12.95 (0-942668-44-8). Sante Fe, NM: Katydid Books, Spring 1995. Tsujii's metaphors exhibit a multilayered freedom of movement, at the same time that they give rise to a sort of narrative power. Takashi Tsujii is the

pen name of Tsutsumi Seiji, founder of the Inter-Continental hotel chain and the Seibu Department Stores. —Katydid Books

Turcotte, Mark. *The Feathered Heart.* 64p. pap. $7.95 (1-877636-12-6). Chicago, IL: March/Abrazo Press, Fall 1995. Turcotte's poetry is sound-vision stirring echoes of an Earth-based relationship in urban places, and offering the hope of a deeper human future. —Louise Erdrich

Tuthill, Stacy Johnson. *House of Change.* 72p. pap. $12.00 (0-938572-16-4). Hedgesville, WV: The Bunny and the Crocodile Press/Forest Woods Media Productions, Fall 1996. Stacy Tuthill is a careful craftsman and a wide-ranging observer of our humanity past and present. —Reed Whittemore

Tzagoloff, Helen. *Waiting.* 24p. pap. $4.00. New York, NY: The New School Chapbook Series, Fall 1995. Helen Tzagoloff combines the understated irony of a great storyteller with the concentration, sharp focus and eye for detail of a poet. The result is a thoroughly entertaining collection of modern fables that are by turn wry, wise, surprising, honest and just plain fun. —Elaine Equi

U

Unbearables. *Unbearables Portfolio One.* Edited by Ron Kolm. 21p. $50.00. Brooklyn, NY: Ackerman Loft Gallery. Each poem is hand-printed on a separate sheet into an unbound limited edition portfolio. The Unbearables are a free-floating, in-your-face Temporary Autonomous Zone of Black Humorists, Immediatists, Neoists, and Beer Mystics. —Ackerman Loft Gallery

Upton, Lee. *Approximate Darling.* 104p. pap. $14.95 (0-8203-1811-6). Athens, GA: University of Georgia Press, Spring 1996. This is the third collection from one of the most generous, intelligent, and trustworthy poets writing in America today. . . . Upton is among those poets most capable of ensuring the safe passage of American poetry into the next millennium. —*Boston Review*

V

Valentine, Jean. *Pilgrims.* 46p. pap. $11.95 (0-88748-206-6). Pittsburgh, PA: Carnegie Mellon University Press/Classic Contemporary Series, Fall 1995.

Valenza, Roberto (She Rab Dorje). *precious umbrella.* 48p. pap. $6.00 (1-878-888-20-X). Winston, OR: nine muses books, Fall 1996. Songs and poems of the lamas and the himalayan life. —nine muses press

Valli, Clayton. Produced by Joe Dannis. *ASL Poetry: Selected Works of Clayton Valli.* Video $24.95 (0-915035-23-5). San Diego, CA: DawnSignPress, Spring 1995. This videotape production of ASL poet Valli's work includes a discussion of poetic structures, meaning and form as they are used in American Sign Language. —DawnSignPress

Van de Kamp, Peter, ed. *Turning Tides: Modern Dutch and Flemish Verse in English Versions by Irish Poets.* 424p. pap. $17.95 (0-

934257-70-1). Brownsville, OR: Story Line Press, Spring 1995. This odd but compelling (and massive) collection transforms Dutch poems into English written with a heavy brogue. The book provides an interesting perspective on the subjective nature of translation and offers much work that is startling, though readers may find themselves partial to the marvelous touch of O'Loughlin and Eamon Grennan. —*Publishers Weekly*

Van Duyn, Mona. *If It Be Not I: Collected Poems 1959-1982.* 308p. $25.00 (0-679-41902-0); pap. $15.00 (0-679-75281-1). New York, NY: Alfred A. Knopf, Spring 1993. This volume collects and restores to print all of the work of Mona Van Duyn, Poet Laureate and 1991 Pulitzer Prize winner, up to *Near Changes.* —Alfred A. Knopf

Van Houten, Lois. *Dancing With the Dead.* 80p. pap. $10.00. Pleasant Hill, CA: Small Poetry Press, Fall 1996.

Van Noord, Barbara Bosma. *The Three Hands of God.* 92p. pap. $12.00 (0-941895-13-0). Amherst, MA: Amherst Writ-

ers & Artists Press, Fall 1995. Barbara Bosma Van Noord is a brave poet. She takes on God, the cosmos, tradition, death, life and ordinary days. The last may take the most courage. She is equal to it. —*Daily Hampshire Gazette*

Vance-Watkins, Lequita, and Aratani Mariko, trans. *White Flash/Black Rain: Women of Japan Relive the Bomb.* 104p. pap. $12.95 (1-57131-402-4). Minneapolis, MN: Milkweed Editions, Fall 1995. The voices in this powerful collection refute the idea that the devastation unleashed on Hiroshima and Nagasaki ended with the war. Their words echo the refrain that the ravages of war live on in body and soul, in victim and victor. —Milkweed Editions. A powerful summons to complete the transformation from a dominator to a partnership world. —Riane Eisler

Vancil, David. *The Homesick Patrol.* 88p. pap. $12.00 (1-885215-15-0). Woodbridge, CT: Viet Nam Generation/Burning Cities Press, Fall 1995. David Vancil is our point-man in [the] battle for sanity. For him cholesterol and the war in Vietnam offer similar lessons about our hunger to get even, our need to explain what we were doing "when the end came." Above all, our need for grace when it's all done. —Jerry Bradley

Varela, María Elena Cruz. Translated by Mairym Cruz-Bernal and Deborah Digges. *Ballad of the Blood*. 117p. $22.00 (0-88001-427-X). Hopewell, NJ: Ecco Press, Fall 1995. Bilingual edition. The survival of this work—written and preserved against censorship, humiliations, beatings, and imprisonment—is evidence of what can happen to the imagination during times of extreme adversity, and evidence that in spite of adversity, the spirit seeks freedom. —Mairym Cruz-Bernal

Vasquez, Robert. *At the Rainbow*. 80p. $24.95 (0-8263-1629-8); pap. $9.95 (0-8263-1630-1). Albuquerque, NM: University of New Mexico Press, Fall 1995. Combines autobiographical poems, political themes, love poems, and surrealistic-dream poems [demonstrating that] poetry by contemporary Chicano poets is one of the most exciting and unpredictable genres today. —Ray Gonzalez

Vazirani, Reetika. *White Elephants*. 68p. pap. $12.00 (0-8070-6833-0). Boston, MA: Beacon Press, Spring 1996. Vazirani writes about "citizenship," in its profoundest sense. [*White Elephants*] engages and compels the reader with its tales of voyages and languages, its vivid-voiced characters, its unduped absence of nostalgia. —Marilyn Hacker

Vega. *Phoenix Rising*. 128p. pap. $10.00 (1-880729-12-1). Sicklerville, NJ: Vega Press, Spring 1995. From his first sexual experience at age 17, to a gay marriage complete with children, and a journey of self-awareness, the author shares his joys and disappointments, as he rises like a 'Phoenix' to meet each new challenge. —Vega Press

Vega, ed. *Milking Black Bull: 12 Gay Black Poets*. 176p. pap. $12.00 (1-880729-11-3). Sicklerville, NJ: Vega Press, Spring 1995. The next wave has arrived. Twelve gay black poets continue the work of Melvin Dixon, Essex Hemphill and Assotto Saint, exploring the diversity of gay black life in our time. Meditative and lyrical, celebratory and angry—verse that takes on black homophobia, desire, friendship and family. —Vega Press

Vega, Janine Pommy, ed. *These Are Successful Hands.* 45p. pap. $7.00 (0-937804-58-4). New York, NY: Segue Books, Fall 1994. A collection of poems by staff and residents of Huntington House, a residence for female prison inmates preparing to re-enter society. —Segue Books

Vega, José Luis. *Solo de pasión / Teoría del Sueño.* 45p. pap. $6.95 (0-8477-0257-X). San Juan, PR: University of Puerto Rico Press, Fall 1996. Erotically charged lyrical verses. In Spanish only. —University of Puerto Rico Press

Velarde, Ramón López. Translated by Margaret Sayers Peden. *Song of the Heart: Selected Poems.* 122p. $19.95 (0-292-74685-7). Austin, TX: University of Texas Press, Spring 1995. López Velarde left us a few poems in verse and prose—fewer than 30—so perfect that it is foolish to lament those that death prevented him from writing. —Octavio Paz

Verga, Angelo. *Across the Street From Lincoln Hospital.* 24p. pap. $4.00. New York, NY: The New School Chapbook Series, Fall 1995. "I read you some poems/ of ordinary life" Angelo Verga writes, "the things I know." He knows plenty. He knows of the poet's commitment not only to the line but to his community. He knows of the power true poetry has to get beneath any "official" story. He knows how to turn the small details of everyday folks into wonderful lyrics. —Cornelius Eady

Verity, Kenneth. *Awareness Beyond Mind.* 128p. $12.95 (1-85230-819-2). Rockport, MA: Element Books, Spring 1996. A collection of original haiku which goes straight to the essence of life and relationships. The author traces the development of the essential philosophy of haiku from its source in India to the present. —Element Books

Vertreace, Martha. *Cinnabar.* 30p. pap. $6.50 (1-886226-00-8). Chico, CA: Flume Press, Spring 1995. Her work is rich with subtleties, careful imagery, agreeable varieties of music. It is obvious that she . . . will say *nothing* that she does not feel. —Gwendolyn Brooks

Vial, Noelle. *Promiscuous Winds.* 106p. pap. $10.95 (1-885266-13-8). Brownsville, OR: Story Line Press, Fall 1995. Winner of the 1994 Hennessy Award for Best Poetry by an Emerging Writer. In a world where others ask her to "love them at the cost of her own happiness," Vial writes to liberate both the writer and reader from the suffocating molds which, she writes, "even our words have imposed on us." —Story Line Press. Noelle Vial's poetry is underlined by a very raw and genine honesty. It is sharply and beautifully written, with a great sense of immediacy. She is a poet with a superb capacity to communicate experience on a very human, sensual, and direct level. —*The Sunday Tribune (Ireland)*

Vieira, John. *Reality Slices.* 34p. pap. $5.00 (1-57141-020-1). Port Charlotte, FL: Runaway Spoon Press, Spring 1996. A collection of textual and visual poetry. —Runaway Spoon Press

Viereck, Peter. *Tide and Continuities: Last and First Poems 1995-1938.* 344p. $36.00 (1-55728-313-3); pap. $20.00 (1-55728-314-1). Fayetteville, AR: The University of Arkansas, Fall 1995. Peter Viereck is one of the most important of our living poets. One reads [his work] with the same amazement and trembling that *The Wasteland* must have inspired in its first readers. The language blazes out as if it had never been used before. —Frederick Turner. Heart-rending, gorgeous, outrageous, Vierck's work is a brand new art form. —Joseph Brodsky

Villanueva-Collado, Alfredo. *Entre la inocencia y la Manzana.* 121p. pap. $6.95 (0-8477-0260). San Juan, PR: University of Puerto Rico Press, Fall 1996. An intense and deeply moving testimony of the pain wrought by the AIDS epidemic. In Spanish only. —University of Puerto Rico Press

Villanueva, Tino. Translated by James Hoggard. *Chronicle of My Worst Years.* 84p. $34.95 (0-8101-5009-3); pap. $12.95 (0-8101-5034-4). Evanston, IL: Northwestern University Press/ Triquarterly Books, Fall 1994. Bilingual edition. As a Chicano writer working in Spanish, Villaneuva voices complex and compelling historical, literary, and cultural questions as impassioned personal utterances, which invests his work with unusually appealing intimacy and seriousness. His eloquent, elegant work portrays American realities absent from mainstream poetry. —Northwestern University Press

Vogelsang, Arthur. *Cities and Towns.* 96p. pap. $10.95 (1-55849-021-3). Amherst, MA: University of Massachusetts Press, Spring 1996. Winner of the Juniper Prize. We have in Vogelsang a poet furious with history but attempting a mad escape. It's a swollen poetry, maximal at the least and packed with his rare rage. —David Shapiro. Vogelsang's newest poems are rich and complicated, yes, and altogether alluring. —James Tate

Voigt, Ellen Bryant. *Kyrie.* 80p. $17.95 (0-393-03796-7). New York, NY: W.W. Norton & Company, Fall 1995. Under the growing shadow of AIDS and other epidemics, Voigt's new collection of sonnets conjures up the influenza pandemic of 1918-1919. Though little recorded in our imaginative literature, this harrowing event claimed over twenty-five

million lives worldwide. —W.W. Norton & Company. The beauty and intensity of this sustained elegy leave us feeling much as we do after listening to Mozart's *Requiem*: grief stricken, transformed, and exalted. —Francine Prose. Seldom have panic and despair been depicted so lyrically. —*Publishers Weekly*. [These poems combine dignity] with mute outrage at being present at the Day of Judgment. —Frank Allen, *Library Journal*

Voigt, Ellen Bryant. *The Forces of Plenty.* 63p. pap. $11.95 (0-88748-227-9). Pittsburgh, PA: Carnegie Mellon University Press/Classic Contemporary Series, Fall 1996.

Volkman, Karen. *Crash's Law.* 64p. $18.95 (0-393-03956-0). New York, NY: W.W. Norton & Company, Spring 1996. In their solitude and wonder, these poems seek the roots of an American woman's entitlement to speech, and find the restoration of an old eloquence in her proverbial yet invented rhyme: "the body / is my heart . . . my hunger is my art." The whole book is a revelation of originality and invention! —Richard Howard.

Reading Volkman's *Crash's Law*, a 1995 National Poetry series winner selected by Heather McHugh, provides the same difficult joy as sucking on a jawbreaker, candy that is pleasant yet hard as rock. For readers interested in the aesthetic side of contemporary poetry. —Frank Allen, *Library Journal*

Voss, Fred. *Maybe It's All True.* 36p. pap. $6.00 (0-9628094-9-7). Long Beach, CA: Pearl Editions, Fall 1994. Voss's 13th collection, a sequence of meditative poems, reveals his lyrical paterfamilias side and compassion for the weary contemporary world at large. —Pearl Editions. An armature of wit, satire, and profundity measured in terms of emotional truth and psychological depth. —George Messo, *London Magazine*

Vreeland, Sandra. *The Sky Lotto.* 72p. pap. $12.00 (1-886435-03-0). Sag Harbor, NY: Canio's Editions, Fall 1995. Underlying the aura of these poems and their quick observant joy, is an anguish she admits. Vreeland cannot ignore the illness that imperils her poetry; she confesses to a panic of the soul.

This confession and our immediate sympathy with it, deepens a book of small wonders. —Barbara Guest

Wagner, Anneliese. *Murderous Music.* 33p. pap. $7.95 (0-9619111-8-2). Goshen, CT: Chicory Blue Press, Spring 1995. Autobiographical poems about a Jewish girl who escapes Nazi Germany and comes to the United States as a refugee, shorn even of her memories of childhood. —Chicory Blue Press. This is an important testimonial and a powerful lyrical voice. —Maxine Kumin

Wagner, Maryfrances. *Salvatore's Daughter.* 64p. pap. $10.00 (1-886157-00-6). Kansas City, MO: BkMk Press of the University of Missouri-Kansas City, Spring 1995. Wagner writes beautifully and lovingly from her Italian-American heritage, on family and neighborhood, on tradition, and on humanity's bond with the natural world. —William Trowbridge

Wagoner, David. *Walt Whitman Bathing*. 104p. pap. $11.95 (0-252-06570-0). Champaign, IL: University of Illinois Press, Fall 1996. When Wagoner looks at something, he brings it to vivid and immediate life through [the] extraordinary power [of] love. He is as formally various as Thomas Hardy, as playful as Dickinson, as wry as Frost. —Dave Smith. Wagoner is a sharp-eyed, even gutsy nature poet, and the deftest and tenderest of love poets. —X.J. Kennedy

Wakoski, Diane. *The Emerald City of Las Vegas: The Archaeology of Movies & Books, Volume 3*. 202p. $25.00 (0-87685-972-4); pap. $13.50 (0-87685-971-6); sig. $35.00 (0-87685-973-2). Santa Rosa, CA: Black Sparrow Press, Fall 1995. Wakoski here charts an engagingly self-revealing "map of thinking"— interspersing poems, letters and dream narratives with quotes from Frank Baum's *The Wizard of Oz* and Nick Herbert's *Quantum Reality* to create an extended meditation on personal history and the nature of consciousness. —Black Sparrow Press

Wald, Diane. *Double Mirror*. 37p. pap. $5.00 (1-57141-023-6). Port Charlotte, FL: Runaway Spoon Press, Spring 1996.

Walden, Gale Renée. *Same Blue Chevy*. 71p. pap. $10.95 (1-882688-10-4). Chicago, IL: Tia Chucha Press, Spring 1996. Gale Walden's first book of poems is a profound series of meditations illustrating the power of place in shaping our histories and perceptions. Walden moves from the prairie to the city and back again, drawing the reader through the living rooms and main streets of a past that is in constant flux. Each poem is saturated with images echoing of myth, an enigmatic journey into our collective past. —Tia Chucha Press

Waldman, Anne. *Fast Speaking Woman: Chants and Essays*. 176p. pap. $10.95 (0-87286-316-6). San Francisco, CA: City Lights Books, Spring 1996. In these spells, invocations, laments & ritual rants, archaic beliefs in magic and ecstasy meet current notions of the power of the spoken word. —City Lights Books. Anne Waldman is one of the fastest, wisest women to run with the wolves in some time. —*The New York Times Book Review*

Waldman, Anne, ed. *The Beat Book: Poems and Fiction of the Beat Generation.* 352p. $24.00 (0-57062-000-8). Boston, MA: Shambhala Publications, Spring 1996. Forward by Allen Ginsberg. Here are selections from the Beat classics, as well as more recent prose and poetry demonstrating the continued vitality of the Beat experiment. Included are short biographies of the contributors, an extensive bibliography of Beat literature, and a unique guide to "Beat places" around the world. —Shambhala Publications

Waldrop, Rosmarie. *A Key Into the Language of America.* 96p. pap. $10.95 (0-8112-1287-4). New York, NY: New Directions, Fall 1994. Waldrop's themes are the legacy of cultural imperialism, the consequences of gender, and the marginalization of the conquered. —New Directions. [Roger] Williams's *A Key Into the Language of America* was the first extensive vocabulary and study of an Indian language printed in English. Waldrop's *Key* is a return and a reinscription. She intersplices, turns, overturns, plots, weaves and threads, line for line, at least three structural

systems. Waldrop's *A Key* is a witty, and deeply moving, translation of sexual and textual division and witness. —Susan Howe

Walker, Sue. *The Appearance of Green.* 52p. pap. $9.95 (1-879205-62-9). Troy, ME: Nightshade Press, Fall 1995.

Wallace, Mark. *Sonnets of a Penny-A-Liner.* 86p. pap. $9.00 (1-886353-05-0). Washington, DC: Buck Downs Books, Fall 1996. "The road to wisdom / has lots of stores and restaurants" Mark Wallace's wonderfully sharp, self reflexive, and darkly humorous sonnets are wisdom teeth stolen from the golden mouths of metaphysical hucksters, penny-a-line journalists, and poetic hit-men. Wallace is always the witty, wandering versifier behind the dry jibe and the existential stool. His poems and essays have played a major role in helping to define what has become post "language" poetry. —Charles Borkhuis

Wallace, Ronald. *Time's Fancy.* 75p. $24.95 (0-8229-3894-4); pap. $10.95 (0-8229-5548-2). Pittsburgh, PA: University of Pittsburgh Press, Fall 1996.

Wallace's work is not only sure in its craftsmanship, but humanly important in its subject matter and treatment. Best of all, it is exuberantly alive. —Lisel Mueller. What a fine poet Wallace is! . . . I recognize so much here with delight and am grateful to have it said at last. —May Sarton

Walter, Eugene. *Lizard Fever: Poems Lyric, Satiric, Sardonic, Elegiac.* 94p. pap. $12.95. Livingston, AL: Livingston University Press, Fall 1994. Original and unexpected . . . witty and unfashionable. —Louise Bogan. [Walter provides an] unexpected combination of the lyric and the humorous. —*The Manchester Guardian*

Walter, Hugo. *Amaranth-Sage Epiphanies of Dusk-Weaving Paradise.* 160p. $16.95 (0-56474-109-5); pap. $8.95 (1-56474-061-7). Santa Barbara, CA: Fithian Press, Spring 1995. Typical of Walter's poems are the vibrant splashes of color, the driving meters, and the whirlpool of lush images. Even more striking are his references to a shared, pan-national human culture and his highly developed word-play. —J.M. Daniel

Walter, Hugo. *Dusk-Gloaming Mirrors and Castle-Winding Dreams.* 90p. pap. $8.95 (1-56474-077-3). Santa Barbara, CA: Fithian Press, Spring 1995.

Walton, Anthony. *Cricket Weather.* 32p. pap. $8.95 (0-942396-71-5). Nobleboro, ME: Blackberry Books, Fall 1995.

Ward, Diane. *Human Ceiling.* 76p. pap. $9.95 (0-937804-62-2). New York, NY: Roof Books, Spring 1996. Diane Ward is among those rare poets, who have found new ways to address the political in lyric forms, creating a body of verse which opens the politics of language and consciousness to us rather than assuming to instruct. —A.L. Nielsen. To read Ward and other 'logo-scientists' is to become a participant in a dynamic building up and tearing down of language and idea. —Kenneth Funsten, *Los Angeles Times Book Review*

Warn, Emily. *The Novice Insomniac.* 96p. pap. $12.00 (1-55659-112-8). Port Townsend, WA: Copper Canyon Press, Fall 1996. In her second collection, Warn continues her artistic attempt to walk a fine line between the ethereal and the earthly. —*Publishers Weekly*

Warren, Shirley. *The Bottomfeeders.* 28p. pap. $5.00 (1-877801-30-5). Galloway, NJ: Still Waters Press, Fall 1995. From the editor of Still Waters Press, poems about the family of fishing men and women she is a part of, each a little story of love or loss or both, with "water" playing a major role in the recurring images of survival. —Still Waters Press

Washington, Peter, ed. *Friendship Poems.* 256p. $10.95 (0-679-44370-3). New York, NY: Alfred A. Knopf/Everyman's Library Pocket Poets, Fall 1995.

Washington, Peter, ed. *Prayers.* 256p. $10.95 (0-679-44466-1). New York, NY: Alfred A. Knopf/Everyman's Library Pocket Poets, Fall 1995.

Wasserman, Rosanne. *No Archive on Earth.* 110p. pap. $10.00 (0-922792-68-2). Port Washington, NY: Gnosis Press, Fall 1995. Rosanne Wasserman's music changes into flesh and memory before our eyes, telling us what went on, poignantly, memorably. —John Ashbery

Wasserman, Rosanne. *The Lacemakers.* 78p. pap. $8.00 (0-922792-52-6). New York, NY: Gnosis Press, 1992.

waterman, margareta. *astarte calling clytemnestra.* 11p. pap. $4.00 (limited edition). Winston, OR: nine muses books, Fall 1994. In these poems a goddess awakens a modern woman by speaking to her of the mystery and power of the ancient archetypes. —nine muses books

waterman, margareta. *five songs from the primordial alphabet.* 26p. pap. $5.50 (1-878888-22-6). Winston, OR: nine muses books, Spring 1996. Poems that link the metaphysics of field and hologram and the mathematics of language with the rhythms and meanings of romantic passion. —nine muses books

waterman, margareta. *some south american colors.* 26p. pap. $4.00 (limited edition). Winston, OR: nine muses books, Fall 1995. Word-sketches from the poet's 1995 South American journals. —nine muses books

Watson, Carl. *Beneath the Empire of the Birds.* 250p. pap. $14.95.

Baltimore, MD: Apathy Press, Spring 1995.

Watson, Robert. *The Pendulum: New and Selected Poems.* 114p. $19.95 (0-8071-1972-5); pap. $10.95 (0-8071-1973-3). Baton Rouge, LA: Louisiana State University Press, Spring 1995. Robert Watson's poetry reminds me of the best that is in Rilke and Frost, a startling sense of the wonder of life, a refreshingly masculine accent, a confident boldness. —Heather Ross Miller. [*The Pendulum*] is a double vision, conjoining the factual and the imagined, the sober and the humorous, the real and the unreal in lines whose dry and sometimes bitter ironies are as bracing as a Key West gin-and-tonic. —Fred Chappell, *Raleigh News and Observer*

Watson, Ron. *A Sacred Heart.* 12p. pap. $6.00. Pocatello, ID: Redneck Press, Fall 1994. Exquisite love poems. —Redneck Press

Watson, Stephen. *Song of the Broken String: Poems From a Lost Oral Tradition.* 75p. pap. $12.95 (1-878818-43-0). Riverdale-on-Hudson, NY: Sheep Meadow Press, Fall 1995. The /Xam Bushmen were a stone-age people who survived nearly 5000 years in a region now known as Cape Province of South Africa, but were destroyed by the European settlement of the interior. *Song of the Broken String* has its provenance in the oral tradition of this ancient culture. Translated into English prose by the German linguist W.H. Bleek in the 1860s, these songs, folktales and personal narratives have been rendered into poems by contemporary South African poet Stephen Watson. —Sheep Meadow Press

Wayne, Jane O. *A Strange Heart.* 70p. pap. $9.95 (1-884235-18-2). Kansas City, MO: Helicon Nine Editions, Fall 1996. Winner of the 1995 Marianne Moore Poetry Prize. *A Strange Heart* takes its primary theme from the heart transplant that gave the author's husband 2½ extra years of life, and from the grief and pain of his death. Although their subject matter is necessarily dark, the poems are filled with unexpected light. Reading these poems is like taking a walk with a close friend at night, where every word comes out of deep silence, and every word rings true.

—Howard Schwartz, *St. Louis Post-Dispatch*

Weaver, Michael S. *Timber and Prayer: The Indian Pond Poems.* 126p. $24.95 (0-8229-3873-1); pap. $10.95 (0-8229-5554-7). Pittsburgh, PA: University of Pittsburgh Press, Fall 1995.

Webb, Kim. *Abstract Cores.* 60p. pap. $10.00 (1-56439-061-6). Roseville, MI: Ridgeway Press, Fall 1996. Kim Webb is a master of both the spoken word and poetry for the page. His work fits comfortably somewhere between the Iowa Workshop and Lollapalooza rants and chants. A wonderful first book! —M.L. Liebler

Webb, Robert T. *Stations of the Cross: An AIDS Poem.* 16p. pap. $5.00 (0-936545-20-8). Bakersfield, CA: Amelia Press, Spring 1995. Winner of the 1991 Louis Sadler Prize for the Arts. *Stations of the Cross* is a long poem in 14 cantos about the loss of a loved one to AIDS. —Amelia Press

Weber, Mark. *Existential Hum.* 43p. pap. $6.00 (1-888219-03-3). Long Beach, CA: Pearl Editions, Spring 1996. After decades of herion and alcohol abuse, Mark Weber tells about the hell on earth wherein he dwelled. —Joan Jobe Smith. He is one of a kind, an original. —Gerald Locklin

Weber, Mark. *Obligatos for Terpsichorean Dipsomaniacs.* 44p. pap. $4.00. Albuquerque, NM: Zerx Press, Spring 1996. Available on CD, $13.00. Mark Weber is one of the best poets writing today. —Ben L. Hiatt, *Mountain Trader*

Weber, Mark. *The Pittsburgh Poems.* 22p. pap. $4.00. Albuquerque, NM: Zerx Press, Spring 1996. A double book, bound back-to-back with Gerald Locklin's *Not the Pittsburgh Poems.*

Weber, Mark. *The Return of Harriet, Wandering Jew Mom.* 16p. pap. $3.00. East Liverpool, OH: Non Compos Mentis Press, Fall 1995.

Weber, Mark. *Transitory Like Smoke.* 45p. pap. $4.00. Albuquerque, NM: Zerx Press, Fall 1995. Bound back-to-back with Gerald Locklin's *Two Jazz Sequences.*

Weber, Mark; Brent Leake, and Larry Goodell. *Assembled Zen.*

48p. pap. $4.00 (Zerx #42). Albuquerque, NM: Zerx Press, Fall 1996. A hodgepodge of poems, songs, narrations and explorations used in a performance and published in chapbook form as a program to the show. —Zerx Press

Weems, Ann. *Kneeling in Bethlehem.* pap. $10.00 (0-664-25516-7). Audiotape $14.00 (0-664-25682-1). Louisville, KY: Westminster/John Knox Press, Fall 1993. A collection of inspirational poems covering the theme and symbols of the Advent and Christmas seasons. Weem's meditations are down to earth, yet portray a striking view of these traditional subjects. —*Booklist*

Weems, Ann. *Psalms of Lament.* 128p. $12.00 (0-664-22074-6). Louisville, KY: Westminster/John Knox Press, Fall 1995. Ann Weems offers poetry and reflection more poignant than anything she has yet published. She brings to this task her finely contoured, well-seasoned faith, which is mature and knowing. She brings, as well, her peculiar finesse with words. —Walter Brueggemann

Weigl, Bruce. *Sweet Lorain.* 66p. $29.95 (0-8101-5053-0); pap.

$11.95 (0-8101-5054-9). Evanston, IL: Northwestern University Press/TriQuarterly Books, Spring 1996. As an elegist of the lives of those who have been changed by hardship and suffering—especially by war—Bruce Weigl has become one of the most admired American poets of his generation. In this, his seventh book of poems, Weigl returns not only to Vietnam but to the Lorain, Ohio, of his youth. —Northwestern University Press. Bruce Weigl's unique verbal music is a song indivisible from its experiential roots. Events of childhood in the industrial midwest, of young manhood flung unwitting into another land and culture, of the years of ongoing pain, of rare joy, of striving and illumination, are one fabric, not episodic. —Denise Levertov

Weiner, Hannah. *We Speak Silent.* 67p. pap. $9.95 (0-937804-68-1). New York: NY: Roof Books, Fall 1996

Weinstein, Debra. *Rodent Angel.* 75p. $25.00 (0-8147-9308-8); pap. $12.95 (0-8147-9307-X). New York, NY: New York University Press, Spring 1996. Weinstein's poetry could at first seem sensational: her subjects *are* often sensational; but this is her life, given and chosen, lived, but never used. This poet is an original, refusing to 'grieve, love, give,' and all through this book doing nothing else. —Jean Valentine. In language that is at times lyrical, at times harsh, the poet's vivid, exact images conjure pictures of wrenching violence and betrayal. —*Publishers Weekly*

Weinstein, Sharon. *Celebrating Absences.* 104p. pap. $10.95 (1-880016-17-6). Painter, VA: Road Publishers, Spring 1995. How can the borderless worlds of yearning, absence, and acceptance be mapped with such economy? Only in Sharon Weinstein's poetry. If she were a painter, she could create a landscape with a single undulating line. —Shelly Wagner

Weiss, Irving. *Visual Voices: The Poem as a Print Object.* 145p. pap. $20.00 (0-926935-95-X). Port Charlotte, FL: Runaway Spoon Press, Fall 1994. Visual poetry variations on pre-1900 classical poems. —Runaway Spoon Press

Weiss, T. and R. *QRL Poetry Series, Vol. 34, 1995.* 58p. $20.00 (0033-5819); pap.

$12.00 (0033-5819). Princeton, NJ: Quarterly Review of Literature, Spring 1995. Contains full-length collections of poems by: Suzanne Paola, Robin Fulton, Werner Aspenström, James Bertolino, Frederick Feirstein; and a play by Paula Blue Spruce. —Quarterly Review of Literature

Weiss, T. and R. *QRL Poetry Series, Vol. 35, 1996.* 342p. $20.00 (1-888545-00-3); pap. $12.00 (1-888545-01-1). Princeton, NJ: Quarterly Review of Literature, Spring 1996. Five prize-winning poetry books selected in international competition and printed under one cover, including works by Lynn Knight, David Citino, Jean Hollander, Barbara D. Hollander and Maria Banus. —Quarterly Review of Literature. QRL's dazzling roster of writers is a tribute to their unerring eye for talent and their pursuit of excellence. —*Parnassus*

Weiss, Theodore. *Selected Poems.* 330p. $49.95 (0-8101-5037-9); pap. $15.95 (0-8101-5040-9). Evanston, IL: Northwestern University Press/TriQuarterly Books, Fall 1995. Weiss explores paradox, history, and love. His distinctive, idiosyncratic poems, noted for their syntactic compression, linguistic playfulness, and characteristic linking of intimate experience and historical incident, are a major accomplishment. —Northwestern University Press

Wenderoth, Joe. *Disfortune.* 88p. $25.00 (0-8195-2222-8); pap. $11.95 (0-8195-1226-5). Middletown, CT: Wesleyan/ University Press of New England, Fall 1995. Joe Wenderoth is one of the true originals in contemporary American poetry. He takes the political and human disconnection felt by many young writers with a new philosophical seriousness, which issues in a new language—funny, compacted; dazzling. He makes me think of Paul Celan more than his obvious American antecedents; and I can imagine no higher compliment. —Alan Williamson. These tightly compressed poems exhibit an acute awareness of the transience of any given thought. —*Publishers Weekly*

Wenthe, William. *Birds of Hoboken.* 64p. pap. $12.95 (0-914961-49-6). Alexandria, VA: Orchises

Press, Fall 1995. William Wenthe's *Birds of Hoboken* frankly considers the postmodern assumption that our every view of reality is a construct: "maybe," he concedes, *"we're invented / by a form—/ 'love'* like syntax/ the theorist might say." In his brilliant first collection the writer *affirms* our capacity to craft, crucial, aesthetic, social and domestic relations. Indeed, in *Birds of Hoboken*, craft is supremely and everywhere evident, in all its senses. —Sydney Lea

Wheatcroft, John. *Alfresco.* 8p. pap. $45.00 (0-916375-23-4). Lewisburg, PA: The Press of Appletree Alley, Fall 1996. A lyrical poem written especially for this letterpress chapbook edition. Wood engravings by Colleen Shannon. —The Press of Appletree Alley

White, Julie Herrick. *Unfinished Business.* 36p. pap. $7.95 (1-879205-65-3). Troy, ME: Nightshade Press, Spring 1996. A narrative poem, but written in fragments—very moving. —Nightshade Press

Whited, David Lloyd. *Wet Way Home.* 26p. pap. $5.00. Portland, OR: 26 Books, Spring

1996. Whited's poems are rooted in the rain and the earth, in the rhythms of salmon and the rhythms of survival. —26 Books

Whitman, Ruth, trans. *An Anthology of Modern Yiddish Poetry, Third Edition.* 200p. pap. $16.95 (0-8143-2533-5). Detroit, MI: Wayne State University Press, Fall 1994. Originally published in 1966, *An Anthology of Modern Yiddish Poetry* was the bilingual anthology to feature the rich, spirited, and passionate Yiddish poetry of the twentieth century. —Wayne State University Press. Wonderful. [Ruth Whitman] has managed to make the translations highly faithful to the Yiddish and at the same time beautiful in English. The choice of poets is excellent. —Isaac Bashevis Singer, from his Note to the Second Edition

Whitman, Walt. *Civil War Poetry and Prose.* 96p. pap. $1.00 (0-486-28507-3). Mineola, NY: Dover Publications, Spring 1995.

Whitman, Walt. Edited by Stephen Mitchell. *Song of Myself.* 158p. pap. $6.00 (0-87773-950-1). Boston, MA: Shambhala Publications/Shambhala Pocket Classics, Fall 1995. Also available in a boxed set with editions of Dickinson, Thoreau and Emerson: *Four American Classics,* $24.00 (1-57062-126-8).

Whitman, Walt. Edited by David Groff (poetry), and Richard Berman (photography). *Whitman's Men: Walt Whitman's Calamus Poems Celebrated by Contemporary Photography.* 80p. $18.95 (0-7893-0022-2). New York, NY: Rizzoli/Universe Publishing. Photographs by Mark Beard, John Dugdale, Robert Flynt, Bill Jacobson, Russell Maynor, Steve Morrison, and Frank Yamrus pay tribute to the bard. —Rizzoli/Universe Publishing

Whitman, Walt, and Emily Dickinson. Edited by Hershel Parker. *Walt Whitman, Emily Dickinson: Selections from the Norton Anthology of American Literature, 4th edition.* 223p. (0-393-96464-7). New York, NY: W.W. Norton & Company, Fall 1994.

Whitney, J.D. *sd & done.* 40p. pap. $6.00 (1-882983-19-X). Greensboro, NC: March Street Press, Spring 1995.

Whitson, Robley. *Miró Mirror.* 45p. pap. (1-55605-260-X).

Bristol, IN: QH Books, Fall 1995.

Whitson, Robley. *Mytholog.* 101p. pap. (1-55605-354-5). Bristol, IN: QH Books, Fall 1995.

Whitt, Michael. *Wild Harvest: Poems From the Land.* 160p. pap. $15.00 (0-912449-48-9). Cedarville, CA: Floating Island Publications, Fall 1995. Dr. Whitt is a physician with a general practice who has served as a country doctor in West Marin for the past twenty-five years. This is his fourth published book and collects all of his poems to date on nature, wildlife and landscapes. Many of the poems are set in West Marin, Nevada and New Mexico. —Floating Island

Widmark, Anne Heath, ed. Photographs by Kent Reeves. *Between Earth and Sky: Poets of the Cowboy West.* 218p. pap. $22.50 (0-393-31565-7). New York, NY: W.W. Norton & Company. Winner of the Western Heritage Wrangler Award for Outstanding Poetry Book of 1995. [Cowboy poetry] is sort of like country music. It's straight talk, dealing with fundamentals, using images you

can touch. Widmark has compiled the work of twelve Western bards who excel at the form. —*Portland Oregonian*

Wilcox, Dan. *Ireland Poems: July 1995.* 12p. pap. $3.00. Albany, NY: A.P.D., Fall 1995. Poems written during a summer trip to Ireland. —A.P.D.

Wild, Peter. *Exotic Dancers.* 12p. pap. $6.00. Pocatello, ID: Redneck Press, Fall 1994.

Wildsmith, Dana. *Alchemy.* 40p. pap. $6.00 (1-885912-05-6). Abingdon, VA: Sow's Ear Press, Spring 1995. *Alchemy,* a first chapbook, has as its main themes the intertwinings of love, sex, and friendship. —Sow's Ear Press

Willard, Nancy. *Swimming Lessons: New and Selected Poems.* 240p. $25.00 (0-679–44639-7). New York, NY: Alfred A. Knopf, Fall 1996. [Willard's poems are] exquisite miniatures, each filled with the luminosity and reverence for detail of a Vermeer painting. —Jonathan Holden, *Open Places*

Williams, C. K. *Selected Poems.* 290p. pap. $12.00 (0-374-52455-6). New York, NY:

Farrar, Straus and Giroux, Fall 1994. Williams's *Selected Poems* is a superb distillate of his work. —James Marcus, *Voice Literary Supplement*

Williams, James. *Toward the Blue Peninsula.* 32p. pap. $3.50 (0-935331-17-4). Bristol, RI: Ampersand Press, Fall 1995.

Williams, Jeanie C., and Victor di Suvero, eds. Translated by Consuelo Luz. *i saludos! Poemas de Neuvo México.* 287p. pap. $15.00 (0-938631-33-0). Tesuque, NM: Pennywhistle Press, Fall 1995. Bilingual edition. Finally! This collection transcends illusory boundaries of language and culture through powerful images that sing the secret wonders of this unique land and its people. —Richard Harris

Williams, Lydia Frances. *Let's Go Git a Pint an' Be's Somebody: A Poetic Journey From Slavery to Forgiveness.* 88p. pap. $12.95 (0-9648045-0-6). Denver, CO: LFW Enterprises, Fall 1996. Williams voices the anger, fear, and powerlessness that led to the sometimes violent struggle for integration and points the way to the healing of forgiveness, hope and love. —LFW Enterprises

Williams, Miller. *Points of Departure.* 88p. $18.95 (0-252-02142-8); pap. $12.95 (0-252-06451-8). Champaign, IL: University of Illinois Press, Fall 1995. Mostly narrative and dramatic, these indelible poems are populated by individuals who go about their lives in fear of pain and loneliness, in hope of something like love. —University of Illinois Press

Williams, Nancy Webb. *The Soul Side: Big Mama Remembers.* 60p. pap. $10.00 (0-9635690-9-0). Brooklyn Center, MN: TA Publications, Fall 1996. [The poetry of Nancy Webb Williams] is funny, clear, and hardhitting as white lightning. —A.D. Hopkins, *Nevadan.* On a more humorous but stinging note, Nancy Webb Williams offers "wry commentary about white racist panic." —Prairie Miller, *Village Voice*

Williams, William Carlos. *Asphodel, That Greeny Flower & Other Love Poems.* 64p. pap. $5.00 (0-8112-1283-1). New York, NY: New Directions, Fall 1994. "Asphodel, That Greeny Flower," celebrating Williams' love for his wife Floss, was published in 1955, when he was 72 years old. It forms the heart of this new selection of his love poems. —New Directions

Williams, William Carlos. Edited by Christopher MacGowan. *Paterson*. 336p. $38.00 (0-8112-1225-4); pap. $11.95 (0-8112-1298-X). New York, NY: New Directions, Spring 1996. *Paterson* is Whitman's America, grown pathetic and tragic, brutalized by inequality, disorganized by industrial chaos, and faced with annihilation. No poet has written of it with such a combination of brilliance, sympathy, and experience, with such alertness and energy. —Robert Lowell

Williamson, Alan. *Love and the Soul*. 80p. $25.00 (0-226-89932-2); pap. $10.95 (0-226-89933-0). Chicago, IL: University of Chicago Press, Fall 1995. In highly wrought elegiac sequences and breathless meditations, Alan Williamson's beautiful *Love and the Soul* explores the vicissitudes of desire with eloquence and subtlety. Few contemporary poets have dissected either *psyche* or *eros* so truthfully, so incisively—and so poignantly. —Sandra Gilbert

Williamson, Greg. *The Silent Partner*. 86p. pap. $11.95 (1-885266-11-1). Brownsville, OR: Story Line Press, Fall 1995. Winner of the 1995 Nicholas Roerich Poetry Prize. Greg Williamson's excellent first book is the work of a meditative mind and a sharp eye devoted to concrete reality. He is concerned with such matters as the desire to shape the world, the risk of fraud and imposition in all shaping, and the fugitive nature of all orderings. This debut publication is a real event. —Richard Wilbur

Willis, Elizabeth. *The Human Abstract*. 96p. pap. $12.95 (0-14-024935-4). New York, NY: Penguin Books, Fall 1995. Winner of the 1994 National Poetry Series. In her first full length collection Elizabeth Willis recovers the originating lyric impulse and brings it forward into a haunting contemporary song. This is poetry of amazing intelligence and grace. —Ann Lauterbach

Willis, Helen. *Looking Glass Falls and Other Poems*. 46p. pap. $8.50 (1-55618-158-2). Lawrenceville, VA: Brunswick Publishing, Fall 1996.

Willis, Irene. *They Tell Me You Danced*. 88p. $19.95 (0-81310-1358-5); pap. $10.95 (0-81310-1371-2). Gainesville, FL: University Press of Florida, Fall 1995. This is a wonderful book, in which those griefs and grievances that can overwhelm a life take, intead, their places as part of the dance; its song weds wisdom and gaiety as only a mature and richly experienced life can. —Linda Mc-Carriston. Lilt, laughter, lunge. —Gwendolyn Brooks

Wilmarth, Richard. *The Henry Miller Acrostics*. 60p. pap. $5.95 (0-880743-06-X). Boulder, CO: Dead Metaphor Press, Fall 1996. An incredible little book. One can not only see the name of Henry Miller indelibly stamped on every poem in the collection, but also the connection between writer and subject, with glimpses into the writing life of both. —Craig Peter Standish. A valid, much needed, self-lived approach to the new reality. —Bern Porter

Wiloch, Thomas. *Decoded Factories of the Heart*. 52p. pap. $3.00 (0-57141-003-1). Port Charlotte, FL: Runaway Spoon Press, Spring 1995. A collection of surrealistic haiku with collages by the author. —Runaway Spoon Press

Wilson, Don D., and Stella Kostova, trans. *Daydreams and Nightmares: Bulgaria, Balkan Goddess*. 64p. pap. $9.00 (1-880286-33-5). Canton, CT: Singular Speech Press, Spring 1995. Georgi Borisov, Vasil Dragonov, Boris Hristov, Ivailo Kozuharov, Alexander Shurbanov, Pavlina Stamenova— these are six exemplars of the surprising diversity and the remarkable power of the contemporary Bulgarian poetry anthologized here. —Singular Speech Press

Wilson, Keith. *The Way of the Dove*. 16p. pap. $3.00. Las Cruces, NM: Whole Notes Press, Spring 1995. *The Way of the Dove* is the culmination of Keith Wilson's *Priesthood Quartette*, in which he explores the art and the discipline of writing poetry. —Whole Notes Press

Wilsun, Don. *Frog Legs/Les Cuisses de Crapeaux*. 16p. pap. $2.00 (1-878888-25-0). Winston, OR: nine muses books, Fall 1996. The frog world, the cajun voice. —nine muses books

Winch, Terence. *The Great Indoors*. 110p. pap. $11.95 (0-934257-89-2). Brownsville, OR: Story Line Press, Fall 1995. Winner of the 1996 Columbia Poetry Prize. Sexy, goofy, lyrical, and astute. —Ed Friedman. Whew! There is something about Winch's poetry that leaves you breathless. Perhaps it's the grand, imagistic leaps: 'quiet as brides / skirting along on sheets of ice.' Brides? Ice? Following his poems in their majestic, airy ballet is thrilling because he's working at the edge of sense, tossing off similies and metaphors in an apparent recklessness that nevertheless seems perfectly controlled. —*Booklist*

Wing, Linda. *Lover's Leap*. 28p. pap. $3.95 (0-9641986-6-5). Duluth, MN: Poetry Harbor, Spring 1995.

Winters, Mary. *A Pocket History of the World*. 54p. pap. $9.95 (1-879205-66-1). Troy, ME: Nightshade Press, Spring 1996. Wry and sophisticated poems about twentieth century urban life. —Nightshade Press

Winters, Mary. *Staple It Down*. 24p. pap. $4.00. Kew Gardens, NY: New Spirit Press, Fall 1995. Winner of the 1995 New Spirit Press Quarterly Chapbook Contest. A collection of insightful and amusing poems about the author's experiences as a poverty lawyer. —New Spirit Press

Winters, Nancy. *Talking to Birds*. 26p. Edgewood, KY: Robert L. Barth (R.L.B.), Spring 1995.

Winters, Paul Victor. *Muscle & Bone* 32p. pap. $8.00 (0-9624178-5-8) Tarrytown, NY: Slapering Hol Press, Fall 1995. *Muscle & Bone* is a mesmerizing first collection of poems spoken in a voice at once alert and dreamy, nervy and vulnerable, tentative and flighty. On the page, the poems are lean and plainly spoken, but they are alive with surprises and bright maneuvers. The result is a fine combination of deftness of craft and ease of expression. —Billy Collins

Woessner, Warren. *Clear to Chukchi: Poems From Alaska*. 24p. pap. $3.95 (0-9641986-8-1). Duluth, MN: Poetry Harbor, Fall 1995. Here is the precise economy of true vision, rendering its simple, sometimes terrifying and complicated beauty. —Jonis Agee

Wojtyla, Karol (Pope John Paul II). Translated by Jerzy Peterkiewicz. *The Place Within: The Poetry of Pope John Paul II.* pap. $10.00. New York, NY: Random House, reissued Fall 1994. Originally published by Random House in 1982, this is a complete collection of the poems written by Wojtyla between the years 1939 and 1978, the only English version approved by the Vatican. Written throughout Wojtyla's adult life, while he was a worker, a student, a priest, and a bishop, his verse reflects the concerns of a man with a spiritual mission. —Random House

Wolf, Michele. *The Keeper of Light.* 24p. pap. $7.00. Philadelphia, PA: Painted Bride Quarterly, Fall 1995. Long, easy lines and flashes of sharp imagery offer up universal situations, a clear voice and persona. —*Bostonia*

Wolfe, Elinor J. *Green Leaves, Tender Leaves.* 126p. $15.95 (0-944957-76-5). New York, NY: Rivercross Publishing, Fall 1994.

Woodring, Carl, and James Shapiro, eds. *The Columbia Anthology of British Poetry.* 891p.

$29.95 (0-231-10180-5). Irvington, NY: Columbia University Press, Fall 1995. Superb—the ideal introduction to British poetry. —Mark Strand. Among countless anthologies of poetry, one always looks for a book in which both scholarship and taste contribute at the highest levels. For anyone who writes or reads poetry, or has the sensibility to be drawn to it, this is the book. —James Dickey

Woody, Elizabeth. *Luminaries of the Humble.* 129p. $36.00 (0-8165-1488-7); pap. $15.95 (0-8165-1465-8). Tucson, AZ: University of Arizona Press, Fall 1994. Native American voices are among the strongest in contemporary American poetry, and among them Elizabeth Woody speaks with extraordinary power. This book gathers itself slowly, like a mountain lion, and then leaps. Rich, strange, a fractured tongue remaking itself to speak true, this is poetry doing the work of poetry. —Ursula K. Le Guin

Wordsworth, William. Edited by Peter Washington. *Wordsworth.* 256p. $10.95 (0-679-44369-X). New York, NY: Alfred A. Knopf/

Everyman's Library Pocket Poets, Fall 1995.

Wright, C. D. *The Lost Roads Project: A Walk-in Book of Arkansas.* 96p. pap. $10.00 (1-55728-362-1). Fayetteville, AR: University of Arkansas Press, Spring 1995. With photographer Deborah Luster, poet C.D. Wright documents the most significant places and authors in Arkansas's literary history. Replete with photographs, biographies, excerpts from novels and stories, poetry collections, and memoirs. —University of Arkansas Press

Wright, C. D. *Tremble.* 60p. $20.00 (0-88001-458-X); pap. (0-88001-512-8). Hopewell, NJ: The Ecco Press, Spring 1996. The dramatic and emotional vitality of C.D. Wright's language, the authenticity and daring of her tone and speech, make her poems, one after the other, surprising, outrageous, exciting, moving, funny. —W.S. Merwin. C.D. Wright's language lies on the page half pulled out of the earth and rivers—still holding onto the truth of the elements. I love her voice and pitch and the long snaky arms of her language that is willing to hold every-

thing—human and angry and beautiful. —Michael Ondaatje

Wright, Charles. *Chickamauga.* 96p. $19.00 (0-374-12108-7). New York, NY: Farrar, Straus and Giroux, Spring 1995. A collection of intense moments used as lenses through which to see the world beyond them, *Chickamauga* is a virtuoso exploration of the power of concision in lyric poetry and of the flexible music of the long line Wright has made his own. —Farrar, Straus and Giroux

Wright, Franz. *Rorschach Test.* 83p. pap. $11.95 (0-88748-209-0). Pittsburgh, PA: Carnegie Mellon University Press, Spring 1995. Wright is a visionary collagist. His poems depend on juxtaposition and the aesthetic of surprise. The voice in the poems is both personal and anonymous. He works off the long lyric tradition. With their compactness and reliance on imagery, his poems go against today's trend. —Charles Simic. Franz Wright is a real poet, and I'm deeply moved by these poems. —James Tate

Wrigley, Robert. *In the Bank of Beautiful Sins.* 96p. pap.

$12.95 (0-14-058716-0). New York, NY: Penguin Books, Spring 1995. With this book of poems, Robert Wrigley takes his place as one of the country's finest poets. *In the Bank of Beautiful Sins* reminds us of our lives as we have forgotten them. Wrigley speaks to us as very few poets have done. —James Welch

Wyrebek, M. *Be Properly Scared.* 64p. pap. $11.95 (1-884800-08-4). Marshfield, MA: Four Way Books, Spring 1996. Beauty and terror fuse in the fierce gaze of language scrutinizing the body self at the edge of its own mortality. —Gregory Orr

Yagley, Robert, ed. *Poems From the Table: The Fruits of the Earth in Verse.* 112p. $2.99 (1-56619-761-9). Lanham, MD: Barnes & Noble Books, Fall 1995. *Poems From the Table* seeks to enhance the mixture of writing and cooking, of the recipe and the poem, and of the meal and the act of reading. —Barnes & Noble Books

Yau, John. Photographs by Bill Barrette. *Berlin Diptychon.* 96p. pap. $19.95 (0-943221-23-4). New York, NY: Timken Publishers, Fall 1995. Yau starts from appearances, which—just barely concrete—are transformed into the surreal, and which then glance off their origins again in order to lose themselves in a place of poetic surprise. —Joachim Sartorius. To see familiar cities with new eyes is to recover their poetry and their metaphysics. I can't think of a more successful collaboration between the eye and the ear and between two people and two art forms. —Charles Simic

Yerkes, C. Noël. *Lightships.* 112p. pap. $14.95 (1-887256-00-8). Newburyport, MA: Ray of Light Publishing, Fall 1995. *Lightships* is a rare spiritual journey. Grieving is the theme, love the goal and transfiguration the destiny in this meticulously observed and intelligent work. —*The Book Reader*

Youkeles, Dollie Carpenter. *A Flight Odyssey.* 80p. pap. $9.95 (1-880016-16-8). Painter, VA: Road Publishers, Spring 1995. Poems about the wonder of birds and all flying things, the poet's central image and guide. —Road Publishers

Youmans, Rich, and Frank Finale, eds. *Under A Gull's Wing: Poems and Photographs of the Jersey Shore.* 207p. $25.00 (0-945582-36-6). Harvey Cedars, NJ: Down the Shore Publishing, Spring 1996.

Young, David. *Night Thoughts and Henry Vaughan.* 72p. $19.95 (0-8142-0652-2); pap. $13.95 (0-8142-0653-0). Columbus, OH: Ohio State University Press, Fall 1994. 1994 Winner of the Ohio State University Press/The Journal Award in Poetry. Young's range is spectacular. The ease with which he moves through personal, historical, literary, and scientific idioms creates a powerful impression that each of these realms is part of a single whole. —*Harvard Review*

Young, Geoffrey. Drawings by James Siena. *Pockets of Wheat.* 48p. pap. $8.00 (0-935724-85-0). Great Barrington, MA: The Figures, Fall 1996.

Young, Kevin. *Most Way Home.* 100p. $20.00 (0-688-14032-7). New York, NY: William Morrow & Company, Spring 1995. National Poetry Series Selection. The language seamlessly shifts from highfalutin diction to backyard vernacular to urban slang and knowing whispers. Observant and empathetic, Young's voice speaks to us about events that are real in the sense that gossip, home remedies, family secrets, and a wild imagination are real. *Most Way Home* is a rock solid book. —John Yau. This poet's gift of storytelling and his understanding of the music inherent in the oral tradition re-creates for us an inner history which is compelling and authentic and American. —Lucille Clifton.

Z

Zarin, Cynthia. *Fire Lyric.* 72p. pap. $12.00 (0-679-74998-5). New York, NY: Alfred A. Knopf, Fall 1993. Zarin's marvelous gift for linguistic play, her gentle humour and her sheer delight in imaginative stanza form and rhyme punctuate this collection and provide a relief that serves to sharpen the reflective edge of the serious poetry. —Robert Hosmer, *The Southern Review*

Zawinski, Andrena. *Traveling in Reflected Light.* 139p. pap. $10.95 (0-917530-36-5). Youngstown, OH: Pig Iron Press, Fall 1995. This is an articulate, urbane, sophisticated voice, [which derives] power and integrity from the refusal to simplify. The poems seethe with savvy and a bristling ironic intelligence. —Lynn Emanuel

Zeidenstein, Sondra, ed. *The Crimson Edge: Older Women Writing.* 280p. pap. $16.95 (1-887344-01-2). Goshen, CT: Chicory Blue Press, Spring 1996. Not only are these women wonderful writers and poets, their accounts of coming to truth at this vital stage in life are mesmerizing. Indeed, the question arises whether women *under* sixty can ever tell the absolute truth about women's lives, about motherhood, work, passion, being female. A revolutionary book! —Carolyn G. Heibron. Editor Zeidenstein breaks new ground with her compilation of fiction, memoir and verse by seven women aged 63 to 87. The collection deserves to find [a] broad audience. —*Booklist*

Zeiger, Gene. *Leaving Egypt.* 79p. pap. $12.00 (1-877727-50-4).

Fredonia, NY: White Pine Press, Spring 1995. It's an ancient theme, leaving Egypt, and we are all called to find a way out of exile. Gene Zeiger's poems, so earthy and moist with family, love, and everyday things and so gently passionate about finding your own territory and so full of memory, offer a way home for us all. —Thomas Moore

Zepeda, Ofelia. *Ocean Power: Poems from the Desert.* 96p. $19.95 (0-8165-1517-4); pap. $9.95 (0-8165-1541-7). Tucson, AZ: University of Arizona Press, Fall 1995. Zepeda centers her poems on her experiences growing up in a Tohono O'odham family and on her perceptions as a Tohono O'Odham woman. The critical importance of weather and climate to native desert peoples is reflected with grace and power in this personal collection of poems, the first written creative work by an individual in Tohono O'odham and English, a landmark in Native American literature. —University of Arizona Press

Zimmer, Paul. *Crossing to Sunlight: Selected Poems.* 176p. $29.95 (0-8203-1818-3); pap.

$14.95 (0-8203-1829-9). Athens, GA: University of Georgia Press, Spring 1996. A collection of more than one hundred selected poems, *Crossing to Sunlight* offers both a retrospective of his 35 years of writing and a current look at the work of Paul Zimmer. —University of Georgia Press. I don't know anything in recent poetry that can match its shrewd humor and tonic high spirits. —Raymond Carver. Zimmer's poems are lucid and bright. —Maxine Kumin

Zimmerman, Julie, ed. *Untidy Candles: An Anthology of Contemporary Maine Poets.* 111p. pap. $10.00 (1-879418-17-7). Brunswick, ME: Biddle Publishing Company, Fall 1995. *Untidy Candles* was conceived and created in order to highlight Maine Writers and Publishers Alliance's encouragement of Maine poets and to provide an opportunity for a collection of worthy poems to find their way into print. —Biddle Publishing Company

Zimroth, Evan. *Giselle Considers Her Future.* 61p. pap. $11.95 (0-88748-230-9). Pittsburgh, PA: Carnegie Mellon University Press/Classic Contemporary Series, Fall 1996.

Zinnes, Harriet. *My, Haven't the Flowers Been?* 117p. pap. $12.00 (0-913660-26-4). Bozeman, MT: Magic Circle Press, Fall 1995. These are poems with rigor and purity, passion and playfulness, mystery and urgency. In an age of slack romanticism and empty classicism, she is a true high modernist. —Bruce Bawer. With an eye for the surreal, Harriet Zinnes creates pantoums, prose poems, and zesty free verse. Here are poems whimsical, lyrical, bold and sage. —Molly Peacock

Ziolkowski, Thad. *Our Son the Arson.* 72p. pap. $9.00 (0-9646535-1-6). Providence, RI: What Books, Spring 1996. Like Kurt Schwitters before him, Thad Ziolkowski has designed a house out of found objects and fragments, echoes of the language of the law, of patriotism, the news such as we receive it, idioms floating in the air. Through this tableau we pass, only to discover that going left takes us right, inside means outside, and in the attic we find what was hidden in the basement. Nothing is to be taken for granted. —Michael Palmer

26 Books
6735 SE 78th
Portland, OR 97206
Phone: 503-777-0406
Cont: Dan Raphael, Pub/Ed
• Averill, Diane, 15
• Bush, Casey, 43
• Drake, Barbara, 78
• LaMorticella, Barbara, 165
• Shively, Bill, 269
• Shugrue, Jim, 270
• Steinman, Lisa M., 285
• Whited, David Lloyd, 314
96 Tears Press
PO Box 3749
Los Angeles, CA 90078
Phone: 213-463-8975
Fax: same, *51
Cont: Mark Salerno, Publr
Dist by: B&T, Bpl, SPD
• Salerno, Mark, 257
A.P.D.
280 S Main Ave
Albany, NY 12208
Phone: 518-482-0262
Cont: Dan Wilcox, Publr
• Nattell, Tom; Charlie Rossiter, and Dan Wilcox, 213
• Rossiter, Charlie, 251
• Wilcox, Dan, 316

Abrams, Harry N.
100 Fifth Ave
New York, NY 10011
Phone: 212-206-7715
Fax: 212-645-8437
Cont: Tracy Smith, Mktg;
Elisa Urbanelli, Ed
• Blum, Joshua; Bob Holman, and Mark Pellington, eds., 28
• Sullivan, Charles, ed., 289
Ackerman Loft Gallery
215 Willoughby Ave #1409
Brooklyn, NY 11205
Phone: 718-399-5102
Cont: Ron Kolm, Ed
• Unbearables, 299
Adams Press
500 N. Michigan Ave
Chicago, IL 60611
To order: Joshua Meander, PO Box 232, Flushing, NY 11385
Cont: Joshua Meander
• Meander, Joshua, 197
Adastra Press
101 Strong St
Easthampton, MA 01027
Phone: 413-527-3324
Cont: Gary Metras, Publr
Dist by: SPD
• Casey, Michael, 48
• Catlin, Alan, 49
• Daniels, Jim, 66
• Davis, Cortney, 68
• Ehrhart, W.D., 82

Delhi, NY 13753
Phone: 607-746-7453
Fax: same
Cont: Tom Tolnay, Pub/Ed
• Glass, Jesse, 106
• Nelson, Stanley, 214
• Stevens, Elisabeth, 286

BkMk Press of the University of Missouri-Kansas City
University House
5100 Rockhill Rd
Kansas City, MO 64110-2499
Phone: 816-235-2558
Fax: 816-235-2611
Cont: Michelle Boisseau, Ed;
   Kelly Freeman, Man Ed
Dist by: B&T
• Bauer, Bill, 20
• Guenther, Charles, 115
• Hall, Irving C., 120
• Wagner, Maryfrances, 305

Black Belt Press
1123 S Hull St
PO Box 551
Montgomery, AL 36104
Phone: 334-265-6753
Fax: 334-265-8880
Cont: Wiley White; Randall
   Williams
• Thompson, Jeanie, 295

Black Buzzard Press / Visions-International
1110 Seaton Ln
Falls Church, VA 22046
Phone: 703-241-8626
Cont: Bradley R. Strahan,
   Publr; Shirley G. Sullivan,
   Assoc Ed
• Mott, Michael, 209
• Napoli, Donna Jo; Bradley
   R. Strahan, and Emily Nor-

wood Rando, eds., 212
• Strahan, Bradley R., ed.,
   287

Black Classic Press
PO Box 13414
Baltimore, MD 21203
Phone: 410-358-0980
Fax: 410-358-0987
To order: 800-476-8870
Cont: Apryl Motley, Ed Asst
Dist by: Red Sea Distribution
• Mataka, Laini, 188
• Miller, E. Ethelbert, 203

Black Sparrow Press
24 Tenth St
Santa Rosa, CA 95401
Phone: 707-579-4011
Fax: 707-579-0567
Cont: Michele Filshie, Asst to
   the Publr
Distributed by: B&T, Koen,
   Ingram
• Bukowski, Charles, 41
• Clark, Tom, 53
• Kelly, Robert, 153
• Malanga, Gerard, 183
• Meltzer, David, 199
• Myles, Eileen, 211
• Sanders, Edward, 259
• Wakoski, Diane, 306

Black Star Press
PO Box 6165
Lincoln, NE 68506-0265
• Gilbert, Virginia, 103

Black Thistle Press
491 Broadway
New York, NY 10012
Phone: 212-219-1898
Fax: 212-477-2714
Cont: Rebecca Pitts
Dist by: SPD

Edwards, Melvin, with Jayne
Cortez, 81
Bordighera
Foreign Lang. & Lit.
Purdue University
1359 Stanley Coulter Hall
W Lafayette, IN 47907-1359
Phone: 317-494-3839
Fax: 317-496-1700
To order: PO Box 1374,
Lafayette, IN 47902-1374
Cont: Anthony Julian Tam-
burri, Pres
• Condini, Ned, 58
• Gioseffi, Daniela, 105
Bottom Dog Press
c/o Firelands College
Huron, OH 44839
Phone: 419-433-5560
Fax: 419-433-9696
Cont: Larry Smith, Dir
Dist by: B&T, Partners
• King, June, and Larry
Smith, eds., 156
Bradypress
5050 Pratt St
Omaha, NE 68104
Phone: 402-554-2773
Cont: Denis Brady, Proprietor
• Dante Alighieri, 66
Braziller, George
60 Madison Ave
New York, NY 10010
Phone: 212-889-0909
Fax: 212-689-5405
• Kane, Paul, ed., 150
• Nasrin, Taslima, 212
Breeze/Street Press
PO Box 772
Sound Beach, NY 11789-0772

Cont: Graham Everett, Publr
• Everett, Graham, 85
Bright Hill Press
PO Box 193
Treadwell, NY, 13846
Phone: 607-746-7306
Fax: 607-746-7274
email: wordthurs@aol.com
Cont: Bertha Rogers, Dir
• Blevins-Church, Adrian, 27
• Rogers, Bertha, ed., 248,
249
Bristol Banner Books
PO Box 1219
Bristol, IN 46507
Phone: 219-825-POEM
Fax: 219-825-7636
Cont: Melody Myers
• Frantz III, William F., 94
• Myers, M., ed., 211
Brito & Lair
200 W 70th St, Ste 10G
New York, NY 10023
Phone: 212-362-6277
Fax: same
Cont: Leila Brito, Publr
Dist by: SPD
• Jones, Sonya, 149
Broadside Press
1301 W Lafayette #102
Detroit, MI 48226
Phone: 313-963-8526
Fax: 313-934-1231
To order: PO Box 04257, De-
troit, MI 48204
Cont: Donald S. Vest, Vice-
Pres; Hilda F. Vest, Ed
• Allen, Ron, ed., 6
• Chavis, William Muse, 51
• Crews, Stella, ed., 63

Creighton University Press
2500 California Plaza
Omaha, NE 68178
Phone: 718-817-4782
Fax: 718-817-4785
To order: Fordham University
Bookmasters Distribution
Services, 1444 US Rte 42,
PO Box 2039, Masfield,
OH 44903; 800-247-6553
Dist by: B&T, Bookmasters,
Ingram
• Liddy, James, 172

Cross-Cultural Communications
239 Wynsum Ave
Merrick, NY 11566-4725
Phone: 516-868-5635
Fax: 516-379-1901
Cont: Stanley H. Barkan,
Publr/Exec Ed
Dist by: B&T
• Barkan, Stanley H., 18
• Barkan, Stanley H., and
Darrell Bourque, eds., 18
• Boss, Laura, 31
• Garcia, Carlos Ernesto, 99
• Levchev, Vladimir, 169
• Matherne, Beverly, 188
• Rav-Hon, Orna, 239
• Rilke, Rainer Maria, 246

Crown Publishers
201 E 50th St
New York, NY 10022
Phone: 212-572-6122
Fax: 212-572-6192
To order: 800-733-3000, 800-
659-2436 (fax)
Cont: Michael Denning, Ed;
John Clark, Asst Ed
• Ehrmann, Max, 82

• Foster, Thomas E., and
Elizabeth C. Guthrie, eds.,
93
• Hanson, Jeanne K., ed., 123
• Hempel, Amy, and Jim
Shepard, eds., 130
• Lassell, Michael, ed., 166
• Mayerson, Charlotte, 190
• Pearlberg, Gerry Gomez,
ed., 228
• Sirowitz, Hal, 273

Crown Publrs / Harmony Books
• Pickles, Sheila, ed., 232

Cryptic Press
One Riverdale Ave, Ste 452
Bronx, NY 10463
• Mannion, James, 184

Cummington Press
1803 S 58th St
Omaha, NE 68104
Phone: 402-554-2715
To order: Nebraska Book Arts
Center, University of Ne-
braska at Omaha, FA Rm
210A, Omaha, NE 68182-
0173; 402-554-2773
Cont: Harry Duncan, Publr;
Denise Brady, Nebraska
Book Arts Center Coordina-
tor
• Gibbs, Barbara, 102
• Lieberman, Laurence, 172

Curbstone Press
321 Jackson St
Willimantic, CT 06226
Phone: 860-423-5110
Fax: 860-423-9242
Cont: Alexander Taylor, Ed;
Donna Nicolino, Mktg Asst
Dist by: Consortium

- Alegria, Claribel, 4
- Connellan, Leo, 59
- Dalton, Roque, 65
- Herrera, Juan Felipe, 132
- Major, Devorah, 183
- Montejo, Victor, 206
- Savageau, Cheryl, 261
- Silex, Edgar Gabriel, 271

Cycle Press
715 Baker's Ln
Key West, FL 33040
Phone: 305-294-6979
Cont: Kirby Congdon; Ralph
  Simmons, Jr.
- Congdon, Kirby, 58, 59

Cypress House Press
155 Cypress St
Fort Bragg, CA 95437
Phone: 707-964-9520
- Adams, 1

Da Capo Press
233 Spring St
New York, NY 10013-1578
Phone: 212-620-8000
Fax: 212-463-0742
Cont: Gretchen Griffin, Publi-
  cist
- Levy, Julien, 170
- Melville, Herman, 199

Dalkey Archive Press
Campus Box 4241
Normal, IL 61790-4241
- Giscombe, C.S., 105

Daniel, John, and Company
PO Box 21922

Santa Barbara, CA 93121
Phone: 805-962-1780
- Haberman, Daniel, 116

Dark Regions Press
PO Box 6301, Concord, CA
  94524
- Boston, Bruce, 31

DawnSignPress
9080 Activity Rd, Ste A
San Diego, CA 92126-4421
Phone: 619-549-5330
Fax: 619-549-2200
Cont: Bernadette Rice, Mktg
- Valli, Clayton, 299

DDDD Publications
9715 Foster, Ste A
St. Louis, MO 63114
Phone: 314-427-3329
Fax: same
Cont: Della Koster, Owner
Dist by: B&T
- Frances, Dee, 94

Dead Metaphor Press
PO Box 2076
Boulder, CO 80306-2076
Phone: 303-939-0268
Cont: Richard Wilmarth,
  Publr; Norman Charles,
  Asst Ed
Dist by: SPD
- Bernstein, Tree, 24
- Wilmarth, Richard, 319

Design Systems Printing
280 S River St
Wilkes-Barre, PA, 18702
To order: c/o J.K. Nelson, 622
  Newberry Estate, Dallas,
  PA 18612, 717-675-8107
Cont: June Nelson
- Nelson, June, 214

Fax: 941-954-5083
Cont: Patrick J. Powers, Consulting Dir; John Patrick, Ed
Dist by: B&T, Inland, Koen
- Anderson, Ken, 10
- Childers, Joanne, 52
- Grenier, Arpine Konyalian, 113

Flume Press
773 Sierra View Way
Chico, CA 95926
Phone: 916-342-1583
Dist by: B&T
- Allred, Joanne, 7
- Matthews, Mary, 189
- Vertreace, Martha, 302

Fly by Night Press
PO Box 20693
Tompkins Sq. Station
New York, NY 10009
Phone: 212-674-8262
- Anderson, 9

Fly by Night Press and A Gathering of the Tribes, copublishers
- Black, Star, 26

Forward Movement Publications
412 Sycamore St
Cincinnati, OH 45202
Phone: 800-543-1813
Fax: 513-421-0315
Cont: Sally B. Sedgwick, Assoc Dir
- Fandel, John, 86

Four Walls Eight Windows
39 W 14th St #503
New York, NY 10011
- Ginsberg, Allen, 104
- Kunstler, William M., 163

Four Way Books
PO Box 607
Marshfield, MA 02050
Phone: 617-837-4887
Fax: same
Cont: Dzvinia Orlowsky, Founding Ed; Martha Rhodes, Ed
Dist by: B&T, SPD
- Brox, Jane; Dzvinia Orlowsky, and Martha Rhodes, eds., 39
- Domina, Lynn, 75
- Friebert, Stuart, 95
- Gorham, Sarah, 110
- Kircher, Pamela, 157
- Knauth, Stephen, 158
- Nurkse, D., 218
- Sasanov, Catherine, 261
- Stahlecker, Beth, 283
- Standing, Sue, 283
- Wyrebek, M., 323

Fox, David
14 Dey Rd
Plainsboro, NJ 08336
Phone: 609-799-0719
- Fox, David, 94

Galiens Press
173 Slater Blvd
Staten Island, NY 10305
- Saint, Assotto, 256

Garden Street Press
PO Box 1231
Truro, MA 02666
Phone: 508-349-1991

Cont: Naomi Feigelson Chase, Pub/Ed
Dist by: B&T
- Chase, Naomi Feigelson, 51
- Duhamel, Denise, 79
- Goodman, Miriam, 109

Generator Press
3203 W 14th St #13
Cleveland, OH 44109
Phone: 216-241-6935
Cont: John Byrum, Pub/Ed
Dist: SPD
- Barone, Dennis, 19
- Deisler, Guillermo, 70
- Falleder, Arnold, 86
- Selby, Spencer, 266

Gilmore • Loftus
6087 Porter Ave
E Lansing, MI 48823
Phone: 517-333-0906
Cont: Richard Gilmore Loftus
- Loftus, Richard Gilmore, 174

GLB Publishers
1028 Howard St #503
San Francisco, CA 94103
Phone: 415-621-8307
Fax: 415-621-8037
To order: PO Box 78212, San Francisco, CA 94107
Cont: W.L. Warner, Pub/Ed; John Hanley, Ed
- Smith, Winthrop, 277

Gnosis Press
New York, NY
c/o The Groundwater Press
67 Edgewood Rd, 2nd Fl
Port Washington, NY 11050
Phone: 516-767-8503
Fax: 212-346-1754

Cont: Anton Rouner, Ed; Eugene Richie, Ed
Dist by: SPD
- McKane, Richard, 195
- Wasserman, Rosanne, 309

Godine, David R., Publisher
Box 9103
Lincoln, MA 01773
Phone: 617-259-0700
Fax: 617-259-9198
Cont: Lissa Warren, Mktg Dir
- Padgett, Ron, 224
- Tillinghast, Richard, 295

Goldschmidt, Allan David
33-06 34th Ave #2A
Long Island City, NY 11106
Phone: 718-786-1585
- Goldschmidt, Allan David, 108

Gramercy Books
c/o Random House Value Publishing
40 Engelhard Ave
Avenel, NJ 07001
Phone: 908-827-2700
Fax: 908-827-2641
To order: 400 Hahn Rd, Westminster, MD 21157; 800-733-3000; 800-659-2436 (fax)
Cont: Susan George, Mktg Asst
- Blake, William, 26
- Browning, Elizabeth Barrett, 38
- Bryant, William Cullen, ed., 40
- Byron (George Gordon, Lord Byron), 44
- Gesner, George, ed., 101
- Kipling, Rudyard, 157

- Rossetti, Christina, 251
- Shelley, Percy Bysshe, 268

Graywolf Press
2402 University Ave, Ste 203
St. Paul, MN 55114
Phone: 612-641-0077
Fax: 612-641-0036
Cont: Jeff Shotts, Ed; Christy
 DeVillier, Mktg Asst
Dist by: Consortium
- Grennan, Eamon, 114
- Haines, John, 119
- Kenyon, Jane, 155
- Melnyczuk, Askold, ed.,
 199
- Phillips, Carl, 231
- Seshadri, Vijay, 267

Great Elm Press
1206 County Route 60
Rexville, NY 14877
Phone: 607-225-4592
- Franklin, Walt, ed. 94

Green Point Press
PO Box 131
Monhegan, ME 04852
Phone: 207-596-6732
To order: 83 Water St #12,
 Waterville, ME 04901;
 207-877-0353
Cont: Glenn McKee, Publr
- McKee, Glenn, 195

Greenfield Review Press
PO Box 308
Greenfield Center, NY 12833
Phone: 518-584-1728
Fax: 518-583-9741
Cont: Joseph Bruchac, Pub/Ed
Dist by: Bpl, Talman
- Blaeser, Kim, 26
- Midge, Tiffany, 202

Grindstone Press
107 Moore St
Princeton, NJ 08540
Phone: 609-924-2445
Cont: Aminta Marks
- Afif, Kaissar, 3

Groundwater Press
67 Edgewood Rd, 2nd Fl
Port Washington, NY 11050
Phone: 516-767-8503
Fax: 212-346-1754, Attn:
 Eugene Richie
Cont: Rosanne Wasserman,
 Ed; Eugene Richie, Ed
Dist by: SPD
- Black, Star, 25
- Manrique, Jaime, 184

Grove Press
841 Broadway
New York, NY 10003-4793
Phone: 212-614-7850
Fax: 212-614-7886
- Ryan, Kay, 256

Gut Punch Press
PO Box 105
Cabin John, MD 20818
Cont: Derrick Hsu, Publr
- Peabody, Richard, 227

Hammond, Raymond P.
236 E 5th St
Brooklyn, NY 11218
- Hammond, Raymond P.,
 123

Hanging Loose Press
231 Wyckoff St

Brooklyn, NY 11217
Phone: 212-206-8465
Fax: 212-243-7499
Cont: Robert Hershon,
  Pub/Ed
Dist by: Bpl, Koen, SPD
• Agüeros, Jack, 4
• Alexie, Sherman, 5
• Friedman, Ed, 95
• Ha Jin, 116
• Hartman, Yukihide Mae-
  shima, 126
• Lourie, Dick; Mark Pawlak,
  Robert Hershon, and Ron
  Schreiber, eds., 177
• Maurer-Alvarez, Pansy, 189
• McDaniel, Wilma Eliza-
  beth, 193
• Peterson, Robert, 230
Harcourt Brace / Harvest
Books
15 E 26th St
New York, NY 10010
Phone: 212-592-1000
525 B St, Ste 1900, San Di-
  ego, CA 92101-4495
Phone: 619-231-6616
Fax: 619-699-6320
To order: Trade Order Fulfill-
  ment, 6277 Sea Harbor Dr,
  Orlando, FL 32887-4300;
  800-543-1918; 800-235-
  0256 (fax)
Cont: Lynne Walker, Mktg
  Assoc; Beverly Fisher, Pub-
  licist
• Grass, Gunter, 112
• Milosz, Czeslaw, ed., 204
• Sandburg, Carl, 259
• Shinder, Jason, ed., 269
• Simic, Charles, 271

• Szymborska, Wislawa, 293
Hard Press
PO Box 184
West Stockbridge, MA 01266
Phone: 413-232-4690
Fax: 413-232-4675
Cont: Jon Gams, Ed; Chad
  Odefey, Asst Ed
Dist by: Consortium
• Brodey, Jim, 36
• Smukler, Linda, 278
Hard Press and The Figures,
copublishers
• McCain, Gillian, 191
Harlem River Press
see Writers and Readers Pub-
  lishing / Harlem River
  Press
Harlequinade Press
12 Flagstaff Hill Terrace
Canton, MA 02021
Phone: 617-828-3978
Cont: Edward Locke
• Locke, Edward, 173, 174
HarperCollins Publishers
10 E 53rd St
New York, NY 10022
Phone: 212-207-7000
To order: Mail Order Dept,
  PO Box 599, Dunmore, PA
  18512-0588; 800-331-
  3761; 800-822-4090 (fax)
• Dillard, Annie, 72
• Ginsberg, Allen, 104
• Gordon, Ruth, ed., 110
• Halpern, Dan, ed., 121
• Hass, Robert, and Stephen
  Mitchell, eds., 127
• Johnson, Denis, 147
HarperCollins / HarperPeren-
nial

Robin Heyeck, Ed
- Mayes, Frances, 190

Hiram Poetry Review
PO Box 162
Hiram, OH 44234-0162
- Cook, Geoffrey, 59

Hogan, Wayne
PO Box 842
Cookeville, TN 38503
- Hogan, Wayne, 135
- Hogan, Wayne, and Edmund Conti, 135

Hohm Press
PO Box 2501
Prescott, AZ 86302
Phone: 520-778-9189
Fax: 520-717-1779
Cont: Regina Sara Ryan, Man Ed; Rabia Tredeau, Publicist
Dist by: SCB (800-729-6423)
- Red Hawk, 240
- Rumi, Jelaluddin, 255

Holocene Publishing
Box 101
Wofford College
Spartanburg, SC 29303
Phone: 864-597-4518
Fax: 864-597-4549
Cont: John Lane
- Sandy, Stephen, 259

Holt, Henry, and Company
115 W 18th St
New York, NY 10011
Phone: 212-886-9200
Fax: 212-633-0748
To order: VHPS, attn: Order Entry, 175 Fifth Ave, New York, NY 10010; 800-488-5233; 800-258-2768 (fax)
Cont: Judith Sisko, Dir of

Special Sales; Sydra Mallery, Mktg Asst
- Eady, Cornelius, 80
- Holman, Bob, 137

Holt, Henry, and Company Books for Young Readers
- Duffy, Carol Ann, ed., 78

Holy Cow! Press
PO Box 3170
Mount Royal Station
Duluth, MN 55803
Phone: 218-724-1653
Cont: Jim Pulman, Pub/Ed
- Jenkins, Louis, 146
- Smith, Thomas R., 277

Hot Pepper Press
PO Box 39
Somerset, CA 95684
Phone: 916-621-1833
To order: CB Follett, 116 Cloud View Rd, Sausalito, CA 94965; 415-331-2503
Cont: Taylor Graham, Publr
- Follett, C.B., 92

Houghton Mifflin Company
215 Park Ave South
New York, NY 10003
Phone: 212-420-5800
Fax: 212-598-5757
222 Berkeley St, Boston, MA 02116
Phone: 617-351-5000
Fax: 617-351-1202
To order: Order Processing, 181 Ballardvale St, Wilmington, MA 01887; 800-225-3362; 508-661-1323 (fax)
Cont: Peter Davison, Ed; Mindy Keskinen, Asst to the Ed
- Atwood, Margaret, 14

- Gregerson, Linda, 113
- Hall, Donald, 120
- Hudgins, Andrew, 141
- Jones, Rodney, 149
- Kinnell, Galway, 156
- Lux, Thomas, 179
- Matthews, William, 189

Hummingbird Press
PO Box 7301
Winston-Salem, NC 27109-7301
Phone: 910-759-5084
Fax: 910-759-5668
- Johnson, Dave, 147

Hyperion
114 Fifth Ave
New York, NY 10011
Phone: 212-633-4400
Fax: 212-633-5935
To order: 800-759-0190
- Neruda, Pablo, 215

I

Ietje Kooi Press
4336 Copper Cliff Ln
Modesto, CA 95355
Phone: 209-524-3066
To order: 209-521-4537; 209-572-1276 (fax)
Dist by: Bpl, Ingram
- Chadwick, Irene, 50

Igneus Press
310 N Amherst Rd
Bedford, NH 03110
Phone: 603-472-3466
Cont: Peter Kidd, Pub/Ed
- Dorbin, Sanford, 76

- Ferrini, Vincent, 89
- Kemmett, William, 153
- Kidd, Peter, 156
- Martin, Richard, 186

Incommunicado Press
PO Box 99090
San Diego, CA 92169
Phone: 619-234-9400
Fax: 619-234-9479
Cont: Sandra Zane
Dist by: Consortium
- Alvin, Dave, 8
- Belile, Elisabeth A., 22
- Berry, Iris, 24
- Borrus, Beth, 31
- Gehman, Pleasant, 100
- Heinowitz, R. Cole, 130

Insight to Riot Press
2300 Pine St #9
Philadelphia, PA 19103
Phone: 215-546-7499
Cont: James M. Cory, Man Ed
- Broughton, James, 37

Interlink Publishing
46 Crosby St
Northampton, MA 01060
Phone: 413-582-7054
Fax: 413-582-7057
To order: 800-238-LINK
Cont: Michel Moushabeck, Pub/Ed
- Qabbani, Nizar, 236

International Forum
PO Box 7000-350
Palos Verdes Peninsula, CA 90274
Phone: 310-377-2339
Fax: 310-544-6015
Cont: Jacqueline Miller Bachar, Pres/Ed
Dist by: Bpl, L-S

- Bachar, Jacqueline Miller, ed., 15

J

Jade Mountain Press
16651 Marchmont Dr
Los Gatos, CA 95032
Phone: 408-867-6502
- Rotella, Alexis K., and Florence Miller, 251

Joe Miller's Company
3080 Olcott St, Ste 210A
Santa Clara, CA 95054
Phone: 408-988-2924
Fax: 408-727-9941
- Callahan, Laura, 45

Johns Hopkins University Press
2715 N Charles St
Baltimore, MD 21218
Phone: 410-516-6900
Fax: 410-516-6968
To order: Hampden Station, Baltimore, MD 21211; 800-537-5487; 410-516-6998 (fax)
Cont: Willis Regier, John Irwin, Eds; Margaret Galambos, Karen Willmes, Mktg
- Burt, John, 53
- Carper, Thomas, 47
- Hearne, Vicki, 129
- Jacobsen, Josephine, 144

Journey Editions
153 Milk St, 5th Fl
Boston, MA 02109
Phone: 617-951-4080

Fax: 617-951-4045
To order: Airport Industrial Park, RR1 Box 231-5, N Clarendon, VT 05759; 800-526-2778; 800-FAX-TUTL (fax)
Cont: Laurel S. Peppino, Publicist; Katheryn Sky-Peck, Ed
- James, Anthony, 145

Juggernaut Press
PO Box 3824
Chicago, IL 60654-0824
Phone: 312-368-7134
Fax: 312-236-7516
Cont: Daniel X. O'Neil, Dir
Dist by: SPD
- O'Neil, Daniel X., 219

Jukebox Press
c/o Meridien PressWorks
PO Box 640024
San Fransisco, CA 94164
Phone: 415-928-8904
Cont: Jeanne Powell, Assoc Ed
- Powell, Jeanne, 234

Just Buffalo Literary Center
2495 Main St, Ste 436
Buffalo, NY 14214
Phone: 716-832-5400
Fax: 716-832-5710
Cont: Debora Ott, Dir; Lisa Fuller, Mktg Dir
- Cohen, Betty, ed., 56

Cont: Alexander Kim, Mktg
Dir
- Cypser, Cora E., 64

Kings Estate Press
870 Kings Estate Rd
St. Augustine, FL 32086-5033
Phone: 800-249-7485
Cont: Ruth Moon Kempher,
Pub/Ed
Dist by: Spring Church
- Elsberg, John, 83
- Hathaway, Michael, 128
- Hogan, Wayne, 135
- Holt, Rochelle Lynn, 137
- Jenks, Dorothy, 146
- Sobel, Carolyn, 279

Knopf, Alfred A.
201 E 50th St. 22-2
New York, NY 10022
Phone: 212-572-2593
Fax: 212-572-2662
To order: Random House Dis-
tribution Center, Order
Dept, 400 Hahn Road,
Westminster, MD 21157;
800-733-3000; 800-659-
2436 (fax)
Cont: Harry Ford, Ed; Nelly
Bly, Asst to the Ed
Dist by: Random House
- Bradley, George, 33
- Brock-Broido, Lucie, 35
- Carson, Anne, 47
- Clampitt, Amy, 53
- Cole, Henri, 56
- Davison, Peter, 69
- Digges, Deborah, 72
- Gilbert, Jack, 103
- Halpern, Daniel, 121
- Haxton, Brooks, 128
- Hecht, Anthony, 129

- Hirsch, Edward, 134
- Hollander, John, 136
- Justice, Donald, 150
- Kenney, Richard, 154
- Kinzie, Mary, 157
- Koch, Kenneth, 160
- Levine, Philip, 170
- Merrill, James, 200
- Merwin, W.S., 201
- Olds, Sharon, 221
- Rice, Stan, 244
- Salter, Mary Jo, 257
- Sheck, Laurie, 268
- Swander, Mary, 29
- Van Duyn, Mona, 300
- Willard, Nancy, 316
- Zarin, Cynthia, 324

Knopf / Everyman's Library
- Herbert, George, 131

**Knopf / Everyman's Library
Pocket Poets**
- Brontë, Emily, 37
- Donne, John, 75
- Hardy, Thomas, 124
- Hollander, John, ed., 136
- Hopkins, Gerard Manley, 139
- Milton, John, 205
- Poe, Edgar Allen, 232
- Rilke, Rainer Maria, 246
- Washington, Peter, ed., 309
- Wordsworth, William, 321

Knott, Bill
WLP Dept. Emerson College
100 Beacon St
Boston, MA 02116
- Knott, Bill, 159

Kore Press
101 W 6th St #4
Tucson, AZ 85701
Phone: 520-882-7542

Fax: 520-621-5566
Cont: Karen Falkenstrom,
Board of Dirs
• Broumas, Olga, and T Beg-
ley, 37
• Deming, Alison, 70
KTAV Publishing House
900 Jefferson St
Hoboken, NJ 07030
• Greenberg, Blu, 112
Kumarian Press
14 Oakwood Ave
West Hartford, CT 06119
Phone: 860-233-5895
Fax: 860-233-6072
To order: 800-289-2664
Cont: Krishna Sondhi, Publr
• Mayo-Smith, Ian, 190

L

L I A Publishing
PO Box 5373
New York, NY 10185-5373
Phone: 718-846-4778
Cont: Bernard Holland
• Holland, Bernard, 136
La Alameda Press
9636 Guadalupe Trail NW
Albuquerque, NM 87114
Phone: 505-897-0285
Fax: 505-897-0751
To order: UNM Press, 1720
Lomas Blvd NE, Albuquer-
que, NM 87131; 800-249-
7737
Cont: J. B. Bryan, Cirrelda
Snider-Bryan, Publrs

• Harter, Penny, 126
• Logghe, Joan, 174
• Merrill, C.S., 200
LALA Press
1007 Abbot Kinney B1 #4
Venice, CA 90291
Phone: 310-452-1692
email: buddhafun@aol.com
Cont: Kathy Yoo, Ed
• Han, Stephanie, 123
**Land-Ship Bookstore Publish-
ers**
PO Box 112
Nogal, NM, 88341
Phone: 505-354-2610
Fax: same
Cont: Wayne Steele, Ed
• Bailey, R.W., 16
**Lantow, David, and Jordan
Trachtenberg**
111 E 14th St, Ste 169
New York, NY 10003
Phone: 212-456-3134
• Trachtenberg, Jordan N.,
ed., 296
Larkspur Press
340 Sawdridge Creek West
Monterey, KY 40359
Phone: 502-484-5390
• Berry, Wendell, 25
Laterthanever Press
3751 First Ave
San Diego, CA 92103
Phone: 619-574-1481
Fax: same
Cont: Fred Moramarco,
Pub/Ed
• Harding, Deborah, 123
**Latin American Literary Re-
view Press**
121 Edgewood Ave

Pittsburgh, PA 15218
Phone: 412-371-9023
Fax: 412-371-9025
Dist by: B&T
• Neruda, Pablo, 214
Ledge Press
64-65 Cooper Ave
Glendale, NY 11385
Cont: Timothy Monaghan,
Publsiher
• Miller, Philip, 204
Left Hand Books
Station Hill Rd
Barrytown, NY 12507
Phone: 914-758-6478
Fax: 914-758-4416
Cont: Bryan McHugh, Publr
Dist by: SPD
• Keith, Bill, 153
• Knowles, Alison, 160
• Nash, Susan Smith, 212
• Polkinhorn, Harry, 233
LFW Enterprises
PO Box 370234
Denver, CO 80237-0234
Phone: 303-750-1040
Fax: 303-727-4889
Cont: Lydia Frances Williams,
Publr
• Williams, Lydia Frances,
317
Libraries Publishing Company
Box 3283
San Diego, CA 92163-1283
• Tibbon, George, 295
Library of America
14 E 60th St
New York, NY 10022
Phone: 212-308-3360
Fax: 212-750-8352
Cont: Karen Iker, Mktg Assoc

• Frost, Robert, 97
Limberlost Press
HC33, PO Box 1113
Boise, ID 83706
Phone: 208-344-2120
Fax: 208-345-5347
Cont: Rick and Rosemary
Ardinger, Publrs
• Embree, Bruce, 84
• Haines, John, 119
• Minskoff, Alan, 205
Listening Chamber
1605 Berkeley Way
Berkeley, CA 94703
• McNaughton, Duncan, 196
Liveright Publishing
500 Fifth Ave
New York, NY, 10110
Phone: 212-354-5500
Fax: 212-869-0856
Dist by: Norton
• Cummings, E.E., 63
• Hayden, Robert, 128
Livingston Press
(formerly Livingston Univer-
sity Press)
Station 22
University of W Alabama
Livingston, AL 35470
Phone: 205-652-3717
Fax: same
Cont: Joe Taylor, Ed; Lee Hol-
land Moore, Asst to the Ed
• Smith, R. T., 277
• Walter, Eugene, 308
Logodaedalus Press
PO Box 14193
Harrisburg, PA 17104
• Frost, Celestine, 96
Loose Gravel Press
8 Shady Ln

Petaluma, CA 94952
Phone: 707-769-8931
Cont: Steve Tills, Pub/Ed
Dist by: SPD
• Hill, Crag, 133
Lorien House
PO Box 1112
Black Mountain, NC 28711-1112
Phone: 704-669-6211
Cont: David A. Wilson, Publr
• Anderson, Martha Shelton, 10
• Beck, Al, 21
Los Hombres Press
PO Box 632729
San Diego, CA 92163-2729
Phone: 619-688-1023
Fax: 619-688-1753
Cont: Marsh Cassady, Ed; Jim Kitchen, Publr
• Better, Cathy Drinkwater, 25
• Swist, Wally, 292
Lost Roads Publishers
351 Nayatt Rd
Barrington, RI 02806
Phone: 401-245-8069
Fax: same, transmit before message
To order: SPD
Cont: C. D. Wright, Forest Gander, Eds
• Brathwaite, Kamau, 34
• Foo, Josephine, 92
• Mayes, Frances, 190
Lothrop, Lee & Shepard
c/o William Morrow & Co
1350 Ave of the Americas
New York, NY 10019

Phone: 212-261-6793; 212-261-6792
Fax: 212-261-6785
To order: Wilmor Order Dept, 39 Plymouth St, Fairfield, NJ 07004; 800-843-9389; 201-227-6849 (fax)
Cont: Mike Kirscher, Mktg Asst; Susan Pearson, Ed
• Adoff, Arnold, 3
• Mingfong Ho, trans., 205
Louisiana State University Press
PO Box 25053
Baton Rouge, LA 70894-5053
Phone: 504-388-6666
Fax: 504-388-6461
To order: 800-861-3477; 800-305-4416 (fax)
Cont: L.E. Phillabaum, Ed; Barbara Outland, Mktg Assoc
• Adcock, Betty, 2
• Brosman, Catherine Savage, 37
• Chappell, Fred, 50
• Cooley, Nicole, 60
• Gentry, Jane, 100
• Hoffman, Daniel, 135
• Hummer, T. R., 142
• Pope, Deborah, 233
• Richman, Jan, 245
• Roeske, Paulette, 248
• Slavitt, David R., 275
• Smith, Dave, 275
• Smith, R. T., 277
• Stuart, Dabney, 288
• Watson, Robert, 310
Luna Bisonte Prods
137 Leland Ave
Columbus, OH 43214

N

Nash, Steven J., Publishing
PO Box 7606
York, PA, 17404
Phone: 717-792-4044
Fax: 717-792-9990
To order: 800-843-8545
Cont: Suzanne K. Williams,
   Sr. Vice Pres
Dist by: Ingram
• Kavanaugh, James, 152

Negative Capability Press
62 Ridgelawn Dr East
Mobile, AL 36608
• Page, Carolyn, 224
• Shipley, Vivian, 269

New Directions
80 Eighth Ave
New York, NY 10011
Phone: 212-255-0230
Fax: 212-255-0231
To order: c/o W.W. Norton,
   500 Fifth Ave, New York,
   NY 10110; 800-233-4830;
   212-869-0856 (fax)
Cont: Griselda Ohannessian,
   Ed; Laurie Callahan, Mktg
   Dir
Dist by: Norton
• Bei Dao, 22
• Bobrowski, Johannes, 28
• Brathwaite, Kamau, 34
• Bronk, William, 37
• Carson, Anne, 47
• Davenport, Guy, trans., 68
• Grossman, Allen, 114
• Howe, Susan, 140

• Laughlin, James, 167
• Levertov, Denise, 169
• Li Po, 171
• Neruda, Pablo, 214
• Palmer, Michael, 224
• Pound, Ezra, 234
• Rothenberg, Jerome, 251
• Scott, Peter Dale, 264
• Sisson, C. H., 273
• Sobin, Gustaf, 279
• Waldrop, Rosmarie, 307
• Williams, William Carlos,
   317, 318

New Earth Publications
1921 Ashby Ave
Berkeley, CA 94703
Phone: 510-549-0575
Fax: 510-549-1514
Dist by: Bpl
• Ross, Clifton, 251

New Native Press
PO Box 661
Cullowhee, NC 28723
Phone: 704-293-9237
Cont: Thomas Rain Crowe,
   Publr
Dist by: B&T, Bpl, Ingram,
   SPD
• Daughtry, Philip, 68
• Lane, John, 165
• McLachlan, Meschach, 196

New Poets Series
541 Piccadilly Rd
Baltimore, MD 21204
Phone: 410-828-0724
Fax: 410-830-3999
Cont: Clarinda Harriss, Ed/Dir
• Elledge, Jim, 83
• Parry, Betty, 225

New Rivers Press
420 N 5th St, Ste 910

Minneapolis, MN 55401
Phone: 612-339-7114
Fax: 612-339-9047
Cont: Bill Truesdale, Ed;
    Phyllis Jendro, Mktg Dir
Dist by: Consortium
• Alexander, Robert; Mark
    Vinz and C.W. Truesdale,
    eds., 5
• Crow, Barbara, 63
• Dittberner-Jax, Norita, 73
• Hewett, Greg, 132
• Marquart, Debra, 185
• Reinhard, John, 242
• Sjöberg, Leif, and William
    Jay Smith, trans., 273

New School Chapbook Series
c/o Jason Shinder
New School for Social Re-
    search
66 W 12 St
New York, NY 10011
Phone: 212-289-5902
Cont: Helen Tzagoloff; Jason
    Shinder
• Fraser, Sanford, 94
• Hoover, Susan, 138
• Tzagoloff, Helen, 298
• Verga, Angelo, 302

New Spirit Press
82-34 138 St
Kew Gardens, NY 11435
Phone: 718-847-1482
Fax: same
Cont: Ignatius Graffeo,
    Pub/Ed
• Brooks, Dorothy Howe, 37
• Ciolli, Vivina, 53
• Elyshevitz, Alan, 84
• Farawell, Martin Jude, 87
• Gousseland, Pascale, 111

• Graffeo, Ignatius, 111
• Harrison, Leigh, 125
• Hix, H. Edgar, 134
• Larson, Michael, 166
• Laskin, Pamela, 166
• Simola, Robert, 272
• Tabasso, Gina M., 293
• Winters, Mary, 320

New York University Press
70 Washington Square South
New York, NY 10012
Phone: 212-998-2575
Fax: 212-998-3833
To order: 800-996-6987
Cont: Colin H. Jones, Ed;
    Kathleen May, Mktg
• Anderson, Alice, 9
• Weinstein, Debra, 312

Nightshade Press
Ward Hill Rd & Route 9
PO Box 76
Troy, ME 04987
Phone: 207-948-3427
Fax: 207-948-5088
Cont: Roy Zarucchi, Pub/Ed
• Blomain, Karen, 27
• Bookey, Ted, 30
• Chute, Robert, 53
• Harper, Linda Lee, 124
• Howard, Julie Kate, 139
• Lusk, Daniel, 179
• Presnell, Barbara, 235
• Theriault, Jeri, 294
• Walker, Sue, 307
• White, Julie Herrick, 314
• Winters, Mary, 320

nine muses press
3541 Kent Creek Rd
Winston, OR 97496
Phone: 541-679-6674

Cont: Margareta Waterman, Publr
- David, Gary, 68
- Hureaux, Michael (Mikey Iniko), 143
- Valenza, Roberto (She Rab Dorje), 299
- waterman, margareta, 309
- Wilsun, Don, 319

Ninety-Six Press
English Dept
Furman University
Greenville, SC 29613
Phone: 864-294-3156; 864-294-3152
Fax: 864-294-3001
Cont: Gilbert Allen, Ed
- Flythe, Starkey, Jr., 92
- Freeman, Keller Cushing, 95
- Thompson, Dorothy Perry, 295

Non Compos Mentis Press
240 Thompson Ave
E Liverpool, OH 43920
- Weber, Mark, 311

NoNo Publications
PO Box 10235
Olympia, WA 98502

Nopal Press
2440 16th St #146
San Francisco, CA 94103
- Manyarrows, Victoria Lena, 184

North Star Press
PO Box 115
Hiram, OH 44234-0115
Phone: 216-632-5447
Fax: 216-569-5449
Cont: Hale Chatfield
- Chatfield, Hale, 51

North Valley Press
1932 Candelaria Rd NW
Albuquerque, NM 87107
Phone: 505-344-6766
Cont: Harvena Richter
- Richter, Harvena, 245

Northeastern University Press
360 Huntington Ave, 416 CP
Boston, MA 02130
Phone: 617-373-5480
Fax: 617-373-5483
To order: c/o CUP Services, Box 6525, Ithaca, NY 14851
Cont: Jackie Gambarini, Mktg Asst
- Boisseau, Michelle, 29
- Funk, Allison, 98
- Moolten, David N., 207

Northwestern University Press / TriQuarterly Books
625 Colfax St
Evanston, IL 60208-4210
Phone: 847-491-5313
Fax: 847-491-8150
To order: c/o Chicago Distribution Center, 11030 S Langley, Chicago, IL 60628; 800-621-2736; 800-621-8476 (fax)
Cont: Mary Jo Robling, Mktg Mgr
- Frost, Carol, 96
- Gibbons, Reginald, and Susan Hahn, eds., 102
- Heine, Heinrich, ed., 130
- Louis, Adrian C., 177
- Olsen, William, 221
- Peck, John, 228
- Straus, Marc J., 288
- Villanueva, Tino, 303

P

- Porta, Antonio, 234
- Sardella, Sandro, 260

Paris Press
1117 W Rd
Williamsburg, MA 01096
Phone: 413-628-0051
Fax: 413-268-7205
Cont: Jan Freeman, Ed
Dist by: Consortium
- Oktenberg, Adrian, 221
- Stone, Ruth, 287

Park Lane Press
c/o Random House Value
Publishing
40 Engelhard Ave
Avenel, NJ 07001
Phone: 908-827-2711
- Burns, Christopher, ed., 41
- Dickinson, Emily, 71
- Frost, Robert, 97

PASS Press
c/o A. Sheinman
250 W 24th St #5AE
New York, NY 10011
Phone: 212-366-8830
Fax: 212-366-8899
Cont: Allen J. Sheinman, Ed
- Oisteanu, Valery, 220

Passeggiata Press
(see also Three Continents
Press)
PO Box 636
Pueblo, CO 81002
Phone: 719-544-1038
Fax: 719-546-7889
Cont: Maureen Tingley, Assoc
Ed
- Iskrenko, Nina, 144

Pearl Editions
3030 E Second St
Long Beach, CA 90803

Phone: 310-434-4523
Cont: Marilyn Johnson, Joan
Jobe Smith, Barbara Hauk,
Eds
- Duhamel, Denise, 79
- Glatt, Lisa, 106
- Johnson, Marilyn, 148
- Noguchi, Rick, 217
- Smith, Joan Jobe, ed., 276
- Voss, Fred, 305
- Weber, Mark, 311

Penguin Books / Viking Penguin
375 Hudson St
New York, NY 10014
Phone: 212-366-2000
Fax: 212-366-2952
To order: Consumer Sales,
Penguin USA, PO Box 999,
Dept #17109, Bergenfield,
NJ 07621; 800-253-6476
Cont: Siobhan Reagan, Mktg
- Christopher, Nicholas, 53
- Dischell, Stuart, 73
- Dobyns, Stephen, 74
- Durcan, Paul, 80
- Gillan, Maria Mazziotti,
and Jennifer Gillan, eds.,
104
- Greger, Debora, 113
- Hall, Daniel, 120
- Kerouac, Jack, 155
- McClure, Michael, 192
- Notley, Alice, 218
- Willis, Elizabeth, 318
- Wrigley, Robert, 322

Pennywhistle Press
105 E Marcy St, Ste 123
Santa Fe, NM 87501
Phone: 505-982-0066; 505-
982-2622

Power Trio Press
PO Box 187
Cooper Station, New York,
  NY 10276
Phone: 212-477-3596
• Rutkowski, Thaddeus, 256
Practices of the Wind Press
PO Box 2486
Kalamazoo, MI 49003
Phone: 616-345-7045
Fax: 616-349-0883
Cont: Nicolaus P. Kogon, Ed
• Kogon, Nicolaus P., ed.,
  161
Pratt Press
83 Wooster St
New York, NY 10012
Phone: 212-925-3714
Fax: same
Cont: Corinne Robins, Ed
• Robins, Corinne, 248
Prescott Street Press
PO Box 40312
Portland, OR 97240-0312
Phone: 503-254-2922
Cont: Vi Gale, Pub/Ed
Dist by: Far West
• Gale, Vi, ed., 99
Press of Appletree Alley
PO Box 608
Lewisburg, PA, 17837
Phone: 717-524-7064
Cont: Barnard Taylor, Publr
Dist by: Far West
• Balakian, Peter, 16
• Wheatcroft, John, 314
Princeton University Press
41 William St
Princeton, NJ 08540
Phone: 609-258-4900; 609-
  258-5714

Fax: 609-258-6305; 609-258-
  1335
To order: 1445 Lower Ferry
  Rd, Ewing, NJ 08618;
  609-883-1759; 609-883-
  7413 (fax)
• Seferis, George, 265
Prologue Press
375 Riverside Dr #14C
New York, NY 10025
• Phillips, Louis, 231
Provincetown Arts Press
650 Commercial St
Provincetown, MA 02657
Phone: 508-487-3167
Fax: 508-487-8634
Cont: Christopher Busa, Ed
Dist by: SPD
• Rhodes, Martha, 243
Puckerbrush Press
76 Main St
Orono, M , 04473
Phone: 207-866-4868
Cont: Constance Hunting,
  Publr
• Blair, Farnham, 26
• Nagel, Muska, 212
• Ranzoni, Patricia, 239
• Sharkey, Lee, 268
Puddin'head Press
PO Box 477889
Chicago, IL 60647
Phone: 708-656-4900; 312-
  486-0865
Fax: 708-656-0959
Cont: David Gecic, Pub/Ed
• Kitzis, Lee, ed., 158
Pudding House Publications
60 N Main St
Johnstown, OH, 43031
Phone: 614-967-6060

Cont: Jennifer Bosveld, Publr
- Abbott, Steve, 1
- Aponick, Kathleen, 12
- Baggett, Rebecca, 16
- Bennett, Paul, 24
- Bosveld, Jennifer, ed., 31
- Hague, Richard, 118
- Honton, Margaret, ed., 138
- Krauter, Mary Jackson, 162
- Linville, William, 173
- Moran, Ronald, 208
- Offen, Ron, 220
- RedKitchen Poet's Performance Troupe, 241
- Terris, Susan, 294

Pudding House Publications / Little Stone Books
- Kirschner, Joseph, 157

Purdue University Press
1532 S Campus Courts, Bldg E
W Lafayette, IN 47907-1532
Phone: 317-494-2038
Fax: 317-496-2442
Cont: Margaret Hunt, Ed; Linda Haynes, Mktg Mgr
- Balk, Christianne, 17
- Perillo, Lucia, 229

Pushcart Press
PO Box 380
Wainscott, NY 11975
To order: c/o W.W. Norton & Company (800-233-4830)
Cont: Bill Henderson, Pub/Ed
Dist by: Norton
- Henderson, Bill, ed., 131

Pygmy Forest Press
PO Box 591
Albion, CA 95410
Phone: 707-937-2347

Cont: Leonard J. Cirino, Pub/Ed
- Freeman, John P., 94
- Seffron, Richard A., 265

Pyncheon House
6 University Dr, Ste 105
Amherst, MA 01002
Cont: David R. Rhodes, Pres
Dist by: B&T
- Cole, James, 56

QED Press
155 Cypress St
Fort Bragg, CA 95437
Phone: 707-964-9520
Fax: 707-964-7531
- de Andrade, Eugénio, 69

QH Books
c/o Cloverdale Corporation
52857 County Rd 21
Bristol, IN 46507-9460
Phone: 219-848-4834
Dist by: B&T, Midwest Library Service
- Whitson, Robley, 315, 316

Quarterly Review of Literature
26 Haslet Ave
Princeton, NJ 08540
Phone: 609-921-6976
Fax: 609-258-2230
Cont: Theodore and Renée Weiss, Eds
- Weiss, T. and R., eds., 313

Queen of Swords Press
1736 Moss St #B

- Hansbury, Gia, 123
- Holley, Margaret, 136
- Hurlow, Marcia L., 143

Rizzoli / Universe Publishing
300 Park Ave South
New York, NY 10010
To order: 800-52-BOOKS
- Levin, Gail, ed., 170
- Whitman, Walt, 315

Road Publrs
33412 Lankford Highway
Painter, VA, 23420-0431
Phone: 804-442-9537
Fax: 804-442-5277
Cont: Joseph Adams, Ed
- Adams, Joseph D., ed., 1
- Arthur, Robert P., 14
- Hu, Jane Hwa, 141
- Johnston, Agnes Nasmith, 148
- Souders, Bruce, 281
- Weinstein, Sharon, 313
- Youkeles, Dollie Carpenter, 323

Rodent Press
Boulder, Co
Phone: 303-440-8125 ,
- Foster, Ed, 93
- Hunt, Laird, 142

Roof Books
303 E 8th St
New York, NY 10009
Phone: 212-674-0199
Fax: 212-254-4145
Cont: James Sherry, Ed; Dan
Machlin, Exec Dir
Dist by: B&T, SPD, Seque
- Andrews, Bruce, 11
- Child, Abigail, 52
- DiPalma, Ray, 72
- Doris, Stacy, 76

- Inman, P., 144
- Raworth, Tom, 239
- Silliman, Ron, 271
- Ward, Diane, 308
- Weiner, Hannah, 312

Rose Alley Press
4203 Brooklyn Ave NE
#103A
Seattle, WA 98105
Phone: 206-633-2725
Cont: David D. Horowitz,
Publr
Dist by: B&T
- Ford, Victoria, 93

Routledge
29 W 35th St
New York, NY 10001-2299
Phone: 212-244-3336
Fax: 212-268-6736
To order: 7625 Empire Dr,
Florence, KY 41042; 800-
634-7064; 800-248-4724
(fax)
Cont: William Germano, Ed;
Mark Dewing
- Featherstone, Simon, ed., 88
- Parker, Alan Michael, and
Mark Willhardt, eds., 225

Runaway Spoon Press
1708 Hayworth Rd
Port Charlotte, FL 33952
Phone: 941-629-8045
To order: Box 3621, Port
Charlotte, FL 33949-3621
Cont: Bob Grumman, Pub/Ed
- Bennett, John M., 23
- Bull, Arthur, 41
- Byrum, John, 44
- Chirodea, Doru, 52
- Conti, Edmund, 59
- Cory, Jean-Jacques, 61

S Press Books
Cambridge, MA
To order: c/o Blur, PO Box 357, W Somerville, MA 02144
Sackbut Press
2513 E Webster
Milwaukee, WI 53211
Phone: 414-964-5644
Cont: Angela Peckenpaugh, Pub/Ed
Saenz Publishing
PO Box 7075
Dearborn, MI 48121
Phone: 313-581-8320
Fax: 313-271-3861

To order: 800-247-6553
Cont: Gil Saenz, Publr
Dist by: Brodart
Saffioti, Judith Dingle
1229 Chestnut St #1014
Philadelphia, PA 19107
Sagittarius Press
930 Taylor
Port Townsend, WA 98368
Phone: 360-385-0277
Cont: Rusty North, Publr
Dist by: SPD
Saint Mary's Press / Christian Brothers Publications
702 Terrace Heights
Winona, MN 55987-1320
Salmon Run Press
PO Box 231081
Anchorage, AK 99523-1081
Phone: 907-337-4585
Cont: John E. Smelcer, Ed in Chief
Dist by: ANA, B&T, Bpl, Ingram, Pacific Pipeline
Salt Lick Press
2107 NE Multnomah St

- Hamill, Sam, trans., 123
- Harrison, Jim, 125
- Schelling, Andrew, and Anne Waldman, trans., 262
- Waldman, Anne, ed., 307

Shambhala Publications / Shambhala Pocket Classics
- Dickinson, Emily, 71
- Whitman, Walt, 315

Sheep Meadow Press
5247 Independence Ave
Riverdale-on-Hudson, NY 10471
Phone: 718-548-5547
Fax: 718-884-0406
To order: PO Box 1345, Bronx, NY 10471; 800-972-4491
Cont: Stanley Moss, Pub/Ed; R. Giannetto, Man Ed
- Asher, Elise, 14
- Dolin, Sharon, 74
- Gregor, Arthur, 113
- Mathis, Cleopatra, 189
- Mattawa, Khaled, 189
- Middleton, Christopher, 202
- Rehder, Robert, 241
- Ruddick, Bruce, 254
- Schulman, Grace, 263
- Watson, Stephen, 310

Sherman Asher Publishing
PO Box 2853
Santa Fe, NM 87504
Phone: 505-984-2686
Fax: 505-820-2744
To order: 800-474-1543 (individual); 800-442-2044 (trade)
Cont: Judith Rafaela, Ed; Stella Read, Mktg Dir

Dist by: Gannon
- Fay, Nancy, and Judith Rafaela, eds., 88
- Hill, Judyth, 133
- McGinnis, Mary, 194

Siegel, Donald R.
3 Pine Tree Ln
New City, NY 10956-1807
Phone: 914-638-0231
- Siegel, Donald R., 270
- Siegel, Donald R., and Jeanne R. Siegel, 270

Signature Books
564 W 400 N St
Salt Lake City, UT 84116-3411
Phone: 801-531-1483
Fax: 801-531-1485
Dist by: B&T, Bpl, Ingram, Pacific Pipeline
- Bushman-Carlton, Marilyn, 43

Signpost Press
Mail Stop 9055
Western Washington University
Bellingham, WA 98225
- Collins, Judy, 58

Silverfish Review Press
PO Box 3541
Eugene, OR 97403
Dist by: Spring Church
- Bond, Bruce, 29
- Hamby, Barbara, 121

Simon & Schuster
1230 Ave of the Americas
New York, NY 10020
Phone: 212-632-4947
Fax: 212-632-4957
Cont: Lisa Maslow, Mktg Asst

Lincoln, NE 68501-3686
Phone: 402-466-8689
Cont: David McCleery, Publr
• McCleery, David, ed., 192
• McEwen, R.F., 194
Small Poetry Press
362 Odin Pl
Pleasant Hill, CA 94523
Phone: 510-798-1411
Cont: David Alpaugh, Publr
• Daigon, Ruth, 64
• Lynch, Kathleen, 180
• Van Houten, Lois, 300
Smiling Dog Press
9875 Fritz Rd
Maple City, MI 49664
Phone: 616-334-3695
Cont: Dean Creighton, Pub/Ed
• Creighton, Dean, ed., 62
**Smith, Gibbs, Publishers /
Peregrine Smith Books**
PO Box 667
1877 E Gentile St
Layton, UT 84041
Phone: 801-544-9800
Fax: 801-544-5582
To order: 800-835-4993
Cont: Gail Yngve, Ed; Linda
Nimori, Awards Program
Ed
Dist by: Bpl, Ingram
• Bowman, Catherine, 32
• Buckley, Christopher, and
Christopher Merrill, eds.,
40
• Estes, Angie, 85
• Hix, H.L., 134
• Sensei, Kamishiura, 266
Snake Nation Press
110 #2 W Force St

Valdosta, GA 31601
Phone: 912-249-8334
Fax: 912-242-6690
To order: 912-247-2787
Cont: Nancy Phillips, Ed;
Roberta George, Ed
Dist by: Bpl, DuBoer
• Goldberg, Barbara, 108
Soncino Books
New York, NY
• Torres, Edwin, 296
Sound Attitude Books
110 Blueberry Ln #1
Hicksville, NY 11801
Phone: 516-681-0345
Fax: 516-939-0789
To order: PO Box 7089,
Hicksville, NY 11801
Cont: Kevin Michaels
• Michaels, Kevin, 201
South End Press
116 Saint Botolph St
Boston, MA 02115
• Alexander, Meena, 4
Sow's Ear Press
19535 Pleasant View Dr
Abingdon, VA 24211-6827
Phone: 540-628-2651
Cont: Larry K. Richman,
Pub/Ed
• Brown, Bill, 38
• Clark, Suzanne U., 53
• Maiden, Nell, 182
• Marion, Jeff Daniel, 185
• Quillen, Rita Sims, 237
• Wildsmith, Dana, 316
Spare Change Poetry Press
2115 Clearview NE
Massillon, OH 44646
Phone: 216-837-8758

- Fanthorpe, U.A., 86
- Fitzmaurice, Gabriel, 91
- Gery, John, 101
- Haskins, Lola, 127
- Jarman, Mark, and David Mason, eds., 145
- Mason, David, 188
- McBreen, Joan, 191
- McDowell, Robert, 194
- Morgan, Frederick, 209
- Paschen, Elise, 225
- Rector, Liam, 240
- Simpson, Louis, 272
- Slaughter, Adèle, 274
- Starck, Clemens, 283
- Stefanile, Felix, 284
- Van de Kamp, Peter, ed., 299
- Vial, Noelle, 303
- Williamson, Greg, 318
- Winch, Terence, 320

Sun & Moon Press
6026 Wilshire Blvd
Los Angeles, CA 90036
Phone: 213-857-1115
Fax: 213-857-0143
Cont: Douglas Messerli, Publr
Dist by: Consortium
- Alexander, Will, 5
- Alferi, Pierre, 5
- Andersson, Claes, 10
- Armantrout, Rae, 13
- Celan, Paul, 49
- Coffey, Michael, 56
- Coolidge, Clark, 60
- Copioli, Rosita, 60
- De Angelis, Milo, 69
- Deluy, Henri, 70
- du Bouchet, André, 78
- Giuliani, Alfredo, ed., 106
- Glassgold, Peter, trans., 106

- Guest, Barbara, 115
- Hartman, Charles O., and Hugh Kenner, 126
- Mac Low, Jackson, 180
- Messerli, Douglas, ed., 201
- Rakosi, Carl, 238
- Rehm, Pam, 241
- Ronk, Martha, 250
- Sorrentino, Gilbert, 280
- Tan Lin, 293

Sun-Scape Publications
65 High Ridge Rd, Ste 103
Stamford, CT 06905
Phone: 203-838-3775
Fax: same
Cont: Megan MacQueen, Ed; Valerie Webster, Mktg and Sales Mgr
Dist by: B&T
- Smith, Rolland G., 277

Sunlight Publishers
PO Box 640545
San Francisco, CA 94109
- Kent, Joseph, 155

T

TA Publications
7109 Perry Pl
Brooklyn Center, MN 55429
Phone: 612-566-1842
To order: PO Box 22583, Minneapolis, MN 55422; 612-566-1842
Cont: Leon Knight, Ed
- Clabon, George D., 53
- Knight, Ginny, 159

- Knight, Leon, 159
- Williams, Nancy Webb, 317

Talent House Press
1306 Talent Ave
Talent, OR 97540
To order: 221 E 12th St #12,
New York, NY 10003;
212-477-3596
- Rutkowski, Thaddeus, 256

Talisman House, Publishers
129 Wayne St
Jersey City, NJ 07303-3157
Phone: 201-938-0698
Dist by: Consortium
- Donahue, Joseph, 75
- Lansing, Gerrit, 165
- Pettet, Simon, 230
- Schwartz, Leonard; Joseph Donahue, and Edward Foster, eds., 263

Tesseract Publications
PO Box 164
Canton, SD 57013
Phone: 605-987-5070
Fax: 605-987-5071
Cont: Janet Leih, Publr
- Stuefen, Fern, 288

Texas Tech University Press
PO Box 41037
Lubbock, TX 79409-1037
Phone: 806-742-2982
Fax: 806-742-2979
To order: 800-832-4042
Cont: Dr. Walt McDonald, Ed; Anne Towery, Mktg Mgr
Dist by: B&T, Booksource, Ingram
- Burnham, Deborah, 41

- Fargas, Laura, 87
- Fink, Robert A., 90

Thin Ice Press
San Francisco, CA
- Ackerman, Pat, 1

Third World Press
7822 S Dobson Ave
PO Box 19730, Chicago, IL 60619
Phone: 312-651-0700
Fax: 312-651-7286
Cont: Haki Madhubuti, Publr
- Baraka, Amiri, 18
- Plumpp, Sterling, 232

Thomas Jefferson University Press
NMSU MC111L
Kirksville, MO 63501
Phone: 816-785-4665
Fax: 816-785-4181
Cont: R.V. Schencker, Dir
- Ray, David, 239

Thomas, Laurence W.
174 Greenside Up
Ypsilanti, MI 48197
Phone: 313-434-2409
- Thomas, Laurence W., 295

Three Continents Press / Lynne Rienner Publishers
(see also Passeggiata Press formerly Three Continents Press)
1800 30th St
Boulder, CO 80301
- Arbuthnot, Nancy, trans., 12
- Boullata, Kamal, ed., 32
- Darwish, Mahmud, 67

Three Mile Harbor
PO Box 1335
Grand Central Station

New York, NY 10163
- Levi, Toni Mergentime, 170

Threshold Books
139 Main St
Brattleboro, VT 05301
Phone: 802-254-8300
Fax: 802-257-2779
Cont: Edmund Halminski, Ed
Dist by: Atrium
- Rumi, Jelaluddin, 255

Tia Chucha Press
PO Box 476969
Chicago, IL 60647
Phone: 312-252-5321
Fax: 312-252-5388
To order: Northwestern University Press, 625 Colfax St, Evanston, IL 60208-4210, 800-621-2736; 800-621-8476 (fax)
Cont: Luis Rodriguez, Dir
Dist by: Northwestern University Press
- Carbó, Nick, 46
- Cumpián, Carlos, 64
- Dixon, Melvin, 73
- Mori, Kyoko, 209
- Rodrigues, Andres, 248
- Salach, Cin, 257
- Walden, Gale Renée, 306

Tilbury House, Publrs
132 Water St
Gardiner, ME 04345
Phone: 207-582-1899
Fax: 207-582-8227
Cont: Jennifer Elliott, Assoc Publr; Michelle Gifford, Mktg and Sales
Dist by: Consortium
- Robinson, Edwin Arlington, 248

Timberline Press
6281 Red Bud
Fulton, MO 65251
Phone: 573-642-5035
Cont: Clarence Wolfshohl, Pub/Ed
- Swist, Wally, 292

Time Being Books
10411 Clayton Rd #201-203
St. Louis, MO 63131
Phone: 314-432-1771
Fax: 314-432-7939
To order: 800-331-6605
Cont: Jerry Call, Ed in Chief
- Brodsky, Louis Daniel, 36
- Chalmer, Judith, 50
- Early, Gerald, 81
- Goldbarth, Albert, 107
- McFall, Gardner, 194
- Milder, Ben, 202

Times Books
201 E 50th St
New York, NY 10022
- Carter, Jimmy, 48

Timken Publishers
137 Varick St. #6
New York, NY 10013
Phone: 212-627-0706
Fax: 212-627-3919
Cont: Jane Timken, Publr; Myles McDonnell, Assoc Ed
Dist by: Consortium
- Deanovich, Connie, 70
- Yau, John, 323

Torderwarz Publishing Company
PO Box 751205
Forest Hills, NY 11375
Phone: 718-520-1483
Fax: same

- Pack, Robert, 223
- Polito, Robert, 233
- Shapiro, Alan, 267
- Sleigh, Tom, 275
- Stewart, Susan, 286
- Williamson, Alan, 318

University of Georgia Press
330 Research Dr
Athens, GA 30602-4901
Phone: 706-369-6163
Fax: 706-369-6131
To order: 800-266-5842
Cont: Stephanie Hansen, Exhibits Mgr

- Finnell, Dennis, 90
- Gross, Pamela, 114
- Halme, Kathleen, 121
- Svoboda, Terese, 290
- Upton, Lee, 299
- Zimmer, Paul, 325

University of Hawai'i Press
2840 Kolowalu St
Honolulu, HI, 96822
Phone: 808-956-8697
Fax: 808-988-6052
To order: 800-956-2840; 800-650-7811 (fax)
Cont: Colins Kawai, Mktg Mgr

- Cowing, Sue, ed., 62
- Kijima, Hajime, 156
- Nakano, Jiro, and Brien Hallett, eds., 212
- Ooka, Makoto, 221

University of Idaho Press
16 Brink Hall
Moscow, ID 83844-1107
Phone: 208-885-5939
Fax: 208-885-9059
Cont: Peg Harvey-Marose, Mktg Mgr

- Brock, James, 35

University of Illinois Press
1325 S Oak St
Champaign, IL 61820-6903
Phone: 217-333-0950
Fax: 217-244-8082
To order: PO Box 4856, Hampden Post Office, Baltimore, MD 21211; 800-545-4703; 410-516-6969 (fax)
Cont: Laurence Lieberman, Ed; Susie Warren, Mktg

- Berg, Stephen, 24
- Cafagña, Marcus, 44
- Coles, Nicholas, and Peter Oresick, eds., 57
- Fulton, Alice, 97
- Goodison, Lorna, 109
- Harper, Michael S., 124
- Hyett, Barbara Helfgott, 143
- Lea, Sydney, 167
- Rolfe, Edwin, 249
- Smith, Dave, 275
- Stein, Kevin, 284
- Stockwell, Samn, 287
- Wagoner, David, 306
- Williams, Miller, 317

University of Iowa Press
119 W Park Rd
100 Kuhl House, Iowa City, IA 52242-1000
Phone: 319-335-2000
Fax: 319-335-2055
To order: 2222 Old Hwy 218 South, Iowa City, IA 52242-1602; 800-235-2665
Cont: Paul Zimmer, Dir; Kate Capps, Mktg Mgr

- Burns, Ralph, 42

V

W

Wayne State University Press
4809 Woodward Ave
Detroit, MI 48201-1309
Phone: 313-577-6123
Fax: 313-577-6131
To order: 800-WSU-READ
Cont: Renee Tambeau, Mktg
Asst
• Daniels, Jim, ed., 66
• Reed, John R., 241
• Whitman, Ruth, trans., 315
We Press
PO Box 1503
Santa Cruz, CA 95061
Phone: 408-427-9711
• Moe, H. D., 206
Weatherhill
568 Broadway, Ste 705
New York, NY 10012
Phone: 212-966-3080
Fax: 212-966-4860
To order: 41 Monroe Tpke,
Trumbull, CT 06611; 800-
437-7840; 203-459-5095
(fax)
Cont: Carolyn Sevos, Mktg
Asst
• Horiuchi, Toshimi, 139
• Sato, Hiroaki, ed., 261
Weird Sisters Press
369 Maryland St
Buffalo, NY 18201
To order: Penelope, PO Box
482, Fredonia, NY 14063
Cont: Phyllis King
• Schweik, Joanne, ed., 264
**Wesleyan / University Press of
New England**
110 Mt. Vernon St
Middletown, CT 06459
Phone: 860-685-2420

Fax: 860-685-2421
To order: UPNE 24 S Main
St, Hanover, NH 03755;
800-421-1561; 603-643-
1540 (fax)
Cont: Suzanna Tamminen, Ed;
Rick Henning, Mktg Dir
Dist by: B&T, Ingram, Koen,
Pacific Pipeline
• Apollinaire, Guillaume, 12
• Cabral de Melo Neto, João,
44
• Collier, Michael, ed., 57
• Dickey, William, 71
• Graham, Loren, 111
• Hadas, Rachel, 118
• Hartman, Charles O., 126
• Ignatow, David, 144
• McPherson, Sandra, 196
• Retallack, Joan, 243
• Revell, Donald, 243
• Rudman, Mark, 254
• Scalapino, Leslie, 261
• Sobelman, 'Annah, 279
• Wenderoth, Joe, 314
West End Press
PO Box 27334
Albuquerque, NM 87125
Phone: 505-345-5729
Fax: same
Cont: John F. Crawford, Publr
Dist by: Talman
• Olinka, Sharon, 221
• Parson-Nesbitt, Julie, 225
Westminster John Knox Press
100 Witherspoon St
Louisville, KY 40202-1396
Phone: 502-569-5058
Fax: 502-569-5113
To order: 800-227-2872

Cont: Annie McClure, Publicist
• Weems, Ann, 312
Westonian Press
179 Prospect Park W., Ste #2
Brooklyn, NY 11215
Phone: 718-499-2786
Cont: Nicole Andonov, Publr
• Andonov, Nicole, 10
Westview Press
5500 Central Ave
Boulder, CO 80301-2877
Phone: 303-444-3541
• Rustomji-Kerns, Roshni, ed., 255
Wexford Press
185 Claremont Ave #6A
New York, NY 10027
Phone: 212-316-2121
• O'Neil, Thomas, 220
What Books
Providence, RI
• Ziolkowski, Thad, 326
Wheel of Fire Press
PO Box 442219
Lawrence, KS 66044
• Bettis, Carl; Sharon Eiker and Philip Miller, 25
• Eiker, Sharon, and Carl Bettis, 82
Whirlybird Press
10210 Granada Ln
Overland Park, KS 66207
Phone: 913-649-2596; 816-753-8800
Fax: 913-341-7770
Cont: Dr. Vernon Rowe, M.D., Pres
• Rowe, Vernon, 252
Whistle Press
PO Box 709

Winterville, GA 30683
• Fishman, Charles, 91
White Eagle Coffee Store Press
PO Box 383
Fox River Grove, IL 60021-0383
Phone: 847-639-9200
Cont: Frank Smith, Publr
• Baumgaertner, Jill Peláez, 21
• Gibson, Becky Gould, 102
• Spring, Justin, 282
White Pine Press
10 Village Square
Fredonia, NY 14063
Phone: 716-672-5743
Fax: same
Cont: Dennis Maloney, Publr; Donna Carlson, Mktg Dir
Dist by: Consortium
• Agosín, Marjorie, ed., 3
• Blue Cloud, Peter, 27
• Brandi, John, 33
• Hamill, Sam, 122
• Johnson, Nancy, 148
• Romtvedt, David, 250
• Seaton, Jerome P., and Dennis Maloney, eds., 264
• Zeiger, Gene, 325
Whole Notes Press
PO Box 1374
Las Cruces, NM 88004
Phone: 505-382-7446
Cont: Nancy Peters Hastings, Pub/Ed
• Dorsett, Robert, 76
• Scheele, Roy, 262
• Wilson, Keith, 319
Wind Publications
PO Box 24548

Z

Zero Degree Press
PO Box 72
Lancaster, PA 17608
Phone: 717-393-9629
Cont: J.C. Groff, Dir/Ed
• Hoch, James, 134
• Louella, Michael, 177

Zerx Press
725 Van Buren Pl SE
Albuquerque, NM 87108
Phone: 505-255-3012
Cont: Mark Weber, Pub/Ed
• Locklin, Gerald, 174
• Weber, Mark, 311

• Weber, Mark; Brent Leake, and Larry Goodell, 311

Zoland Books
384 Huron Ave
Cambridge, MA 02138
Phone: 617-864-6252
Fax: 617-661-4998
Cont: Roland F. Pease, Jr., Pub/Ed; Heather Hoffman, Mktg Dir
Dist by: National Book Network
• Corbett, William, 60
• Cornish, Sam, 61
• Fogel, Alice B., 92
• Laughlin, James, 167
• Torra, Joseph, 296

Key to the Index
by Publisher

The Index by Publisher provides the office address, as well as phone and fax number, for each of the presses whose books are represented in this volume. Ordering addresses, when they differ, follow. Then a contact person at the press is provided. The distributors and wholesalers who carry the books are given (see below for the phone numbers of those which appear most often). Finally the authors published by the press and described in this volume are listed.

The following abbreviations appear frequently:

Cont:	**Contact: precedes publishing staff members**
Assoc	Associate
Asst	Assistant
Dir	Director
Ed(s)	Editor(s)
Man	Manager
Mktg	Marketing
Pres	President
Pub/Ed	Publishing Editor
Publr	Publisher

Dist by:	**Distributed by: precedes distributors or wholesalers**
B&T	Baker and Taylor, 800–775–1100
	Bookmasters, 800–247–5663
Bpl	Bookpeople, 800–999-4650
	Consortium, 800–283–3572
	Ingram, 800–937–8000
SPD	Small Press Distributors, 8090–869–7553
	Spring Arbor, 800–395–5599